Autism and Developmental Delays in Young Children

Autism and Developmental Delays in Young Children

The Responsive Teaching Curriculum for Parents and Professionals

Curriculum Guide

Gerald Mahoney and James D. MacDonald

8700 Shoal Creek Boulevard
Austin, Texas 78757-6897
800/897-3202 Fax 800/397-7633
www.proedinc.com

8700 Shoal Creek Boulevard
Austin, Texas 78757-6897
800/897-3202 Fax 800/397-7633
www.proedinc.com

ISBN-13: 978-1-4164-0236-7
ISBN-10: 1-4164-0236-5

Art Director: Jason Crosier
Designer: Kim Worley
This book is designed in Nexus Serif TF, Century Gothic, and Tekton.

Printed in the United States of America

2 3 4 5 6 7 8 9 10 11 10

This book is dedicated to the numerous people who have played a direct role over the past 20 years in the development of Responsive Teaching. These include the policy makers who promoted the research initiatives that were used to support the development of this curriculum; the staff at the United States Department of Education, Office of Special Education Programs, who supervised our research and demonstration projects; and, most importantly, the hundreds of parents and professionals who both challenged and trusted us as we struggled together to improve and refine Responsive Teaching. We especially dedicate this book to Frida Perales, who provided the insight and support throughout this process that was so critical to the completion of this project.

Contents

Preface

The methods and procedures of Responsive Teaching (RT) are the result of each of the authors engaging in years of curriculum development, field-testing, research, and model replication. In the course of our work, we have become keenly aware that several of the concepts and strategies presented in this curriculum run counter to many of the practices currently used in early intervention. We recognize that many professionals struggle to understand the rationale of this approach and to implement this type of intervention with parents and their children. We developed Responsive Teaching with the hope that we can minimize this struggle and provide the tools and supports that are needed to implement this intervention effectively.

In this curriculum, we

- provide a detailed description of Responsive Teaching strategies that research shows are effective at enhancing children's development;
- identify and describe numerous discussion points that interventionists can use to help parents understand how these strategies impact children's development;
- provide the Responsive Teaching Planning and Tracking Form, which prescribes a menu of Responsive Teaching strategies and discussion points that can be used to address children's developmental needs;
- describe procedures for planning intervention sessions and evaluating children's progress; and
- present a format for conducting intervention sessions and implementing this program at home.

The Responsive Teaching Curriculum Planning and Tracking Program, available from PRO-ED on a CD-ROM, provides all of the materials and forms necessary to implement Responsive Teaching. Step-by-step instructions for using the computer program are included on the CD-ROM (compatible with Windows 2000 or later).

In designing this curriculum, our intention was to support the notion that *early intervention is a long-term process.* It takes time for most parents not only to learn but also to believe in and routinely use Responsive Teaching strategies with their children. Service providers need to have a variety of concrete, easy-to-follow procedures for helping parents implement this intervention with their children. They need to be proficient at using these strategies so that they can model the various components of Responsive Teaching, coach parents to use Responsive Teaching strategies, and point out how these strategies affect children's behavior. They need to help parents understand how Responsive Teaching promotes their children's development and be able to discuss the child development concepts associated with Responsive Teaching in relation to parents' personal beliefs about development. This curriculum provides the information and tools needed to carry out these complex and demanding tasks.

Our enthusiasm for Responsive Teaching comes from our own experiences in witnessing the astonishing things that have happened to children and parents who have used this intervention. We have had first-hand experience of working with hundreds of children who, when given the opportunity to interact with highly responsive and engaging parents, came to life. Children who looked developmentally delayed—who did not do much while playing; who seldom communicated with others; who were frequently fussy, irritable, and sometimes unpleasant to be with—became children who began taking an interest in being with and communicating with people—active, involved, and persistent in their play with toys as well as with people while appearing happier and more content.

Although these changes represent great accomplishments for these children, and even a greater source of consolation to their parents, they are not the primary reason for using Responsive Teaching. The only justifiable reason for using any intervention model is that it works—it effectively accomplishes what intervention is supposed to do. As we illustrate in our evaluation of 50 children who participated in this intervention, Responsive Teaching is a highly effective developmental intervention. As we report in Chapter 6, after 12 months of services, the children who participated in Responsive Teaching made dramatic improvements in their developmental growth. On average, these children showed a 60% increase in their rate of cognitive development, a 125% increase in their expressive language development, and a 150% increase in their receptive language growth.

Our evaluation sample included 20 children who had severe social–emotional problems as reflected by their diagnoses of autism/Pervasive Developmental Disorders. These children made dramatic improvements in their social–emotional functioning as well. Their scores on standardized tests of social–emotional functioning increased by approximately 25%.

Responsive Teaching is a remarkably effective intervention, far surpassing the effectiveness of any other developmental intervention reported to date. However, even more exciting than the impact Responsive Teaching can have on children's early development is the lifelong influence this intervention can have on parents and children. Many of the parents who have participated in Responsive Teaching have reported that they continue to use Responsive Teaching strategies to promote their children's learning and social–emotional behavior, long after their involvement in early intervention has ended.

How To Use This Guide

We have organized this Curriculum Guide into four sections. Section I: Introduction presents information about the theory and rationale for Responsive Teaching. It describes each of the components of the Responsive Teaching intervention model and provides an explanation of the role that a parent-mediated approach plays in early intervention.

Section II: Theoretical and Research Foundations provides a more detailed explanation of the rationale for Responsive Teaching strategies and pivotal intervention objectives, which are the cornerstones of this curriculum. This section provides a review of theory and research, which have been the basis for the development of each of these components. It also provides a description of the study we conducted to assess the effectiveness of Responsive Teaching. Results from this evaluation provide strong evidence that Responsive Teaching is effective at addressing the developmental and social–emotional needs of young children who have significant developmental problems.

Section III: Implementing Responsive Teaching provides the guidelines and procedures for implementing Responsive Teaching, including guidelines for planning RT sessions and tracking children's progress, recommendations for helping parents follow through with this intervention, and a recommended format for conducting individual sessions with parents and children.

Section IV: Curriculum Materials includes reproducible handouts of all the intervention tools needed to implement Responsive Teaching. These tools include the Responsive Teaching Planning and Tracking Form—which identifies the Responsive Teaching strategies, discussion points, and evaluation criteria for each of the 16 pivotal behaviors—and the Curriculum Outline. For each pivotal intervention objective, the Curriculum Outline provides a definition of the pivotal behavior, a discussion of facts that are relevant to these behaviors, the list of discussion points that can be used to review these facts with parents, and a detailed description of the RT strategies recommended to promote the behavior. (This same information is also included in the Responsive Teaching Curriculum Planning and Tracking Program, which was developed to facilitate the use of this curriculum.)

The parts of this curriculum that are necessary for planning and implementing Responsive Teaching are completely contained in Section IV. Professionals and parents need to be familiar only with the information presented in Section I: Introduction and Section III: Implementing Responsive Teaching to begin to use this curriculum. The information provided in Section II is for the advanced practitioner who would like in-depth information about the rationale and research base for this program. For many, this information will take on greater personal meaning as they begin to discover the effects that Responsive Teaching methods have on children and their parents.

Section I

Introduction

Chapter 1—The Purpose of Responsive Teaching

Chapter 2—The Role of Parents in Child Development Interventions

Chapter 3—Overview of the Responsive Teaching Curriculum

Chapter 1

The Purpose of Responsive Teaching

Responsive Teaching (RT) is an evidence-based child development curriculum that was designed to be implemented by parents and other caregivers who spend significant amounts of time interacting with and caring for young children. RT was developed to help parents and other adults maximize the potential of each of their routine interactions with children so that they support and enhance children's development and well-being. This curriculum encourages children to develop and use the "pivotal behaviors" that are the foundations for developmental learning, such as social play, initiation, problem solving, practice, joint attention, conversation, trust, cooperation, and feelings of confidence. The instructional strategies that are at the heart of Responsive Teaching are easy-to-remember suggestions that adults can incorporate into daily, routine activities with children. The strategies enable parents to continually, but gently, stimulate their children's developmental learning.

The Structure of Responsive Teaching

Responsive Teaching is designed to promote the following three domains of developmental functioning:

- Cognition—Children's ability to think, reason, solve problems, and learn new information about their world and relationships
- Communication—Children's ability to convey their feelings, observations, and intentions and to respond to the feelings, observations, and intentions of others through nonverbal, symbolic, and spoken language
- Social–Emotional Functioning—Children's ability to engage in and enjoy developmentally appropriate interactions with parents, adults, and other children and to comply with reasonable rules and expectations

The instructional methods and objectives of RT are derived from contemporary child development research and theory. Instructional strategies come from the frequently reported research finding that the degree to which parents engage in responsive interactions with children is one of the most important environmental influences on their development and social–emotional well-being. Responsive Teaching strategies help parents engage in this responsive style of interacting with their children by providing practical suggestions that emphasize the following five dimensions of responsive interaction:

- Reciprocity—Frequent episodes of interaction that are characterized by a balanced, give-and-take relationship
- Contingency—Interactions that have an immediate and direct relationship to a child's previous behaviors that support and encourage the child's actions, intentions, and communications

- Shared control—Guidance and direction that facilitates and expands the actions and communications that the child initiates or leads
- Affect—Expressive, animated, and warm interactions that are characterized by enjoyment or delight in interacting with the child
- Match—Interactions and requests that are adjusted to the child's developmental level, current interests, and behavioral style or temperament

The intervention objectives, or child behaviors that RT helps children to learn and use, are referred to as "pivotal behaviors." Contemporary theories of child development claim that these behaviors are the cornerstones for early developmental learning. Responsive Teaching is based upon the following theories:

- Constructivist theories of learning and development (Piaget, 1963; Vygotsky, 1978)
- Communication theories of language development (Bruner, 1974, 1983)
- Attachment theory (Bowlby, 1969; Goleman, 1995)
- Achievement motivation theory (Atkinson, 1964; Weiner, 1980)

Each of these theories stresses that children's developmental learning results from their active participation in routine activities and social interactions.

Unlike most other child development curricula, Responsive Teaching does not recommend specially designed toys or instructional activities to enhance children's developmental growth. Rather, based upon the four theories listed, RT focuses on supporting and encouraging children's enjoyment and participation in *routine activities* they experience each day while playing, communicating, and interacting with others.

Children Who Benefit From Responsive Teaching

We initially developed RT to be an intervention program that parents could use at home to enhance the development of children with disabilities who were younger than 6 years of age. The group of children who participated in this program included 30 children with *developmental disabilities* and 20 children diagnosed with *autism* or *Pervasive Developmental Disorders* (PDD) (Mahoney & Perales, 2005).

Most of the 30 children with developmental disabilities had significant delays in mental development, ranging from mild to severe. All had delays in language development, and many did not have any language at all at the start of intervention. Most of these children did not have formal diagnoses because they were less than 3 years of age; however, they all had developmental characteristics that would have made them eligible to be diagnosed with mental retardation, delayed language development, or related conditions such as developmental apraxia. Some of these children had disabilities associated with genetic or chromosomal abnormalities, such as Down syndrome.

The 20 children diagnosed with autism or PDD ranged in age from 23 to 54 months, with an average age of 32 months when we began using RT with them. These children had mild to severe cognitive and communication delays. They also had severe regulatory disorders. This was manifested by several different problems, including detachment, underreactivity, hypersensitivity–hyperactivity, and problems in self-regulation.

Currently, we are evaluating RT with two other groups of children who are younger than 6 years of age—children who have mental health concerns or behavior problems and children who have been adopted. The behavioral or social–emotional problems manifested by children with mental health concerns are similar to many of the problems presented by children with autism or PDD. Because parental responsiveness is associated with the social–emotional functioning of children from a range of different backgrounds (Bornstein, 1989; Bradley, 1989), it is reasonable to believe that RT will have the same kinds of effects on the social–emotional problems of young children who have not been diagnosed with autism or PDD as it has had on children with autism or PDD.

Our evaluation of RT with adopted children is being carried out to determine whether RT can be used as a preventative intervention program. Although most adopted children do not have significant developmental or social–emotional problems at the time of adoption, there is a great risk that many will develop these problems later in childhood. Because RT has been successful at promoting the development of children who have serious developmental problems, we believe that it should also be effective at preventing the developmental or social–emotional problems of adopted children, whose developmental vulnerabilities tend to be less serious than the children with whom RT has been used.

Identifying RT Candidates

Another way to identify the children and parents that RT can be used with is to consider the underlying premises of this program. Responsive Teaching is based upon the general developmental principles of responsive interaction and pivotal behavior, which have been validated across many different groups of children and parents. As a result, RT can be used as a child development program with all children, whether they have developmental problems or risks or have no special problems at all.

Developmental Capacity

Responsive Teaching is based upon the idea that the development of all children is affected by the same two factors. The first is children's capacity to develop. This is influenced by multiple factors, including children's genetic makeup, their temperament, whether they have medical conditions or biologically based disabilities, or whether they have had disruptive or traumatic early experiences, such as abuse or neglect. For the most part, this capacity to develop is a lifelong characteristic that is resistant to change through education or developmental interventions such as RT, or else is a characteristic that can only be modified gradually over time. However, this does not mean that children's developmental fate is predetermined, or fixed, by their capacity to develop. On the contrary, children's capacity to develop merely restricts the range of developmental outcomes children are likely to attain.

For example, if a child has a condition such as Down syndrome, or any other biologically based disability, no educational or developmental intervention can fully eliminate the impact the condition has on the child's capacity to develop. Most children with Down syndrome will have lifelong difficulties with learning and development that are directly related to this condition.

However, the condition of Down syndrome does not predetermine that children will become mentally retarded; rather, it lowers the range of developmental outcomes they are likely to attain. Typically developing children who do not have Down syndrome are likely to attain an IQ of between 75 and 125, with the majority attaining IQs that fall near the middle of this range (i.e., 100). In contrast, children with Down syndrome are likely to attain an IQ of between 30 to 100, with the majority attaining IQs in the middle of this range (i.e., 70). Although the possibility that children with Down syndrome may become mentally retarded is high, the capacity to develop that is associated with Down syndrome is sufficiently adequate for these children to attain a normal IQ (i.e., 100).

Pivotal Developmental Behaviors

The second premise underlying RT is that, regardless of how much capacity children have to develop, the developmental and social–emotional outcomes they attain during early childhood are strongly influenced by the amount of pivotal developmental behaviors that they use in each of their daily interactions while playing, working, or interacting with others. Thus, if a child has the genetic capacity for genius but uses his or her pivotal behaviors at a very low level, this child is likely to attain an IQ score in the "below average" or "average" range when he or she reaches school age. However, if a child's capacity to develop has been compromised by a disability such as autism, that child is capable of attaining a normal IQ score (i.e., 100) and typical social–emotional well-being if he or she can be helped to become a frequent, high-level user of pivotal behavior.

No matter what children's capacity to learn might be, by using Responsive Teaching strategies parents can have an enormous impact on promoting children's pivotal developmental behavior and thereby enhancing their development and social–emotional functioning. No one really knows how much capacity to develop children actually have—whether they have autism or Down syndrome, have been abused or neglected, or have no developmental problems at all—but recent child development research has shown that all children are more likely to achieve their maximum developmental potential when their parents and caregivers engage in highly responsive interactions with them throughout the early childhood years (MacDonald, 2004).

Benefits of RT to Parents and Other Adults

The primary benefit of Responsive Teaching is that it enhances parents' and caregivers' effectiveness at promoting and nurturing the development and well-being of young children. During the past 50 years, there has been considerable interest in determining whether parents influence the developmental outcomes of their children, how this occurs, and how parents' influence compares to other influences, such as children's biological makeup or the amount and quality of learning opportunities they have. Findings from this research indicate that all of these factors influence children's development, but parents' influence is considerable, perhaps greater than the effects of preschool, childcare, or even the individual therapeutic services (e.g., speech–language therapy) some children receive.

For example, in a national study of the effects of childcare on children's development (Applebaum et al., 2000), findings indicated that, for most children, the amount or quality of childcare services children received had little impact on their rate of development. However, this study reported that the way parents interacted with their children had a considerable effect on children's development, which was nearly five times greater than the effects of childcare.

Even when children receive early intervention services for their disabilities, research suggests that parents may have a greater impact on children's development than do the services children receive. For example, the Infant Health and Development Program was a comprehensive intervention program for low–birth-weight children that provided intensive (25 hours per week), high-quality preschool services from the time children were 12 months old until they were 3 years of age. This large research study showed that children who received these preschool services made on average a 10-point increase in their IQ scores during intervention (Brooks-Gunn et al., 1994). However, subsequent analyses indicated that the way mothers interacted with their children accounted for most of these child development gains (Mahoney, Boyce, Fewell, Spiker, & Wheeden, 1998). Furthermore, the effects that the preschool program had on children were no longer evident when children were 5 years old; yet the way mothers interacted with their children continued to have a substantial relationship to their children's development and academic achievement up through the time children were 7 years old (Fewell & Deutscher, 2004).

In yet another study, we compared the effects of different types of preschool instruction on the development of young children with disabilities (Mahoney, Wheeden, & Perales, 2004). Children in this study attended preschool special education classrooms 4 half-days a week for an entire academic year. They received one of three different types of preschool instruction: developmental (Play Oriented), didactic (Instruction Oriented), or blended developmental–didactic. Results indicated that none of these instructional models increased children's developmental quotients during the study. The way mothers interacted with their children, however, was related to how well their children were developing.

These results, and many other research findings, illustrate the tremendous impact parents have on the early development of young children. How parents interact with their children, especially how responsive they are, can make a major difference in children's level of development, ability to communicate, social–emotional well-being, and readiness for school. Parents' influence occurs whether children are typically developing or have developmental problems and are receiving special education or other therapy services. These research studies also indicate that parents affect their children's development (a) whether they are aware of their influence or not and (b) no matter how effective they are at doing this.

Responsive Teaching provides clear, practical strategies parents can incorporate into their daily routines that greatly increase their ability to promote their children's development and well-being without adding to the burden of caring for their children. Responsive Teaching is based on the most up-to-date research about how parents influence children's learning and development. It is a child development program that has proven to have a profound impact on the development and social–emotional well-being of children who are the most resistant to normal intervention methods—children with autism and developmental disabilities. The results of this research were consistent with the logic model of Responsive Teaching, illustrated in Figure 1.1. It indicated that in 1 year's time, Responsive Teaching helped parents engage in more responsive and enjoyable interactions with their children; as a result, their children not only made dramatic improvement in their use of pivotal behaviors, their rate of cognitive development increased by an average of 64% and their language development increased by 150%. The children with autism/PDD also made clinically significant improvements in several critical social–emotional problem behaviors, including detachment, hypersensitivity–hyperactivity, and self-regulation (Mahoney & Perales, 2003, 2005).

Responsive Teaching's Design

We designed Responsive Teaching to be a highly flexible curriculum that could be used by parents or by child development and mental health professionals who work both with young children and their parents. RT was designed so that anyone familiar with this program can put together a child development plan, or series of intervention session plans, that is individually tailored to the unique developmental needs of a child. These plans can be developed by using the Curriculum Outline (see Curriculum Material 6 in Section IV),

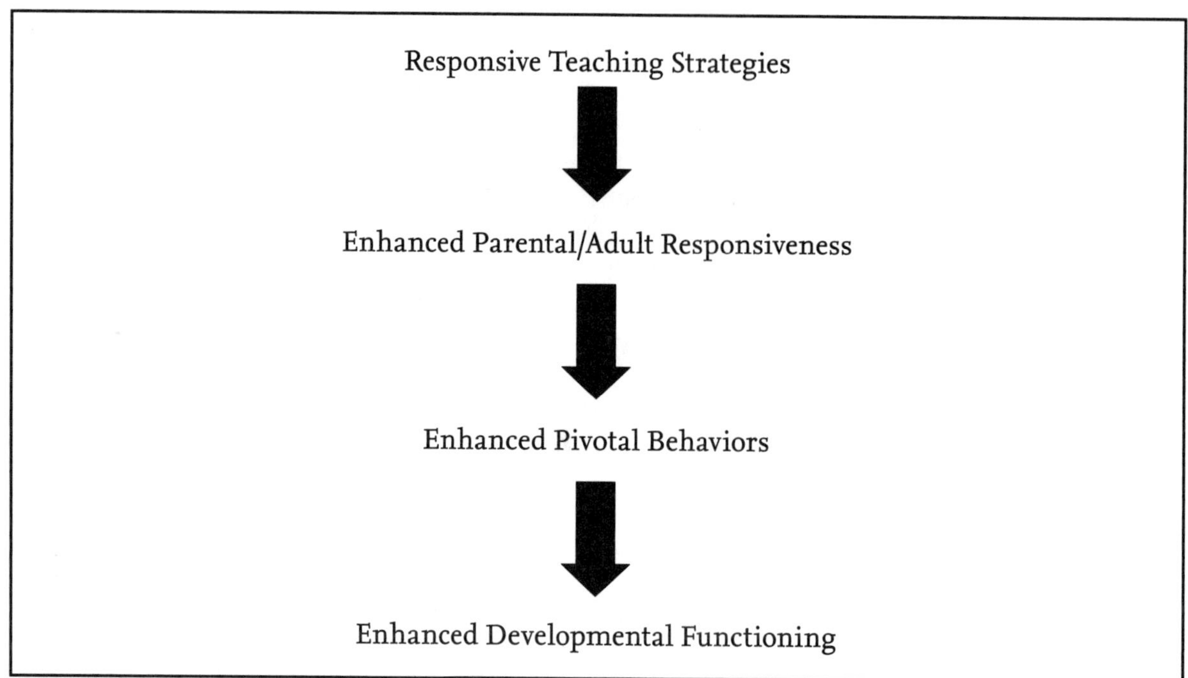

Figure 1.1. Responsive Teaching logic model.

which is a menu of RT strategies, intervention topics, and assessment items that can be used to address pivotal behaviors that are the foundations for cognitive, communication, and social–emotional development. The RT Pivotal Behavior Wizard (see Curriculum Material 2 in Section IV) is a user-friendly tool designed to help select pivotal behavior objectives that are appropriate to a child's developmental needs and current behavior. Once a pivotal behavior has been selected, parents or professionals simply need to select one to two intervention topics and RT strategies to work on from the Curriculum Outline. Session plans can be completed by either (a) developing a handwritten lesson plan using the descriptions of the RT strategies and intervention topics provided in this manual or (b) generating lesson plans on a personal computer using the Responsive Teaching Curriculum Planning and Tracking Program, available on CD-ROM.

Because RT is effective at promoting three domains of developmental functioning, this program can be used by professionals from a variety of disciplines, including professionals who focus on children's cognitive development, such as early intervention specialists, teachers, parent educators, or occupational therapists; professionals concerned with children's language development, such as speech–language pathologists; and professionals concerned with children's social–emotional development, such as nurses, psychologists, psychiatrists, and social workers.

The structure of this curriculum is ideally suited for use by interdisciplinary teams of professionals who are working with a family to address different developmental concerns related to their specialty area. One advantage of RT is that it assures that, even though they are addressing different developmental concerns, professionals are providing information and suggestions that complement each other. This makes it easier for parents to follow through with all of the intervention recommendations that are made. When professionals are working alone with families, the RT curriculum enables these professionals to address problems or concerns that extend beyond their comfort zone or realm of expertise.

Chapter 2

The Role of Parents in Child Development Interventions

One of the central tenets of Responsive Teaching (RT) is that parents are the key to the development and well-being of their young children. No matter how stimulating are the toys and materials children have at home, or how exceptional are the learning activities children receive in preschool, childcare, special education, or therapy, it is the quality of the experiences that parents provide their children that ultimately determines whether children attain their maximum developmental potential. Child development programs such as preschool, childcare, and therapies can play an important role in promoting children's development and well-being, but only if they take seriously their responsibility to help parents nurture and support their children's development (Bronfenbrenner, 1974, 1979). This is as true for children with developmental risks or problems as it is for children who have no developmental problems at all (MacDonald & Blott, 1974; Mahoney, Boyce, Fewell, Spiker, & Wheeden, 1998).

The Importance of Parents

There are at least three major reasons why parents play such a critical role in their children's development. First, all parents, whether they are biological or adoptive parents, have a special social–emotional bond or attachment to their children that no one else can, or should, try to replace. This bond places parents in the unique role of being the most powerful influence in the lives of their young children, even if their time with their children is limited because of work or other responsibilities. Not only is this bond the reason why young children prefer to be with their parents, it is also what makes the things that parents say or do more influential on young children than whatever any other adults say or do.

Second, children's learning and development is a continuous process that can occur in any situation in which children are actively engaged. When or where children learn new developmental information or skills is determined by what children pay attention to and by what interests or excites them; it has little, if anything, to do with whether adults are trying to teach children or provide experiences to help them learn. Young children are as likely to learn new information or skills as they wake up in the morning, eat breakfast, take a bath, play with their parents, or ride in a car as they would in a preschool or childcare classroom, or when they receive special instruction from therapists or other child development specialists. Parents' unique capability to influence their children's developmental learning comes from the fact that they are the ones most likely to "be there" when their children are ready to learn.

Third, the opportunities parents have to interact with and influence their children's development are far greater than the opportunities that any other professionals or adults could ever have. This effect is accentuated by the fact that most parents are a constant influence in their children's lives throughout the early childhood years.

To illustrate these points, we conducted a hypothetical analysis of the opportunities parents have to influence their children's development compared to teachers, therapists, or intervention specialists when children are in preschool special education or early intervention classes. As indicated in Table 2.1, we assumed that preschool special education classes last about 2½ hours per day, 4 days a week, for approximately 30 weeks each year. If children also receive therapy, such as speech–language pathology or physical therapy, these therapy sessions last approximately ½ hour and are usually provided 1 day a week for 35 weeks a year. We also assumed that most parents spend at least 1 hour per day in one-to-one contact with their children.

When we analyzed classrooms in terms of the total amount of time teachers interact with children each week (assuming two teachers in a classroom divided among 12 children and distributed among group instruction, one-to-one interactions, and management activities), we estimated that children receive approximately 33 minutes of one-to-one interaction with their teachers each week. This can be contrasted with approximately 25 minutes of one-on-one time with therapists and 420 minutes with parents.

However, because parents are with children 52 weeks each year—whereas teachers and therapists average between 30 to 35 weeks—the greater amount of one-to-one time parents spend with their children each week is magnified by the number of weeks they are with their children over the course of a year. Assuming that most adults engage in 10 interactions per minute, parents engage in at least 220,000 discrete interactions with their children each year, whereas teachers engage in approximately 9,900 and therapists 8,750 interactions in the same period of time.

As illustrated in Figure 2.1, if a child were enrolled in a special education or early intervention classroom or playgroup and also received therapy once each week, in 1 year parents would have at least 200,000 more interactions, or opportunities to influence their children's development, than teachers and therapists combined.

Table 2.1

Comparison of Opportunities To Engage in One-on-One Interactions with a Young Child in Early Intervention

	Teacher/Classroom	Therapist/Specialist	Mother/ Primary Caregiver
Context for interaction	2½ Hours per day; 4 Days per week, 2 Teachers, 12 Children. Group time; Management time; One-on-one time.	30-Minute session; 1 Day per week.	1 Hour per day, 7 Days per week. Holding; Comforting; Playing; Communicating; Childcare; Feeding; Transporting.
One-on-one time per week (minutes)	33	25	420
Weeks per year	30	30	52
Minutes per year	990	750	22,000
Interactions per minute	10	10	10
Interactions per year	9,900	7,500	220,000
Relative opportunities to influence child compared to mother	4.5%	3.4%	92.1%

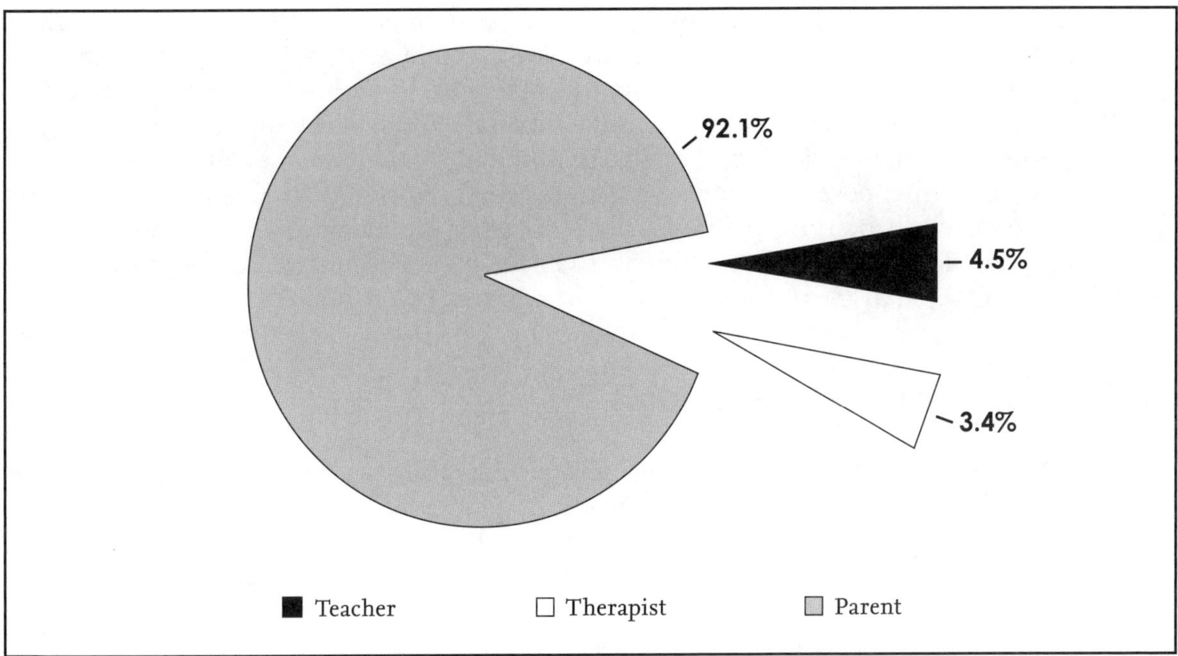

Figure 2.1. Who has the greatest impact on children's development?

This is an extremely conservative estimate of the opportunities parents have to influence their children's development. If parents spend 2 or more hours each day interacting with their children, as many parents do, the discrepancy between the opportunities parents have to interact with their children compared with the opportunities of teachers and therapists would be magnified by 2 or 3 times. Still, our example illustrates how even parents who have limited time with their children because of work or other responsibilities still have substantially more opportunities to influence their children's development than professionals could ever have.

What This Means for Parents

The idea that parents are the key to children's development means that, if parents are truly concerned about enhancing their children's development or social–emotional well-being, they must play a major role and take on the responsibility for bringing about fundamental changes in the types of developmental stimulation their children receive. Even if preschool, childcare, or other child development programs do not work collaboratively with parents, parents still have a major role in enhancing their children's development. As convenient as it might be for parents to assume that educators and professionals can address their children's developmental concerns by themselves, parents are not capable of relinquishing their role as a primary influence on their children's development. Children simply never stop learning from their parents, nor do they benefit more from the stimulation provided by teachers and other professionals than they do from the stimulation provided by their parents.

Responsive Teaching can help parents make fundamental and dramatic changes in the quality of developmental stimulation they provide their children without placing undue stress on them. When parents learn to infuse Responsive Teaching strategies into the more than 220,000 interactions they have with their children each year, they will dramatically enhance the quality of developmental stimulation they provide their children. By continually using RT strategies in routine interactions with their children, parents teach their children the habit of using pivotal behaviors while they play and interact. This optimizes the developmental learning potential of each of the routine activities children experience and helps them to realize their maximum developmental potential.

Parents can choose to implement Responsive Teaching on their own, or they can choose to work collaboratively with teachers and other professionals to learn how to carry out this intervention with their children. In either case, Responsive Teaching will maximize parents' effectiveness at promoting their children's development and well-being.

What This Means for Professionals

In many professional training programs, teachers and child development professionals are trained to implement procedures that are designed primarily to work directly with children alone. Little if any of the training professionals receive adequately prepares them to understand either *what* they should be encouraging parents to do with their children or *how* to go about this process. The instructional and therapeutic procedures that professionals use are often highly effective at encouraging young children to learn and perform important developmental behaviors in classrooms, clinics, or home visits. But no matter how effective professionals are, the activities they implement with children can never offset the influence that parents have on their children.

Although intervention should be a collaborative partnership between parents and professionals, it is not an equal partnership. No matter what professionals do with children, the stimulation parents provide while interacting with their children ultimately accounts for how effectively intervention promotes children's developmental well-being. The time analysis we reported makes it clear that, if children have the potential to learn from each of the interactions they have with adults throughout their day, intervention cannot enhance children's learning and development unless it involves children's parents—the people who have the greatest opportunities to interact with children.

This does not mean that professionals and early childhood teachers need to stop providing direct services to children. On the contrary, professionals provide children exciting and stimulating developmental and educational experiences. These activities broaden children's horizons by giving them experiences they may not typically have with their parents and others. Through these experiences, professionals are able to gain a unique perspective about children's skills and abilities and to identify talents that children may rarely display with their parents and others. By modeling and testing various instructional strategies with children, professionals can develop a better understanding of the unique learning styles and habits of children. This information can be used to help parents and others learn to maximize their effectiveness during routine interactions with their children. What is most important, professionals can monitor children's developmental progress to make sure that children's intervention objectives are being met and to either support and sustain parents' current intervention efforts or change intervention objectives or instructional strategies when necessary. In other words, professionals can continue providing the type of clinical services that they were trained to provide. However, these services need to be limited so that there is sufficient time to work directly with parents to help them learn to support their children's developmental and social–emotional well-being by engaging in responsive interactions during routine interactions with their children.

One example of this type of clinical practice was reported by Koegel, Koegel, Shoshan, and McNerney (1999), who reported a case study of 6 children with autism who received discrete trial training intervention. Results from this case study indicated that the amount these children benefited from discrete trial training was related to how much they "initiated" while interacting with their mothers. Over a period of several years, children who were low initiators decreased their rate of developmental functioning, even though they participated in a modified discrete trial training intervention; children who were high initiators, however, made remarkable developmental improvements.

Based upon these findings, Koegel et al. (1999) taught another group of 4 mothers to use responsive strategies to help their children with autism who were low initiators increase their rate of initiation. Results indicated that mothers were successful in helping their children improve their initiation rate by using responsive strategies. In addition, after several years of intervention, their children benefited from discrete trial training in a manner that was comparable to the children who were high initiators in the case study described. In this situation, the researchers were able to increase the effectiveness of an intervention procedure they had been using for several years by adding a parent component in which they helped parents learn to use responsive interaction strategies with their children at home.

Similarly, professionals can incorporate Responsive Teaching into their service as a means for working collaboratively with parents while using their current clinical procedures with children. To do this, however, professionals must structure intervention sessions so that they have sufficient time not only to work directly with children but also to help parents learn to use Responsive Teaching.

Preschool and childcare classrooms provide several important learning and developmental experiences as well, yet, like professionals, these classrooms are also unlikely to have a meaningful impact on children's development and social–emotional well-being unless they help parents support these objectives by engaging in responsive interactions with their children at home (Mahoney, Wheeden, & Perales, 2004). Preschool and childcare programs serve the important functions of helping children become accustomed to being away from their parents as well as learning to conform to the rules, structure, and expectations of a school setting. These programs expose children to a rich variety of developmental learning activities that are fun and enjoyable. Children not only have the opportunity to benefit from these activities, but, perhaps more important, they also have the opportunity learn how to socialize and form friendships with other children.

For the past several years, we have been implementing a model preschool project for children with special needs in which we have been field-testing different models for both conducting preschool classrooms and working with parents to help them use Responsive Teaching with their children at home (Mahoney & Wheeden, 2000). One model that was not effective was attempting to teach Responsive Teaching strategies to parents in the classroom while their children were there. Teachers found it overwhelming to balance the demands of running a classroom with 12 active preschoolers while at the same time trying to connect with their parents in a meaningful way. However, in subsequent models, we reduced the number of days that we operated the classrooms to either 2 or 3 half days a week, using the remainder of the time for teachers to meet individually with parents and children. These options allowed children to continue to participate regularly in a high-quality preschool program in which they were both exposed to a rich array of developmentally appropriate activities and had the opportunities to socialize and form friendships with other children. These options also gave teachers the time they needed to meet with parents to help them learn to use Responsive Teaching with their children at home. Parents not only reported enjoying the opportunity to learn how to better support their children's development but were delighted that their children continued to have the opportunity to participate in a high-quality preschool program.

Professionals have worried about the propriety of asking parents to use Responsive Teaching with their children during daily routines (McCollum & Hemmeter, 1997). Many teachers and therapists view their job responsibility as "teaching" the child and do not want to make parents do their work for them. They have also struggled with the apparent contradiction between family-centered service philosophy, which asks professionals to minimize the hardships and stressors in parents' lives, and a model of intervention that essentially places the burden of intervention on parents (Baird & Peterson, 1997). These are legitimate and serious concerns.

Parental involvement in Responsive Teaching does not overburden parents, however; rather, it makes it easier and more enjoyable for them to be with their children (Mahoney & Wheeden, 1997). Most parents who have participated in Responsive Teaching have found that caring for their children becomes easier, more productive, and enjoyable when they learn how to fine-tune their daily interactions to their children's learning needs. Responsive Teaching strategies do not interfere with parents' natural interactions with their children. Rather, consistent with the goals of family-centered service philosophy, they enhance the quality of these interactions and transform them into highly efficient learning opportunities.

In our view, it is not "family focused" for professionals to withhold key facts from parents. Intervention does not enhance children's development unless there is a substantial improvement in the developmental stimulation children receive throughout their entire day. If intervention fails to promote responsive parent–child interaction—the most potent influence on children's development—then, as supported by recent evidence, intervention is unlikely to enhance children's developmental functioning (Mahoney et al., 1998). Infants, toddlers, and preschoolers do not reap the benefits from intervention by simply attending services. Interventions that truly work do not happen only in classrooms or therapy sessions. Professionals need to develop their interventions so that they become a continuous activity that happens during children's routine play interactions and activities. Only by collaborating with parents can professionals make this happen.

Summary

In this chapter we discussed how parents are the most important influence on young children's development and social–emotional functioning. We presented a hypothetical analysis of the number of opportunities that children who receive early intervention or special education services have to interact with their teachers and therapists as compared with their parents. Results from this analysis provide overwhelming evidence that, even for children who receive intensive child development services, parents have at least 10 times more opportunities to affect their children's developmental functioning than do all professionals combined.

These data support recent research findings that parents are the key ingredient to effective interventions. Interventions are more likely to be effective when parents support the developmental goals of intervention by engaging in responsive interactions with their children.

Two conclusions can be derived from these observations. First, parents can be their children's developmental interventionists. Parents who are able to use RT on their own and engage in more responsive interactions with their children can take comfort in the fact that they are implementing one of the most powerful child development interventions yet to be discovered. Second, professionals and teachers who primarily provide direct services to children should continue to do this. However, insofar as their primary concern is to enhance children's development and social–emotional well-being, professionals must supplement their services with serious efforts to help parents learn how to support their children's developmental functioning. RT provides an evidence-based curriculum that professionals can use to ensure that parents learn RT strategies and understand how these strategies will help them achieve the outcomes they desire for their children.

Chapter 3

Overview of the Responsive Teaching Curriculum

The design of the Responsive Teaching (RT) curriculum was based upon the idea that, even though this program will be implemented by parents, it must conform to the structure and requirements that professionals are required to follow. Increasingly, professionals from all disciplines must carry out their services using some type of planning or reporting form, such as the Individualized Family Service Plan (IFSP) or an Individualized Educational Program (IEP). These planning forms ask professionals to answer the following questions about their services:

- What is the goal of the intervention?
- What are the objectives or intermediate steps that will be addressed to achieve the goal?
- What activities will be carried out to reach each of the objectives?
- What types of criteria will be used to determine that the objectives have been accomplished?
- How will progress toward attaining the goal be measured?

Generally, these considerations are less important to parents who do not need to complete IEPs or IFSPs and who simply want to know what they can do to help their child. Nonetheless, the structure of this curriculum can still be useful to parents. It helps to clarify important distinctions among

- what parents can do to help their child,
- what children should do as a result of the strategies their parents use, and
- how parents' use of strategies promotes the developmental and social–emotional outcomes they desire for their children.

The Responsive Teaching Quick Start, included in Table 3.1, summarizes the components of this curriculum and the sequence of activities that we recommend for developing and implementing RT intervention sessions or child development plans. In Figure 3.1 we illustrate how the major components of Responsive Teaching can be grouped according to goals, objectives, and intervention procedures. The remainder of this chapter provides an overview of each of the components of Responsive Teaching and describes the process that is used to construct intervention plans.

Table 3.1

Responsive Teaching Quick Start

Responsive Teaching	Parent-mediated intervention designed to enhance children's functioning across three developmental domains
Developmental Domains	Cognition, communication, and social–emotional functioning (These are the *goals* addressed by Responsive Teaching)
Pivotal Behaviors	Behaviors children must use in their routine interactions to progress in a targeted developmental domain (These are the intervention *objectives*)
Discussion Points	Information that guides discussions with parents about what defines a pivotal behavior and the role that the pivotal behavior plays in learning and development
Responsive Teaching Strategies	Intervention activities that parents and others can use during routine interactions to help encourage children's use of pivotal behaviors
Pivotal Behavior Profile	Rating scales used to assess children's progress in acquiring each pivotal behavior
Family Action Plan	Written plan outlining what parents will do to follow through with Responsive Teaching strategies and suggestions
Pivotal Behavior Wizard	Tool that helps select pivotal behaviors that are best suited to the needs of the child
Planning and Tracking Form/Program	Form or CD-ROM used to select and track the discussion points and Responsive Teaching strategies to be covered in an intervention session
Curriculum Outline	Content for the intervention sessions, including • Facts and considerations about each pivotal behavior • Discussion points to be covered with the parent • Responsive Teaching strategies that can be used to promote each pivotal behavior

Developmental Domains

The goals addressed by Responsive Teaching are the developmental domains that child development research has shown to be influenced by parental responsiveness. RT focuses on cognition, communication, and social–emotional functioning because of the considerable research evidence showing that responsive parental interactions promote these aspects of children's development.

In Responsive Teaching, there is only one goal for each developmental domain. These goals reflect the intended outcomes of intervention. Developmental intervention is not simply about children learning the specific skills and behaviors we teach them; rather, it is about promoting fundamental changes in children's development. Developmental goals are the guiding rationale for the activities conducted in intervention and are the benchmarks for assessing whether intervention is accomplishing what is intended.

There are two issues to note about the goals recommended for RT. First, intervention goals are the same for all children, regardless of the severity of their developmental problems. Whether children are only "at risk" for delayed language development or have severe communication problems, the goal of intervention is the same—to help children develop more productive and useful communication. Second, most of the outcomes parents identify for their children can be translated into one or a combination of the Responsive Teaching intervention goals. For example, if a parent wants her child to communicate or

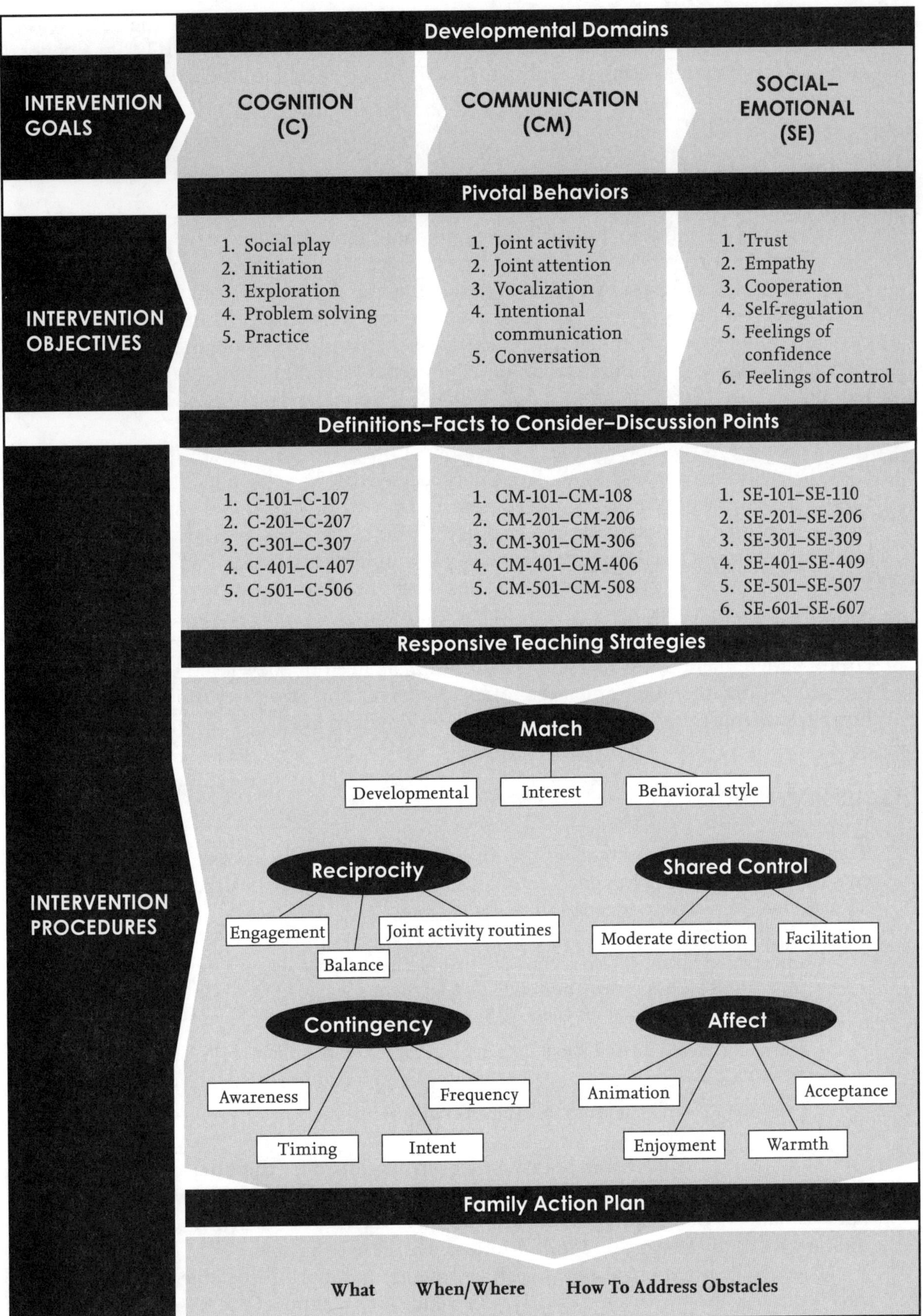

Figure 3.1. Responsive Teaching curriculum.

share his feelings, that parent's concerns can be interpreted as falling in the goal areas of communication or social–emotional functioning. Parents' outcomes point to the general goal or developmental domain that is the focus of the child's individualized intervention program.

Pivotal Behaviors

As indicated in Figure 3.1 for each developmental goal, Responsive Teaching prescribes a small set of intervention objectives. These objectives are the pivotal behaviors children must use to progress in a targeted developmental domain. RT intervention objectives are not the test items or behaviors that are used to assess children's developmental functioning; rather, they are the behavioral processes that child development theory and research have shown to be the basis for developmental learning. They are the behaviors that parents and adults encourage each time they use Responsive Teaching strategies with their children.

There are three noteworthy features of RT intervention objectives. First, although these behaviors do not represent all of the processes that have been identified as contributors to developmental learning, they address the learning processes that are most commonly identified in contemporary child development theory. Second, these objectives are behaviors children must use simultaneously throughout the entire developmental period. Intervention must address these objectives over long periods of time and revisit them whenever children stop using them. Third, individualized intervention or child development plans are developed by targeting those pivotal behaviors that are most relevant to a child's developmental needs. Thus, interventionists need not develop their own objectives for each child; rather, they only need to select intervention objectives from the RT curriculum that are most pertinent to the child's individualized needs.

Discussion Points

Responsive Teaching intervention sessions focus on the strategies and activities that parents can implement during daily interactions. Thus, the activities that take place during RT sessions should help parents

- understand how the pivotal behavior that has been targeted as the intervention objective will both improve the child's developmental learning and help parents attain the outcome they want for their child;
- learn to understand and use RT strategies that will foster their child's use of pivotal behaviors; and
- integrate RT strategies into their child's daily, routine activities.

More than 130 discussion points have been developed for this curriculum. These discuss in simple language the theories of development that are the basis for this curriculum. They explain why certain behaviors are "pivotal" to children's learning and development and how RT strategies encourage children to use these behaviors.

Discussion points have been designed so that parents will be able to complete each intervention session with a few clearly defined ideas that support the RT strategies parents have been asked to use with their children. Discussion points formalize what good professionals typically do. They provide a focused and cohesive structure for providing child development information to parents.

Often, when professionals explain the rationale for what they ask parents to do, two problems occur. First, they provide *too much* information. They fail to help parents focus on one or two critical ideas to think about until the next session. As a result, some parents end the sessions somewhat bewildered, not fully understanding how the discussion that took place was related to the RT strategies demonstrated during the session. Because parents are preoccupied with the day-to-day tasks and responsibilities of their busy lives, too much information can make it difficult to recall anything discussed during the session.

Second, professionals tend to *repeat the same things,* often failing to put a new twist or insight into the information. This results in intervention sessions lacking freshness and limits professionals' effectiveness at helping parents understand what they can do to support and enhance their children's developmental learning.

Discussion points help to address these problems. Each discussion point emphasizes a key idea that reinforces the importance of using RT strategies to address children's developmental needs. Professionals and parents can use these to focus on one or two ideas that underscore the importance of a pivotal behavior to children's developmental progress. By keeping track of the discussion points covered in each session, interventionists are more apt to review them at subsequent sessions and to select different discussion points at following sessions so that parents have the opportunity to learn several key ideas about children's developmental learning.

Responsive Teaching Strategies

Responsive Teaching includes approximately 70 Responsive Teaching strategies. These strategies are brief, easy-to-remember suggestions or reminders (e.g., "take one turn and wait"; "imitate your child") that parents can use to monitor and change how they interact with their children at any time and in any situation. The word *responsive* indicates that these strategies help parents learn to use each of the five dimensions of responsive interaction that we described in Chapter 1. The word *teaching* emphasizes that these strategies are instructional procedures that encourage children's use of the pivotal behaviors that are the foundations for their developmental learning.

To develop Responsive Teaching, we surveyed several "relationship-focused" curricula from which we identified more than 120 different strategies, which we eventually reduced to a list of 66 strategies. As we attempted to categorize these strategies, we realized that they could be grouped into the five dimensions of responsive interaction—including reciprocity, contingency, shared control, affect, and developmental match—with several subcategories in each dimension. In other words, these 66 strategies address the complex parenting qualities that are involved in responsive interaction.

There are not as many different dimensions of responsiveness as there are responsive teaching strategies. Nonetheless, by providing several strategies that address the same dimension, Responsive Teaching gives multiple options for learning to implement these behaviors. For example, the strategies "act as a play partner," "interact for fun," and "turn routines into games" provide three different ways of emphasizing the importance of adults' enjoying interaction with their child. These strategies, which promote the same dimension or quality of responsiveness, give interventionists three different ways of describing the same information. It is not necessary to use all of these strategies; however, when an adult is having difficulty acquiring certain dimensions of responsive interaction, multiple strategies can be used across successive intervention sessions to focus on learning this component of responsiveness.

Pivotal Behavior Profile

One of the most important considerations for any intervention curriculum is determining whether it meets the objectives it intends to address. In Responsive Teaching, the primary objective is to increase children's use of the pivotal behaviors that are the foundations for those areas of developmental functioning that have been targeted as intervention objectives. The RT strategies that parents are asked to use with their child are selected because they are well-suited to promoting the pivotal behavior that has been identified as the child's objective. The question that needs to be assessed is whether parents' use of these strategies is actually helping their child make progress in their use of the targeted pivotal behaviors.

The Pivotal Behavior Profile (see Curriculum Material 3 in Section IV) is the instrument that can be used to assess children's progress. This profile includes 16 individual rating scales that correspond to the 16 pivotal behaviors addressed in Responsive Teaching. Each of these scales rate how well a child is using a pivotal behavior on a 10-point scale (1 = *very low*, 10 = *very high*). The pivotal behaviors and criteria for rating the behavior are written in clear, understandable language so that these scales are basically self-explanatory. The Pivotal Behavior Profile was designed so that parents and professionals can periodically assess the child's behavior. Parents should keep their own personal copies of this scale, which they can display in a convenient area of their home, such as on the refrigerator or a bulletin board, as a reminder of what they are trying to accomplish while incorporating RT strategies into their routine interactions with their children.

Family Action Plans

Family Action Plans (see Curriculum Material 5 in Section IV) are perhaps the most critical component of Responsive Teaching. No matter how effective an intervention session has been, or how much the parent has understood or was able to implement RT strategies during the session, intervention will have little impact on children's developmental functioning if it is not integrated into their daily routine.

Family Action Plans are the part of the intervention where parents take the lead. After parents have been presented information and given the opportunity to practice Responsive Teaching strategies, it is up to them to decide how to follow through with this information. The kinds of activities included in Family Action Plans are based upon where parents are with regard to understanding, accepting, and using Responsive Teaching. If parents have reservations about the value of this approach, it may include activities such as (a) thinking about information presented during the session, (b) discussing intervention concepts with their spouses or others, or (c) observing the child in different situations. If parents are just beginning to learn RT strategies, it could include (a) practicing strategies during focused play activities or (b) integrating strategies into daily routines. If parents want to expand their children's opportunities for responsive interaction, it might include (a) teaching others (spouse, siblings, relatives) to use strategies and (b) discussing the intervention program with professionals who work with the child.

Family Action Plans specify *what* parents are going to do, *when* and *where* they are going to do it, and for *what duration of time*. Family Action Plans include clear, specific suggestions and reminders (e.g., "imitate my child's sounds" when I change his diaper or "take one turn and wait" during bath time). They enhance the developmental effectiveness of Responsive Teaching by helping parents integrate this intervention into children's natural environments.

Menu-Driven Curriculum

Responsive Teaching uses a menu-driven curriculum. This enables professionals to develop intervention session plans that are both responsive to children's current level of functioning and individualized to parents' knowledge, capabilities, and unique family circumstances.

The Responsive Teaching Planning and Tracking Form (see Curriculum Material 4 in Section IV) is designed to assist interventionists in planning and tracking the content provided in each intervention session. This form lists the selection of discussion points and RT strategies that can be used to address each pivotal behavior. Using this form, interventionists or parents can plan and track each of their intervention sessions so that they are tailored to the needs of children and parents in a manner that builds upon the information presented in the previous session.

The RT Curriculum Outline (see Curriculum Material 6 in Section IV) describes the content for intervention sessions including (a) facts and considerations about each pivotal behavior, (b) discussion points to be covered with the parent, and (c) RT strategies that can be used to promote each pivotal behavior. To develop intervention session plans, parents or professionals need only to fill out a session plan form using the descriptions of the RT strategies and discussion points that were selected from the Planning and Tracking Form.

We have also developed the Responsive Teaching Curriculum Planning and Tracking Program, available on CD-ROM, to make the curriculum even easier to use. This program, which is compatible with personal computers that run Microsoft Windows 2000 or more recent versions of Windows, includes the complete Responsive Teaching curriculum. Once a file has been set up for a client, interventionists can construct session plans by using drop-down menus to select the goals, intervention objectives, RT strategies, and discussion points they want to use in a session. The Pivotal Behavior Wizard is also built into this program to assist in selecting intervention objectives. Using this program, interventionists can complete individualized session plans in less than 2 minutes. The program then automatically develops and prints plans that can be used by both professionals and parents.

This menu-driven format combines some of the most desirable features of two common curricular approaches used in early intervention. First, RT is a clinical intervention curriculum. The menu-driven format provides early intervention with sufficient flexibility so that interventions can be tailored to the unique needs and learning styles of children and parents as well as be responsive to new problems or concerns that parents bring up during their session. Interventionists not only have the option of choosing the intervention objectives, RT strategies, and discussion points they want to work on, they also can decide how much information to present during each session and how long to work on this information.

Second, RT is a structured curriculum. Although clinical intervention procedures are helpful for accommodating to the diverse needs of children and parents, many professionals do not have the time needed to plan and carry out individualized services. In addition, clinical interventions that do not follow a fixed sequence of activities run the risk of becoming sidetracked by addressing problems that arise and losing sight of the long-term goal of promoting the child's development.

The menu-driven structure of Responsive Teaching helps to avoid these problems. Responsive Teaching requires professionals to use their clinical judgment to select the objectives and content that they use in an intervention session, and two features have been built into the curriculum to guide this process. First, the Pivotal Behavior Wizard is provided to help select intervention objectives that are best suited to the needs of the child. Second, the information presented in the Planning and Tracking Form, Responsive Teaching Curriculum Planning and Tracking Program, and Curriculum Outline limit the content of the session plan to RT strategies and discussion points that are relevant to the desired child development outcomes. These features assure that the scope of intervention activities implemented over time provide a logical and coherent sequence for promoting the goals desired from this program.

RT Is Adaptable to a Variety of Formats

The core of Responsive Teaching is the 66 RT strategies. The primary objective of this curriculum is to help parents interact more responsively with their children. Any parent or caregiver who takes the time to learn RT strategies and incorporate these strategies into their routine interactions with their children will become more effective at both promoting their children's pivotal behavior and maximizing their children's development and social–emotional well-being. The other previously described components of the Responsive Teaching curriculum simply make it easier for parents to learn these strategies and help to accommodate RT to the structure and requirements of most clinical service programs for young children, such as early intervention, speech–language pathology, and early childhood mental health.

The various components of Responsive Teaching (e.g., intervention objectives, Responsive Teaching strategies, discussion points, Family Action Plan, Pivotal Behavior Profile, Pivotal Behavior Wizard, Responsive Teaching Planning and Tracking Form, Responsive Teaching Curriculum Planning and Tracking Program) can either be used according to the procedures described in this manual or can be used selectively to meet the specific needs of parents and professionals.

How Parents Can Use RT

Parents who are trying to implement Responsive Teaching on their own can develop their own child development plans by following the procedures outlined in this manual for developing RT intervention session plans. Alternatively, parents can choose to use this curriculum by simply selecting a few RT strategies to implement with their child and by using one or more items from the Pivotal Behavior Profile to assess how these strategies are impacting their children's pivotal behavior. This selective use of RT can be especially effective when parents are familiar with the child development theories and principles on which this program is based. However, if parents are unclear about the underlying rationale for this program, it is helpful for them to review the discussion points to gain a greater insight about how pivotal behaviors contribute to their children's development and well-being.

How RT Can Be Adapted for Parent Groups

We have worked with several professionals who have adapted RT for group parent education programs. These professionals have targeted one or more pivotal behaviors that would be of general interest to the group. They have used the RT Curriculum Outline to identify one or more discussion points and to select one or more RT strategies. Group sessions then involve live or videotaped demonstrations of how to use the RT strategies as well as group discussion about the targeted pivotal behavior. One disadvantage of this group format is that it is not individualized to the specific needs or concerns of each of the parents. However, general discussion topics, such as the role of social play in children's development, can be beneficial for a broad range of parents and children and is useful whether or not parents are already engaging in reciprocal social play with their children.

Summary

In this chapter we have described the four main components of Responsive Teaching: intervention objectives, discussion points, Responsive Teaching strategies, and family action plans. We indicated that the structure of this curriculum was designed to meet the requirements that many professionals have for specifying goals, objectives, intervention activities, and criteria for evaluating children's progress. We also described the tools and procedures included in this curriculum for developing intervention session plans. We indicated that the RT components and recommended procedures have been designed to make it easy for professionals to use RT with parents and children. However, we also described how RT is a flexible curriculum that can be used in a variety of ways by parents and professionals. When implemented successfully, Responsive Teaching can have a substantial impact both on parents' responsiveness and children's use of the pivotal behaviors. As children develop the habit of using pivotal behaviors during their daily activities and interactions, they will begin to make substantial improvements in their developmental growth across multiple domains—including cognition, communication, motivation, and social–emotional functioning.

Section II

Theoretical and Research Foundations

Chapter 4—Responsive Teaching Strategies

Chapter 5—Pivotal Behaviors

Chapter 6—The Effectiveness of Responsive Teaching

Chapter 4

Responsive Teaching Strategies

The underlying logic used to develop Responsive Teaching was very simple. It was based upon the notion that if developmental intervention could encourage parents to accentuate the parenting behaviors or qualities that research has found to be most effective at enhancing children's learning and development, then intervention could help parents maximize the impact they have on their own children's development. As a result, there were two critical questions that needed to be answered before developing this intervention curriculum. First, what are the primary qualities and features of parents that make them *most effective* at promoting young children's development and social–emotional well-being? Second, what types of intervention procedures can be used to help parents acquire and accentuate these parenting features in their own interactions with their children?

Positive Parenting Qualities

For several years, researchers have been interested in determining how parents promote children's development. One of the most popular ideas is that parents influence development primarily through the amount of stimulation they provide their children. Hart and Risley (1995) reported a study of a small sample of children of families from three different social classes (i.e., welfare, working class, and professional families) that provided evidence to support this notion. They reported dramatic differences in the amount of verbal stimulation these three groups of children received from their parents in the first 3 years of life. Professional parents talked 50% more to their children than did working class parents, who in turn spoke 100% more to their children than welfare parents. Differences in the amount of verbal stimulation these three groups of parents provided were related to how well their children were developing when they were 3 years old and when they were 9 and 10 years old. Children from welfare families had substantially lower developmental scores than children from the other two groups.

If "amount of stimulation" were the primary influence on children's development, however, then differences in the amount of stimulation that parents from similar family backgrounds provide children should also be associated with their development. We conducted a language-development study with children with Down syndrome who mostly came from middle class homes that failed to support this notion. Although there were considerable differences in the communication abilities of these children, neither the amount of the mothers' communication with their children nor the quality of the mothers' communication affected children's rate of language development. In fact, the children with the best language had mothers who did the least amount of talking and who used the simplest language when they spoke to their children (Mahoney, 1988a, 1988b). These findings do not refute the idea that children's development is promoted through the amount of stimulation they receive; however, they do suggest that when children have frequent opportunities to interact with their parents, the amount of stimulation they receive is not the most important influence on their language development.

Another idea is that parents promote their children's development by providing stimulation that is closely matched to children's current level of functioning. For example, in the field of language development, many have been interested in the unique way that parents modify their language when speaking to their children. Without thinking, parents adjust the language they use to communicate with their children so that it is more childlike—having short utterances, simple grammatical structure, frequent repetition, considerable inflection, and rising intonation.

This style of communication, referred to as "motherese," would appear to make an ideal model for helping children learn language because it closely matches children's own ability to communicate and is easy to comprehend. In fact, young children are more attentive to motherese than to adult forms of language. However, researchers have yet to find that differences in parents' ability to use motherese affect their children's language development (Hampton & Nelson, 1993). Motherese likely plays some role in helping children learn language; however, similar to "amount of stimulation," this feature does not stand alone as a major influence on children's language development.

Investigations of other parenting behaviors commonly believed to promote children's development have yielded similar findings. For example, childcare books frequently emphasize the importance of giving positive reinforcement to children. However, there is no research to indicate that parental reinforcement has any influence on children's rate of development (Brown & Hanlon, 1970; Nelson, 1973).

Asking children to imitate (i.e., elicited imitation) is another parenting strategy that is thought to influence children's learning and development. Although it is true that young children frequently imitate spontaneously during the language-learning period, there is no evidence that parents increase their children's rate of language development by asking their children to imitate them. Even though many intervention curricula use elicited imitation to teach developmental behaviors to children (e.g., "clap your hands" or "say *apple*"), research indicates that, although this strategy can help children learn to say words when asked, it is not very effective at improving children's spontaneous communication (Camarata, Nelson, & Camaratta, 1994).

Parental Responsiveness Promotes Child Development

The most beneficial studies that have explained how parents influence children's learning have attempted to link various parenting qualities with children's long-term developmental outcomes. They have attempted to understand how parenting contributes to general developmental outcomes, such as children's cognitive or language abilities, as opposed to how they teach specific behaviors or concepts. They describe how parents and children interact with each other, instead of testing preconceived ideas about how certain parenting behaviors help developmental learning. There are at least four parenting characteristics that have been observed in these studies:

- Achievement orientation (the extent to which parents encourage their child to use advanced developmental behaviors)
- Affective quality of parent interactions (parents' energy and enthusiasm, as well as the enjoyment and warmth they display)

- Responsiveness (the degree to which parents support and encourage activities and behaviors their child is involved with)
- Control (the degree to which parents, rather than children, decide what to do when they are with their child)

Parents display these characteristics in almost every interaction they have with their children. These qualities also distinguish the wide range of caregiving styles parents use with their children. Researchers believe they contribute to children's development when evidence shows that children's development is related to the degree to which parents manifest these qualities while interacting with their children.

Research investigating how parents enhance their children's cognitive development shows that, compared to the other interactive qualities described previously, responsiveness is the only parenting quality that consistently predicts children's developmental ages or intelligence quotient (IQ) scores (Beckwith & Cohen, 1989; Bradley, 1989; Fewell, Casal, Glick, Wheeden, & Spiker, 1996). Neither the amount of encouragement, toys, nor other opportunities for stimulation contribute to children's scores on these tests; however, responsiveness is consistently reported to have a positive relationship with children's development.

Responsiveness has also been identified as the primary parenting characteristic that influences communication development (Bornstein, Tamis-LeMonda, & Haynes 1999; Hoff-Ginsberg & Shatz, 1982; Nelson, 1973). Children attain higher levels of communication the more often their parents respond to their communicative behaviors and interpret their attempts to communicate as though they were meaningful. For example, Nelson (1973) compared the language development of children whose parents corrected them for using incorrect word forms to children whose parents responded to their incorrect word usage as if it were meaningful. The children whose parents responded to incorrect language as if it were communicative attained higher levels of communication than the children whose parents corrected them when they mispronounced or used language inaccurately.

Responsiveness also appears to promote social–emotional development. Several studies have reported that responsiveness is associated with children's attachment to their parents, which is one of the most important social–emotional behaviors in the early years of life (Birigen & Robinson, 1991; Kochanska, Forman, & Coy, 1999; Vereijken, Ricksen-Walraven, & Kondo-Ikemura, 1997). In addition, during the preschool years, the one parenting characteristic that predicts how well children get along with their peers and act independently is their mothers' responsiveness with them (Crockenberg & Litman, 1990; Isabella, 1993; van den Boom, 1995).

These research findings suggest that when parents engage in responsive interactions with their children, they are also implementing a highly effective developmental teaching strategy. Insofar as teaching means helping children acquire the skills and behaviors needed to achieve higher levels of competence, parents are actually teaching the foundations of development each time they interact responsively with their children.

Responsiveness Is a Universal Feature of Effective Parenting

The influence of responsiveness on learning and development is a universal phenomenon that is not restricted to western or middle class culture, or to children who are developing typically. Across different cultural groups several differences have been observed in the ways that parents raise their children, and within each cultural group there are differences in how parents interact with their children. Investigations of parenting effectiveness within cultural groups suggest that the most responsive parents in each group are the most effective at promoting their children's development. For example, although Japanese parents have been reported to have a different parenting style than parents from western countries (Bassani, 2003), Bornstein (1989) reported that Japanese mothers' responsiveness with their children was related to their children's developmental growth, at least during the early childhood years.

In the United States, there are socioeconomic status (SES) and racial differences in the way parents raise children. Low SES White and Black parents tend to have a more authoritarian style of child rearing than middle SES families. Nevertheless, within low SES groups, parental responsiveness is one of the few factors that contribute to children's rate of development (Bradley, 1989).

Parents of children with developmental problems tend to be highly directive with their children, most likely because of their desire to encourage their children to engage in age-appropriate behavior. Yet even for these parents, responsiveness, not directiveness, is the main influence on their children's development, regardless of the severity of their problems (Brooks-Gunn & Lewis, 1984; Mahoney, 1988a, 1988b; Mahoney, Finger, & Powell, 1985; Siller & Sigmon, 2002).

Responsiveness Is a Complex Behavior

In our own research, we have found that responsiveness comprises several interactive qualities. These qualities are dimensions, or components, of responsive interaction, and they play an important role in promoting child development (Mahoney, 1988a; Mahoney et al., 1985; Mahoney, Fors, & Wood, 1990; Mahoney & Powell, 1988).

Perhaps a better term for responsiveness is *child orientation;* that is, the interactive qualities associated with responsiveness characterize adults who are primarily focused on supporting and encouraging their children's involvement and participation. Responsive adults incorporate reciprocity, contingency, shared control, affect, and match into their interactions with their children. They understand that their children live in a world of sensations and actions—not the adult world of thinking and speaking. Child orientation contrasts with other parenting roles such as the disciplinarian (make sure the child behaves), teacher (make sure the child learns higher level skills), or monitor (make sure the child is safe and secure). The five dimensions of responsiveness which contribute to this child-oriented style of interaction are described next.

Reciprocity

Interactions are reciprocal when parents and children *engage* in *balanced,* back-and-forth exchanges with each other. Each of the partners offers something of him- or herself to the interaction while responding to what the other person does. Reciprocal interactions are shared, cooperative activities where the partners are attentive to each other. This can be contrasted with interactions where

- the child does all the work, attending primarily to what he or she wants to do, and paying little attention to the adult;

- the adult dominates the interaction, giving the child few opportunities to do what he or she wants, and relegating the child to a passive role where he or she is primarily on the receiving end of the adult's initiatives; or
- interactions are uncoordinated such that neither the adult nor the child is successful at getting the other to attend or cooperate with what he or she wants to do.

Although reciprocity refers to the degree to which interactions between parents and their children are balanced, one of the most important consequences of reciprocity is that it promotes longer and more frequent *joint activity routines* between parents and children. As Goldberg (1977) observed, parents feel good about their parenting skills and enjoy being with their children when they are effective at engaging them in joint activities, which is the hallmark of reciprocity. The success and enjoyment parents gain from interacting with their children encourage them to interact more frequently with their children.

Contingency

Contingency refers to adult interactions that have a direct relationship to the previous behaviors produced by the child. Many parents play with their children and are highly animated and expressive, but they do not produce this stimulation in a way that complements the behaviors their children previously produced. These parents may have a warm, loving relationship and engage in developmentally appropriate activities with their children, but unless their interactions are directly related to what their child did previously, their interactions are not responsive.

Parents' interactions are contingently related to their children's behavior when two conditions are present. First, the "time lapse" between the behavior of the parent and the child is very brief. Contingent interactions occur immediately after the child's behavior, or at least before the child produces two other behaviors. Second, the parents' behavior supports not only the child's actions but also his or her intentions. For these conditions to occur, parents must be sensitive to their children's activity or play interests. They must be keen observers of their children, constantly monitoring their children's behavior and detecting interests that children might indicate by subtle communications, such as gaze or facial expressions. They must be able to interpret what their children are doing; for example, if their child is banging toy pots and pans on a play stove, parents need to respond in a way that complements their child's intention to bang and make noise as opposed to "pretending to cook." Contingency is not only displayed by parents responding when children demand their response, such as by crying or calling the parent; it is also reflected by parents responding to the subtle things children do, even when children do not demand or expect their response.

Shared Control

Responsive parents limit the number of times they direct their children so that they respond to their children more than they direct them, and use direction primarily to facilitate the actions and communications their children initiate. Shared control is a crucial component of responsiveness (MacDonald & Gillette, 1986). Responsive parents provide direction and guidance to children, but they limit the number of times they direct their children so that they respond to their children more often than they direct them. This gives children the opportunity to learn how to respond to adults' requests while at the same time it provides opportunities for children to learn to control the behavior of the adult.

Affect

Responsive parents tend to be *expressive* and *animated* with their children. They express enjoyment at being with their children, and their children react with pleasure and excitement at being with them. Parents can be responsive without exhibiting high affect, and affect alone is not what make parents responsive to their children. Affect is, however, an important component of responsiveness—it fosters children's interest in interacting with them and communicates that the main purpose for interacting is to have fun. This encourages children to participate actively and cooperatively with parents and other adults.

Two other affective qualities associated with responsiveness are *warmth* and *acceptance.* Warmth refers to parents' tenderness and physical displays of affection. Acceptance refers to the extent to which parents' verbal and nonverbal behavior conveys that they approve of what their children do. Parents who are highly accepting communicate that they value whatever their children do through nonverbal and verbal interactions. They do this by treating their children's behavior as meaningful and legitimate, regardless of how "correct" or "appropriate" their behavior might be.

Match

Responsive parents make it easier for their children to understand what they are saying, doing, or requesting by matching or adjusting their behavior to their children. This enables children to respond appropriately to them and increases the likelihood that children will learn from the information and activities adults are presenting them.

Responsive parents match three characteristics of their children. First, they match their child's *developmental level.* That is, what they say, do, or request is similar to, or only slightly more complex, than their child's behavior. If their child communicates with one-word utterances, they communicate with one- to three-word sentences. If their child plays by banging toys together, parents join in the play by banging toys, or by modifying this activity only slightly by introducing different objects to bang, banging on different surfaces, or accompanying their banging with words (e.g., "bang, bang, bang").

Second, responsive parents match children's *interests.* They understand that whatever their children are doing are the activities and behaviors that interest them at the moment. By focusing their attention, communication, and behavior on what their children are currently doing, parents support, augment, and encourage their children's interests.

Third, responsive parents match their expectations and interactions to their children's *behavioral style.* If their children interact slowly, are soft spoken and gentle, responsive parents slow their own pace of interaction, soften their tone of voice, and handle their children gently. If children are active, impulsive, or physical, parents engage in active physical activities, and they refrain from forcing their children to stay engaged in interactions or attend for a longer period of time than their children seem capable of doing.

Parents who successfully match their children's behavioral style adjust their expectations so they are compatible with their children's natural tendencies. If their children do not require a lot of sleep, these parents do not expect their children to go to bed at early hours, and they restrict the amount of time they let their children sleep during the day so they will need to sleep more at night. They recognize that many of the individual characteristics of their children's behavior are caused by their biological predispositions. Rather than fighting biology, responsive parents accommodate to their children's predispositions by being flexible and giving their children the space and support they need.

Conclusion

Although responsiveness is the primary parenting behavior that child development research has found to influence children's developmental functioning, the interactive qualities that co-occur with responsiveness also contribute to the impact that responsiveness has on children's development. Parents who consistently interact responsively with their children

- engage in balanced reciprocal interactions with their children;
- respond contingently to activities their children initiate;
- share control insofar as they encourage their children to control the topic or focus of interactions as often as they themselves do;
- are affective and animated while interacting with their children (i.e., focus more on having fun and taking delight in their children than on trying to coax their children to learn and perform higher level behaviors); and
- match their children so that what they ask or expect their children to do is influenced by their children's actions, state, or behavioral style.

Helpful Intervention Procedures

There are at least three different procedures that interventionists can use to enhance parents' responsiveness with their children. One is to *discuss* with parents what responsiveness is and how it can help their children develop. The second is to *model* responsive interaction with the child in the hope that by observing them, parents will be able to learn this style of interacting with their children. The third is to use *interactive strategies* to (a) demonstrate how to interact responsively with a child, (b) encourage parents to modify specific behaviors while interacting with their children, and (c) provide parents feedback.

For some parents the first two procedures are effective; for many others they are not enough. When interventionists *discuss* in global terms how to interact responsively with their children, many parents see themselves as already doing what the interventionist is recommending. We have worked with several parents, who were not very responsive with their children, who not only agreed with the importance of being responsive but also viewed themselves as already engaging in this style of interaction with their children. As a result, they seldom changed how they interacted with their children just by engaging in these discussions.

The second procedure, *modeling*, is more effective for helping parents understand exactly what responsiveness means. However, modeling involves several steps that make it difficult for many parents. First, modeling requires that parents identify from what they have observed the key behaviors they should copy. Second, parents have to incorporate these behaviors into their own interactions based upon their understanding of what they entail. Third, if there are interactive behaviors that parents instinctively engage in that interfere with their carrying out the behaviors the professional modeled (e.g., asking too many questions or changing play activities with which the child is involved), parents also need to identify these behaviors and determine how to stop them.

In contrast to these two approaches, *interactive strategies* have a number of advantages for working with parents. First, interactive strategies provide specific responsive behaviors on which to focus. Rather than trying to attain global goals, such as interacting "more responsively," interactive strategies provide ministeps to becoming more responsive. Second, strategies are easy to remember, so that parents have little difficulty thinking about them while playing or interacting with their children. Third, strategies provide an objective standard that can be used to provide feedback on how parents are currently interacting with their children, and give concrete targets to work toward.

Responsive Teaching (RT) strategies are based upon the principle of "active learning." They help parents engage in responsive interactions before this is their natural style of interacting with their children. As parents use Responsive Teaching strategies, many discover the impact responsiveness has on their children's engagement and participation. These experiences help parents understand and appreciate the implications this style of interaction has for all encounters with their children. It motivates them to incorporate RT strategies into their spontaneous interactions, and eventually results in their instinctively using a responsive style of interacting with their children.

Responsive Teaching Has 66 Interactive Strategies

Most of the strategies included in Responsive Teaching have been described in several other developmental intervention programs, including *Floor Time* (Greenspan & Wieder, 1998), *It Takes Two to Talk* (Pepper & Weitzman, 2004), and *Enhanced Milieu Language Intervention* (Kaiser & Hester, 1994), as well as intervention programs that we ourselves have developed, including the *ECO-Model* (MacDonald, 1989) and *Transactional Intervention Program* (TRIP; Mahoney & Powell, 1986). From these curricula we identified more than 120 separate Responsive Teaching strategies. We eliminated strategies that duplicated each other, renamed some, and classified the remaining strategies into the five dimensions of responsive interaction. Within each dimension of responsive interaction, we divided the strategies into the subcomponents that constitute that dimension. This process ensured that each of the strategies included in this curriculum could be used to help parents focus on a distinct element of interactive behavior that was integrally related to the general construct of responsive interaction. Thus, as indicated in Figures 4.1 through 4.5, each of the strategies included in Responsive Teaching has a unique, identifiable role in helping adults learn to interact more responsively with children.

We decided to include a large number of strategies in this program so that parents and professionals could have several alternatives for promoting the complex array of behaviors that are entailed in responsive interaction. During the extensive clinical work we did to develop Responsive Teaching, we found that different parents felt more comfortable with different strategies. For example, parents who had difficulty learning and using strategies such as "take one turn and wait" could still attain the same types of responsive interactive qualities using other strategies such as "imitate your child" or "communicate like your child communicates." One of the strengths of Responsive Teaching is that the 66 RT strategies provide a rich array of alternatives for helping parents and other adults learn how to modify and monitor their interactive behavior so that it is responsive and child oriented. The detailed descriptions and suggestions for implementing these strategies, included in the curriculum materials in Section IV, help to ensure that almost any parents who make a serious effort to use these strategies will actually become more responsive and effective interactive partners with their children.

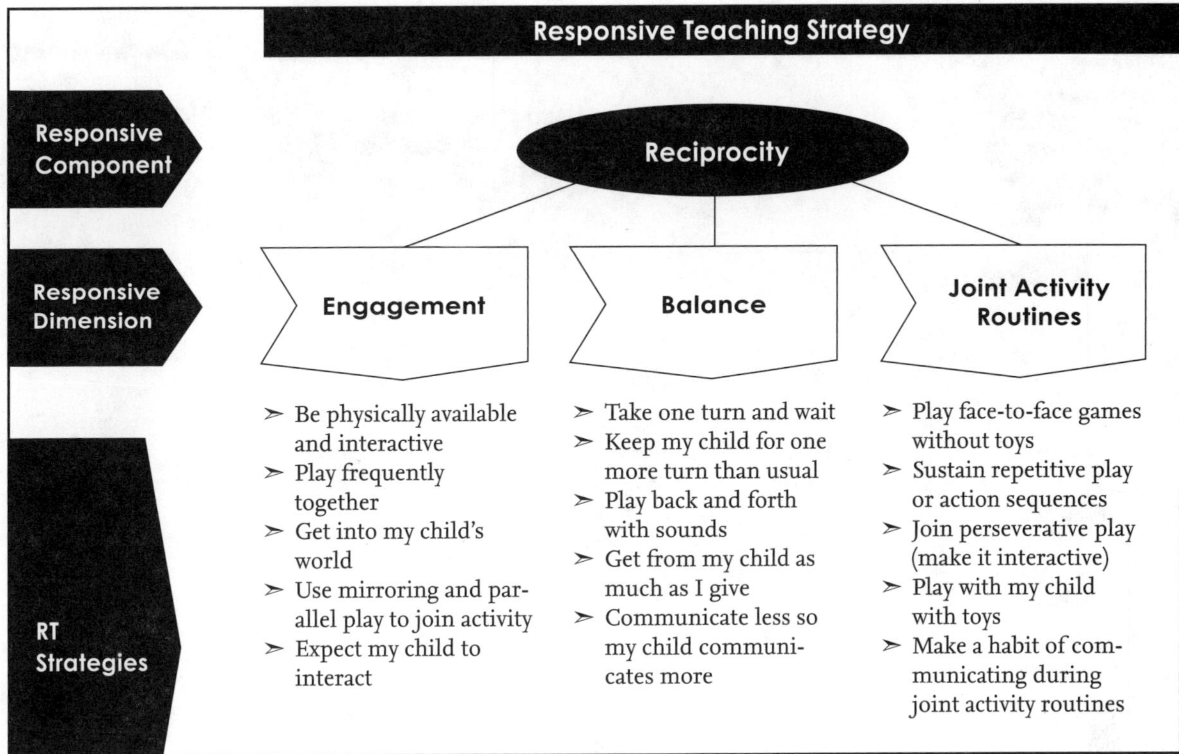

Figure 4.1. Strategies that promote reciprocity.

Responsive Teaching Strategies Are Useful for All Parents

Responsive Teaching strategies are derived from research findings about the types of parental interactions that are effective at promoting children's development. These strategies are not designed to make good parents or bad parents. Rather, they are designed to help parents acquire and use the types of interactive qualities that are most effective at fostering and supporting the development and social–emotional well-being of young children.

Several of the parents with whom we developed these strategies were highly responsive with their children when they first began intervention. Nonetheless, even though Responsive Teaching strategies often encouraged interactions these parents were already doing, they still had some very important benefits. They helped parents feel that they were already engaging in the kinds of behaviors that were necessary to support their children's development and learning. This helped them gain confidence in themselves. Furthermore, the more parents focused on using these strategies, the more they accentuated their natural tendencies to interact responsively, thus increasing their effectiveness at promoting their children's development and social–emotional functioning (see Results, Chapter 6).

If Responsive Teaching strategies are conceptualized only as methods for promoting good parenting or good interaction, we miss the point that responsive interaction is about developmental teaching. We have yet to encounter a parent who was so responsive at the onset of intervention that Responsive Teaching strategies had no additional benefits for his or her child. Responsive Teaching strategies can be beneficial for working with parents identified as having problems in relating with their children (e.g., abuse or neglect). Nonetheless, just like any other instructional technique, they are equally, if not more,

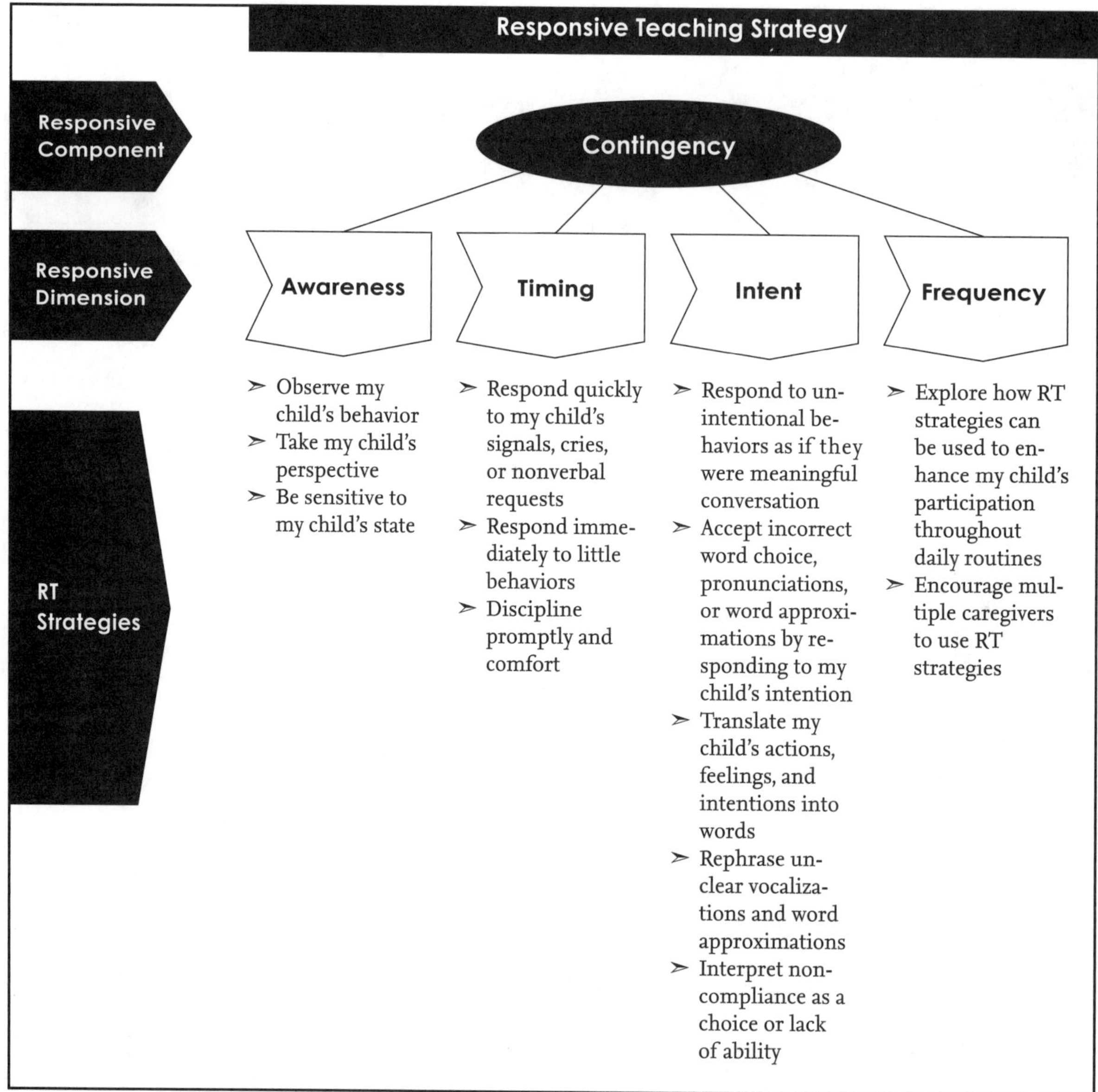

Figure 4.2. Strategies that promote contingency.

effective at helping competent parents become even more capable at nurturing and supporting their children's development and social–emotional well-being.

Summary

In this chapter, we have listed each of the instructional strategies used in Responsive Teaching and described the rationale for these strategies. Responsive Teaching strategies are designed to encourage adults to engage in highly responsive interactions with their children. Responsive interaction is a complex behavior, not just the simple act of reacting to a child. We explain how child development research has reported that responsive interaction is one of the most powerful developmental teaching methods yet to be identified. Detailed descriptions of each of these strategies are presented in the Curriculum Outline (see Curriculum Material 6 in Section IV).

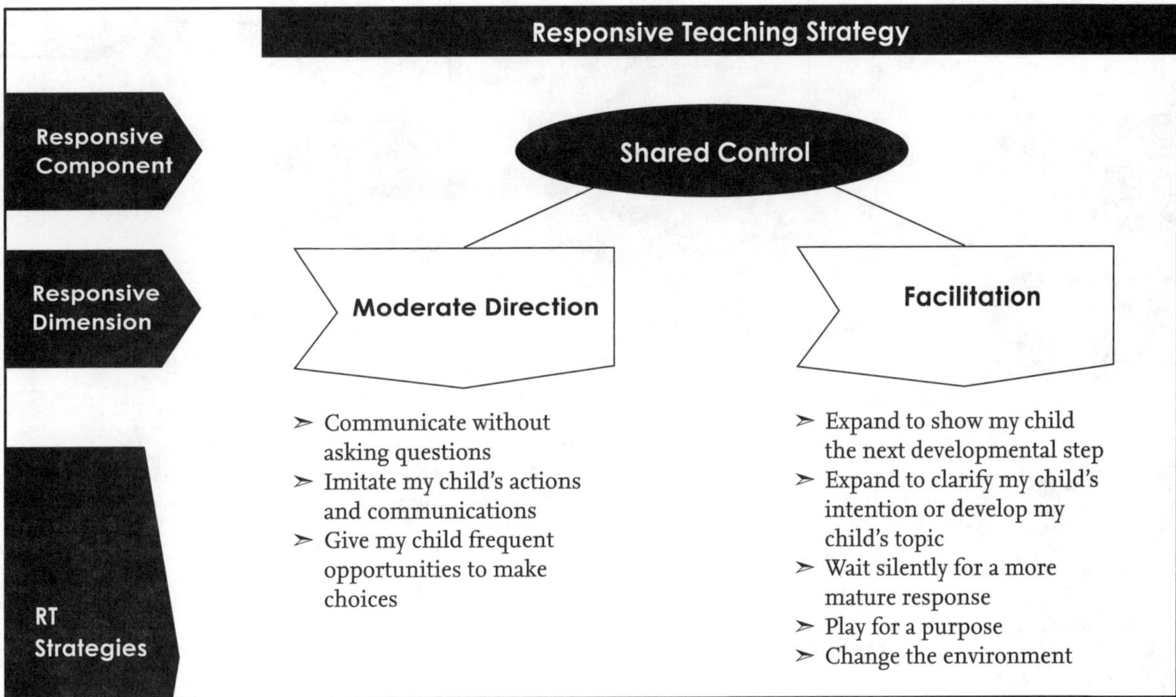

Figure 4.3. Strategies that promote shared control.

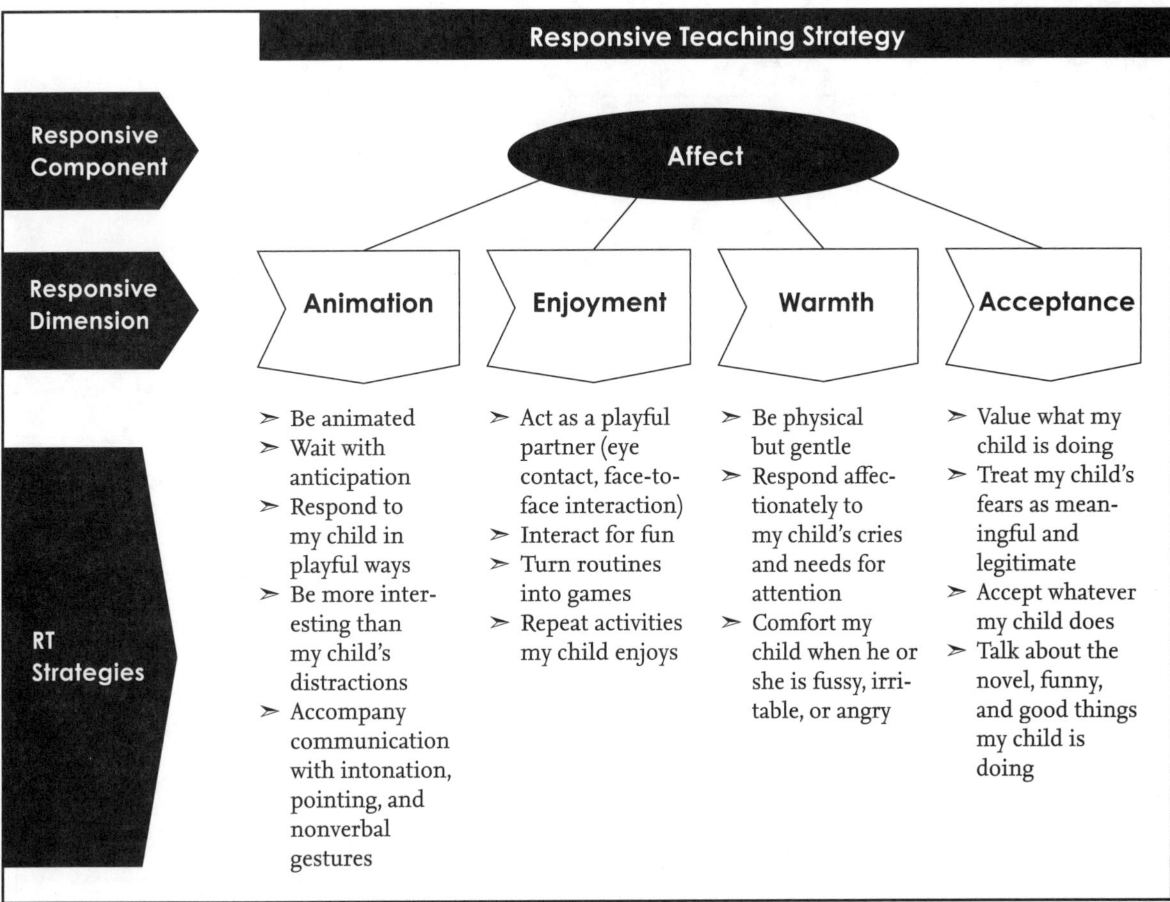

Figure 4.4. Strategies that promote affect.

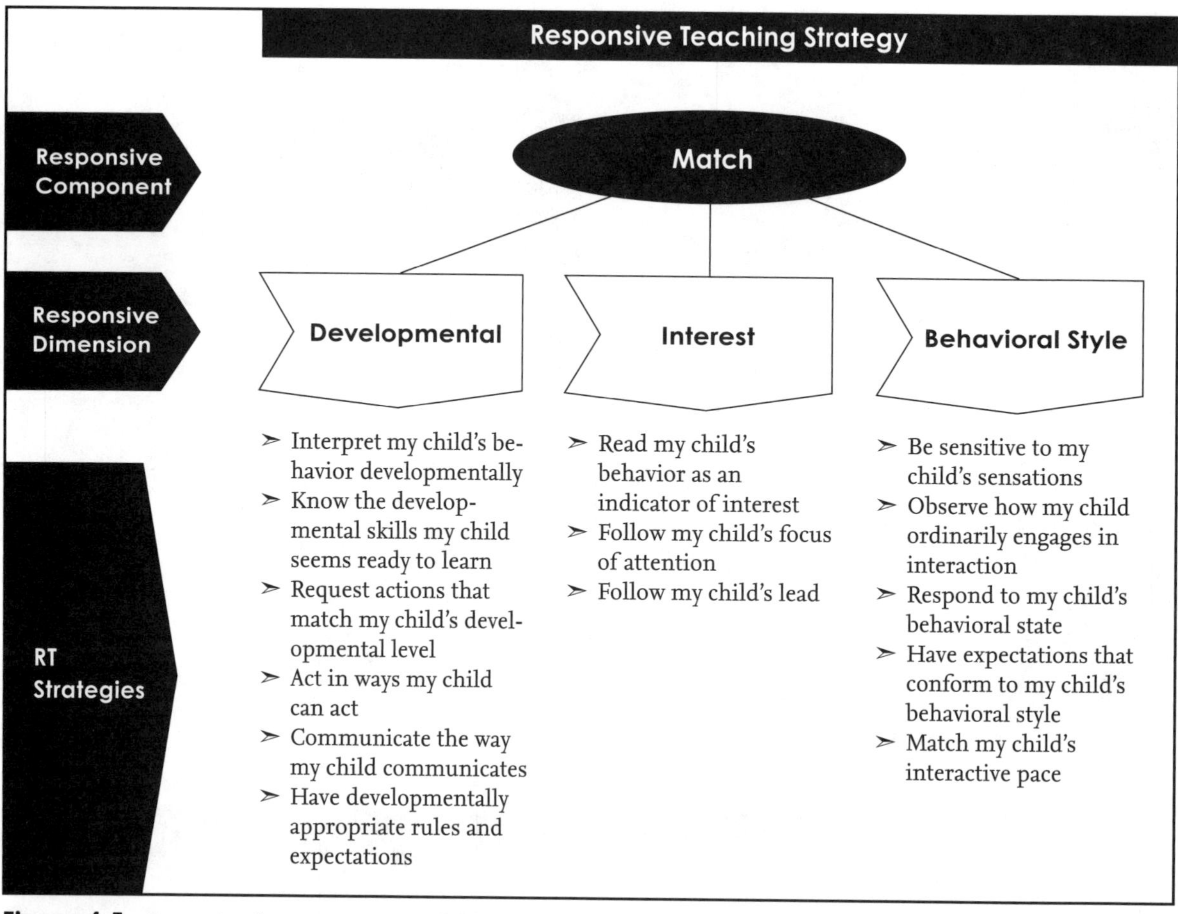

Figure 4.5. Strategies that promote match.

Chapter 5

Pivotal Behaviors

One of the most critical considerations for using Responsive Teaching (RT) is to understand (a) the types of child behaviors that RT strategies promote and (b) how these behaviors help to improve children's developmental functioning. The behaviors that intervention encourages children to learn must have a clear relationship to the goal of intervention—promoting children's development and well-being. Parents and others are likely to use RT strategies only if they understand the underlying logic for these strategies and are confident that they will help to promote their children's developmental well-being.

RT Strategies Do Not Promote Discrete Child Development Skills

In contemporary developmental intervention practice, intervention objectives typically selected for children are developmental skills and concepts that children are not able to do. These skills are the end results of developmental learning and are often items from tests that are used to assess developmental functioning. In many early intervention programs, intervention objectives are selected by identifying the next set of items beyond what a child is able to perform successfully on a developmental test or inventory.

This approach to identifying intervention goals is based upon the idea that development can be thought of as the skills that children are typically capable of doing at a particular age or developmental level. It assumes that children who have developmental problems or delays will "catch up" as they learn and thus use these higher level developmental skills.

Although this is a logical approach to developmental intervention, it is not the way that responsive interaction promotes children's development. When parents interact responsively, they usually encourage their children to say and do things they already know how to say and do. They support their children by joining in their activities and by doing or saying things that are similar to those of their children.

Although responsive interaction strategies are highly effective at promoting children's development, strategies such as "imitate your child" or "follow your child's lead" are simply not effective for getting children to say or do specific, targeted, higher level behaviors. A study reported by Kaiser et al. (1996) provides a startling illustration of this point (see Figure 5.1).

Mothers of 12 children with language delays were asked to use responsive interaction strategies (e.g., balanced turn-taking; follow the child's lead) to help promote their children's language. While using these strategies, mothers were also asked to teach their children a set of discrete language skills or objectives that their children did not yet know. After 6 months of intervention, responsive interaction strategies had almost no impact on the number of language objectives their children learned. As indicated by the bars in the first column of Figure 5.1, children's spontaneous production of targeted language objectives increased from .4 at the beginning of intervention to 4 after 6 months of intervention.

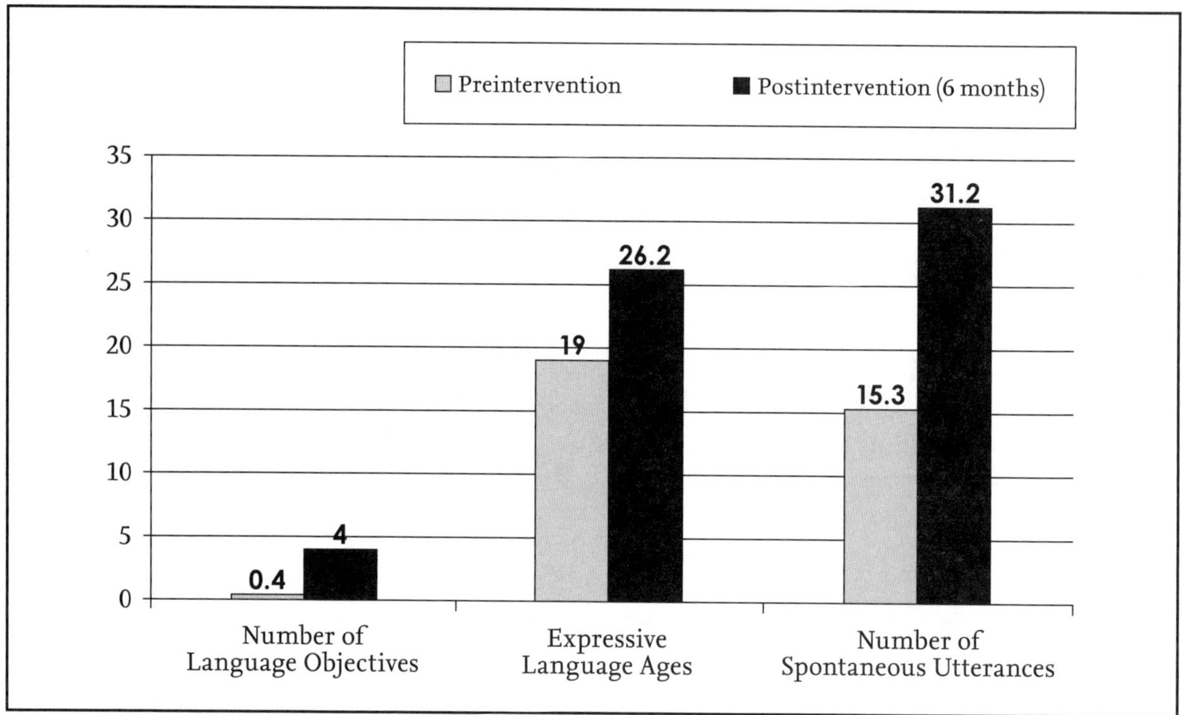

Figure 5.1. Impact of responsive interaction strategies on the communication of preschool-aged children ($N = 12$). *Note.* Data are adapted from "The Effects of Teaching Parents to Use Responsive Interaction Strategies," by A. P. Kaiser et al., 1996, *Topics in Early Childhood Special Education, 16*(3), pp. 375–406.

In other words, these children learned only one language objective or word for every 2 months of intervention.

Despite this, children's rate of language development, as measured by standardized tests (see the middle column in Figure 5.1), increased by approximately 100%, from ½ month of language development per month prior to intervention to more than 1 month of language development per month during the 6 months of intervention. In addition, the amount of language children produced spontaneously in conversation (see the right-hand column in Figure 5.1) doubled during this same period.

Responsive Interaction Teaches Pivotal Behaviors

Why are RT strategies so effective at promoting children's development when they appear to be of so little value at helping children learn targeted higher level developmental skills? We conducted two studies that provide information that helps to explain this paradox.

The first study included 45 infants and toddlers with developmental problems who were enrolled in an early intervention program (Mahoney, Kim & Lin, in press). These children were 25 months old and had a variety of developmental problems. We divided these children into two groups: children of High-Responsive Mothers (n = 28) and children of Low-Responsive Mothers (n = 17), based upon ratings of how mothers interacted with them. We then measured how these children interacted with their mothers using the *Child Behavior Rating Scale* (CBRS; Mahoney & Wheeden, 1998). As illustrated in Figure 5.2, children of High-Responsive Mothers had higher ratings on each of the seven CBRS items than did children of Low-Responsive Mothers.

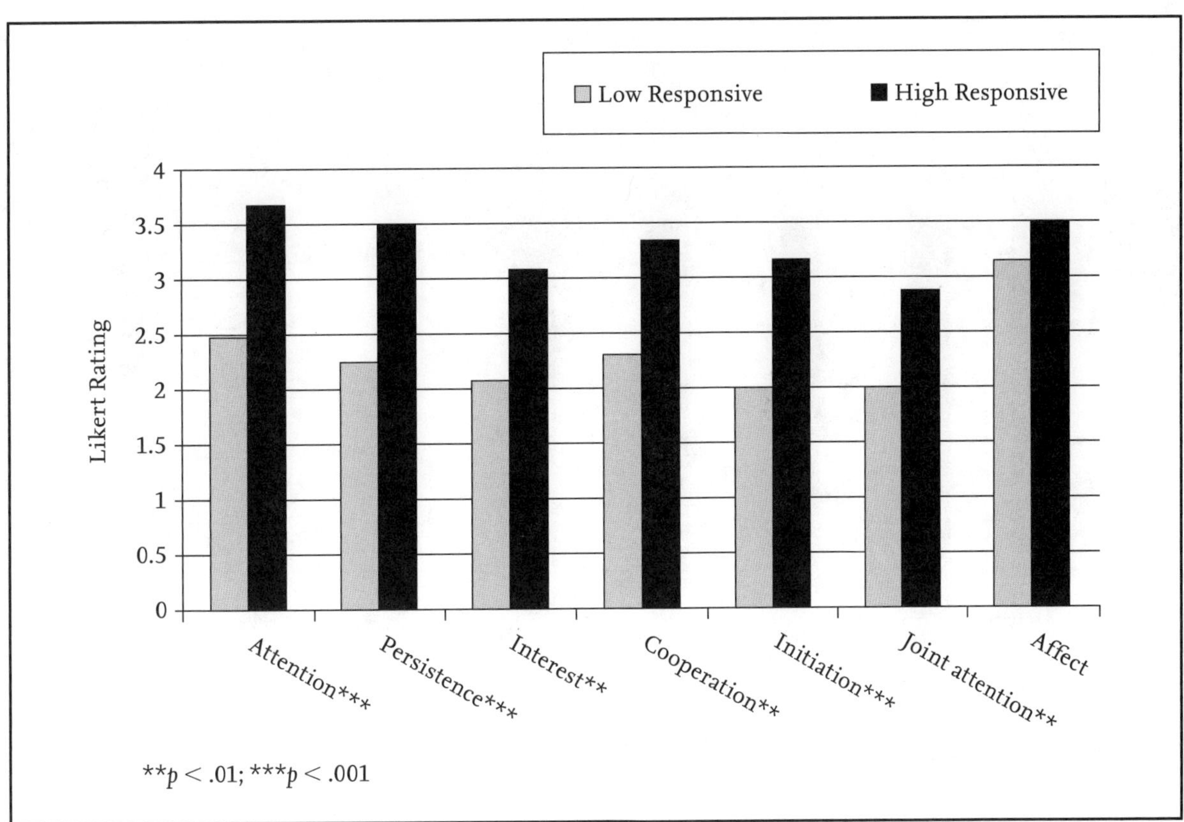

Figure 5.2. Relationship of maternal responsiveness to the scores of infants and toddlers with disabilities (N = 45) on the *Child Behavior Rating Scale* (CBRS; Mahoney & Wheeden, 1998).

We repeated this same study with 70 children in preschool special education while they were interacting with their teachers. The average age of the children was 57.4 months, and their average developmental age was 36.9 months. We divided the children into High-Responsive ($n = 35$) and Low-Responsive ($n = 35$) groups based upon how their teachers interacted with them. As indicated in Figure 5.3, the responsive interactions of teachers had almost the same type of impact on children's behaviors as those of mothers. These children exhibited higher levels of each of the CBRS behaviors with teachers who used a more responsive style of interacting with them.

As we examined the pattern of findings from these two studies, it occurred to us that, although responsive interaction was not effective at teaching targeted developmental skills or concepts, it seemed to be highly effective at teaching a different, but perhaps much more critical, class of developmental behaviors. Most of the behaviors measured by the CBRS are considered by child development experts to be the processes or activities that children must do themselves in order to learn. How much children learn from a particular activity or experience largely depends on how actively they are engaged in these situations.

To test the idea that children's developmental learning is influenced by the amount they used the engagement behaviors measured by the CBRS, we divided the 45 infants and toddlers described into two groups: High Engagers and Low Engagers. High Engagers had average CBRS scores that were above the midpoint, and Low Engagers had scores that were at the midpoint or lower. We then compared the average developmental age scores of these children on two developmental measures, the *Vineland Adaptive Behavior Scale* and the *Transdisciplinary Play-Based Assessment.* As illustrated in Figure 5.4, across the nine developmental subscales from these two assessments, children who were High Engagers had

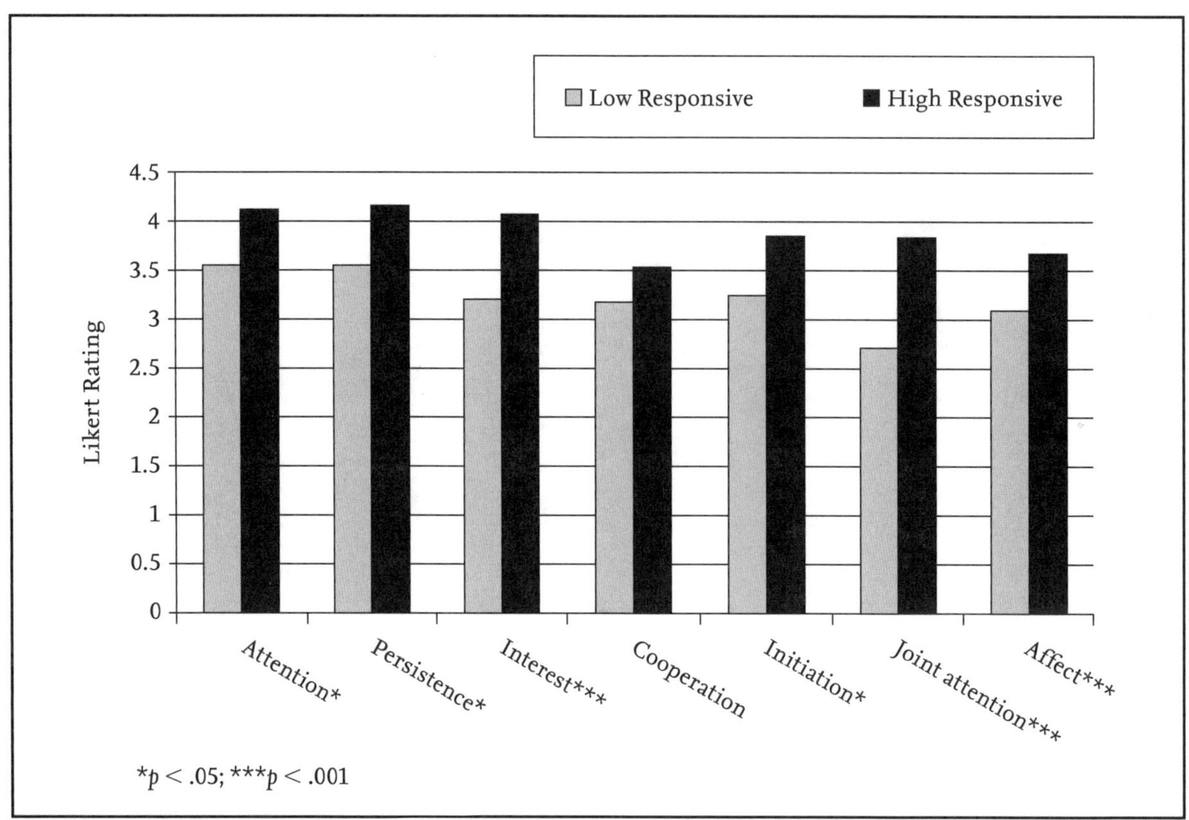

Figure 5.3. Relationship of teacher responsiveness to the scores of preschool children with disabilities ($N = 70$) on the *Child Behavior Rating Scale* (CBRS; Mahoney & Wheeden, 1998).

significantly higher developmental age scores than children who were Low Engagers. These findings are highly supportive of the idea that children's rate of developmental learning is related to the degree to which children use the type of engagement behaviors measured by the CBRS.

These results suggest that the behaviors parents encourage when they interact responsively with their children are the learning processes that are the foundations for developmental learning. Following the work of Koegel, Koegel, and Carter (1999), we refer to these as *pivotal behaviors.* That is, as indicated in Figure 1.1, the child behaviors that parents promote by interacting responsively are pivotal to wide areas of functioning such that improvements in these behaviors enhance children's ability to learn the skills and concepts that are the foundations for higher levels of developmental functioning.

Responsive Teaching is thus based upon the idea that responsive parents promote children's development *less* by directly teaching the skills and concepts that are the benchmarks of higher levels of functioning, and *more* by encouraging children to engage in pivotal developmental learning behaviors. The more responsively parents interact with their children, the more they prompt their children to use these pivotal behaviors. Parents who consistently engage in a responsive style of interacting in each of the more than 200,000 interactive episodes they have with their children each year (see Chapter 2) over time help their children develop habits of using these pivotal behaviors or learning processes, which helps to maximize children's development and social–emotional well-being.

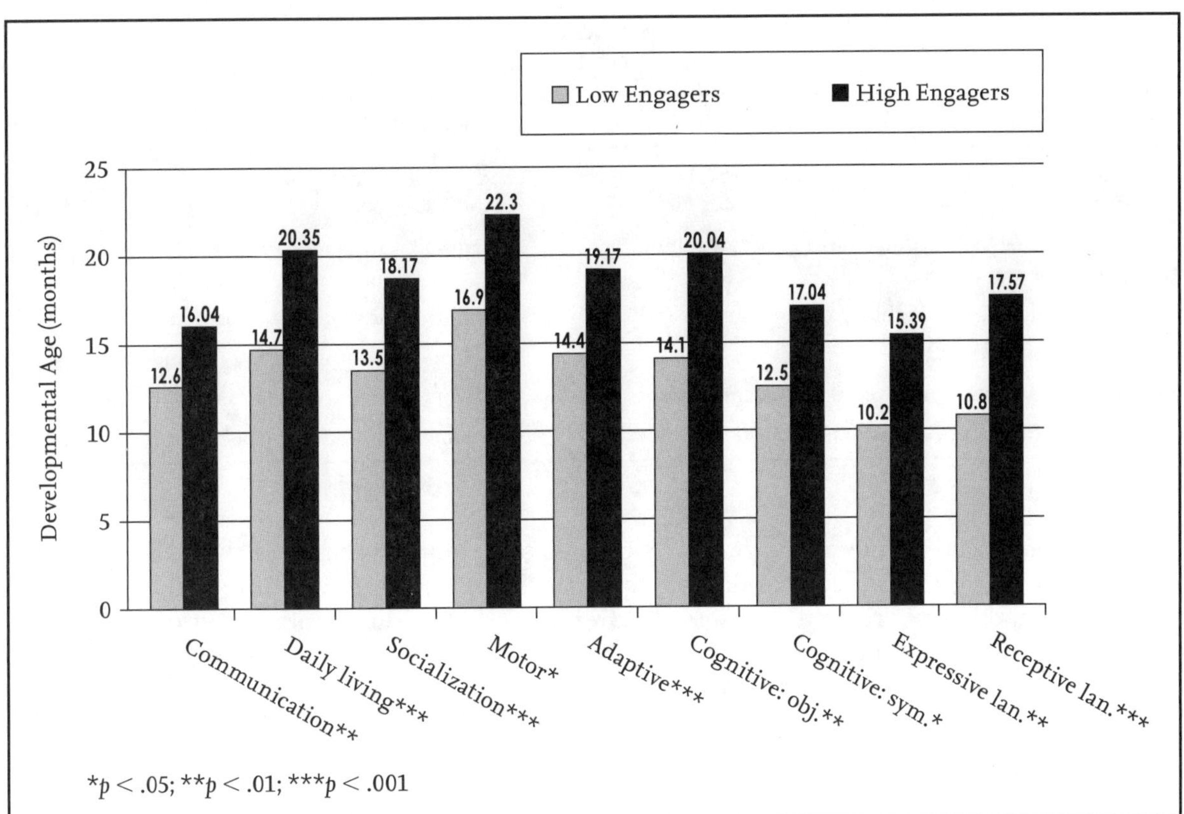

Figure 5.4. Relationship between children's engagement and their rate of development.

Comparison of Pivotal Behaviors and Discrete Skills

As indicated previously, discrete-skill intervention objectives are often defined in terms of specific behaviors, or categories of behavior, that are the benchmarks of higher levels of functioning. Discrete skills are the end results of developmental learning and may be items from tests that are used to assess developmental functioning. Many are hierarchical behaviors that are prerequisites for the next set of developmental behaviors children need to learn. See Table 5.1 for a summary of some of the major differences between the discrete skills and behaviors that are commonly used as early intervention objectives and pivotal behaviors.

When a child masters discrete intervention objectives, these behaviors are no longer useful as intervention objectives. In fact, in some cases children need to stop using a discrete skill that was previously targeted as an intervention objective as they learn new skills that provide a more effective means of doing what the initial objective enabled them to do. For example, although crawling may have been a discrete objective that a child learned at a previous time, the child will need to decrease his or her use of this behavior to learn how to walk.

In contrast, pivotal behaviors are a small set of behaviors that children use to learn developmental skills and competencies throughout early childhood. They are behaviors that most children are able to do from the earliest days of their lives. Most children with

Table 5.1

A Comparison of Pivotal Behaviors and Discrete Skills

Pivotal Behaviors	Discrete Skills
Active learning processes are the bases for developmental learning	Products of learning
Simultaneous behaviors used continually throughout the developmental period	Prerequisites to more complex behavior
Behaviors children are capable of doing from an early age	Behaviors children do not know how to do
Behaviors useful across contexts	Utility of behavior is context dependent
Behaviors seldom used in developmental assessments	Behaviors often used to assess competence
Assessment—frequency and intensity child uses behavior	Assessment—produce the behavior to criterion

developmental problems are generally capable of producing these behaviors, although often at lower intensity levels and less frequently than typically developing children. Seldom are pivotal behaviors used to assess children's level of developmental functioning, yet pivotal behaviors can be used to characterize critical differences in the quality of children's functioning at each developmental level.

RT Promotes the Pivotal Behaviors for Cognition, Communication, and Social–Emotional Functioning

The behaviors targeted as intervention objectives in Responsive Teaching are the 16 pivotal behaviors listed in Table 5.2. Each of these pivotal behaviors has been identified as a critical developmental process in one or more of the major contemporary developmental theories, including constructivist theories of child development, communication theories of language development, and psychosocial theories of social–emotional development. Research evidence shows that these are all behaviors that can be promoted through responsive interaction. The following section provides a description of these pivotal behaviors for each of the three developmental domains.

Pivotal Behavior Promotes Cognitive Development

Cognitive development entails changes in children's perceptions, knowledge, understanding, reasoning, judgment, and the use of these competencies in everyday routines. Cognitive competencies include perception, memory, comprehension, symbolic representation, problem solving, purposeful planning, decision making, discrimination, and idea or intention generation. Cognition is the most basic of developmental competencies, and is the foundation for the development of communication and language as well as social and adaptive behavior. Children's ability to communicate, interact with others, and care for themselves is ultimately dependent upon their level of understanding or reasoning. Until children with developmental problems acquire the prerequisite level of cognitive competence, their ability to communicate or interact with others will be limited (Dunst, Mahoney, & Buchan, 1996).

The constructivist view of child development was popularized through the work of Jean Piaget. Through careful observations and analyses of children's play, Piaget (1963) described how the apparently random and meaningless activities young children engaged

Table 5.2

Responsive Teaching Pivotal Behaviors

Developmental Domains	Cognition	Communication	Social–Emotional Functioning
Pivotal Behaviors	Social play	Joint activity	Trust
	Initiation	Joint attention	Empathy
	Exploration	Vocalization	Cooperation
	Problem solving	Intentional communication	Self-regulation
	Practice	Conversation	Feelings of confidence
			Feelings of control

in while playing or interacting with objects, materials, and people were neither random nor as devoid of meaning as many had thought. Piaget observed that there was a fairly predictable sequence in the way that children's play activities changed over time. These changes suggested that the way that children interacted with objects, materials, and people was primarily a reflection of the current way they perceived, reasoned, and understood their world. For example, young children who frequently bang objects that are within their reach, understand and perceive objects as "things that can be banged." Children whose play is dominated by putting objects in and out of containers may be at a stage of cognitive functioning where they are focused on understanding spatial relationships between objects. Children who begin to use objects according to their intended function, such as using a brush to comb a doll's hair, are beginning to understand that objects can have unique functions or purposes. Children who begin to integrate toys into pretend sequences are beginning to understand that objects and toys can be used as props to represent events, actions, or things that are not possible in the present situation.

The constructivist approach to learning maintains that, particularly in the first 7 years of life, cognitive development does not depend upon children being directly taught new information, such as how to use objects or to reason and understand their world—rather it depends more on the large number of personal experiences children have throughout the day as they interact or play with objects, materials, or people. Children's understanding of their world develops as they use their current mode of understanding as a filter through which they interact with their environment. In doing this, children learn about the usefulness of their current behaviors and ways of thinking. By repeating the same activities over and over again, they become increasingly proficient with their current mode of thinking and reasoning while at the same time they begin to discover some of its limitations and shortcomings. Children's awareness of the uses and limitations of their current mode of thinking motivates them to develop, or construct, different ways of thinking or perceiving, particularly as they become aware of the details of their world.

There are two keys to constructive learning. The first is children's native ability to detect patterns or consequences of their actions and to make connections between different activities and experiences. Children who have high native ability require fewer active learning experiences to move on to more advanced levels of thinking and reasoning than do children with low native ability. The second key is the amount of active learning experiences that children have. For all children, regardless of how much native ability they have, constructive learning can only occur through active engagement with the objects, materials, and people. Children acquire an insight and understanding of their world by repeated use of cognitive pivotal behaviors including initiation, exploration, practice, and problem solving. These behaviors not only help children become more proficient in using their existing skills and competencies but also motivate them to construct more effective means of thinking and reasoning when they become aware of the limitations of their own behavior in dealing with the complexities of their world (Mahoney, Robinson, & Powell, 1992; Spiker, Ferguson, & Brooks-Gunn, 1993).

Play is clearly one of the most important activities for early cognitive growth. While playing, children are constantly using many of the pivotal behaviors that are the foundations for constructive learning to interact with toys and materials. Still, parents and other adults play a major role in children's cognitive growth. Children simply do not learn as much from playing by themselves or with other children as they do from playing with an adult partner. Because of this, social play (i.e., children playing reciprocally with an adult partner) is one of the most critical pivotal behaviors for cognitive development. By playing with children, adults have the opportunity to maximize children's initiation, exploration, practice, and problem solving, particularly if their interactions are highly responsive. In addition, the more children engage in reciprocal social play with adults, the more opportunities adults have to expand the scope and complexity of children's play, such as by directing children's attention to elements of the situation that children were not aware of and by showing children new or slightly different activities that complement children's actions and intentions. Through social play, adults plant seeds or new ideas in children's mind that make it easier for children to construct or discover concepts and abilities that are needed for the next developmental stage of thinking and reasoning.

Table 5.3 outlines how various responsive behaviors that parents and others use encourage children's use of the pivotal behaviors that are the foundation for cognitive learning. By engaging in balanced, reciprocal interactions, by matching children's interactive pace, and by reducing the complexity of their turns, responsive parents virtually force their children to participate actively in social play. By imitating children's actions—by playing

Table 5.3

Responsive Behaviors Promote Cognitive Pivotal Behaviors

Responsive Behavior	Cognitive Pivotal Behaviors
Balanced, reciprocal interactions Match children's interactive pace Reduce complexity of turns	Social play
Imitate children's actions Play with toys and materials the way children do Follow children's lead	Initiation
Sustained repetitive interactive sequences Act as a play partner	Exploration
Expand children's activities by matching their intentions	Problem solving
Be available to children Respond to children during daily routines	Practice

with toys and materials the way their children do and following their children's lead—responsive parents encourage their children to initiate activities. Similarly, by being a play partner with children, by engaging in sustained sequences of repetitive play, and expanding children's activities in a manner that matches their intentions, responsive parents encourage their children to use active learning strategies such as exploration and problem solving (van den Boom, 1994). Furthermore, by being available to their children and implementing responsive interactive strategies throughout the daily routine, responsive parents provide children repeated opportunities to practice and gain mastery of their existing cognitive skills (Feldman & Greenbaum, 1997; Tamis-LeMonda, Bornstein, & Baumwell, 2001).

Pivotal Behaviors Promote Communication and Language

The Responsive Teaching approach to language intervention is derived from communication theories of language development (Bates, Benigni, Bretherton, Camaioni, & Volterra, 1979; Bruner, 1974, 1983: Dale, 1976). Communication theories assert that verbal language is a sophisticated form of communication that evolves from children's emerging social interaction and primitive nonverbal communication exchanges with parents and other adults (Tamis-LeMonda, Bornstein, & Baumwell, 2001).

To build a communication base for language, children need to learn and use several pivotal behaviors in their social interactions with adults and others, including the following:

- Engage in joint activities that provide opportunities for social communication (Bruner, 1983)
- Share attention with another person (Mundy, Sigman, & Kasari, 1990)
- Produce the range of complex vocalizations that approximate the sounds of spoken language
- Communicate specific intentions or meanings through nonverbal behavior, vocalizations, and verbalizations (Bruner, 1983)
- Have conversations by using words and conventional linguistic forms (Bornstein et al., 1999)

Although other factors contribute to children's communication development, including cognitive and vocal–motor behaviors, communication theory asserts that the most critical social influences on language development are the spontaneous exchanges children have with parents and others. In the following sections, we provide a more detailed explanation of each of the pivotal behaviors children need to use in these exchanges to develop their ability to communicate. We also describe the elements of responsive communication that adults typically use to promote children's use of these pivotal behaviors.

Joint Activity

Communication theories of language development are based upon the idea that language learning is a social activity. Language development occurs in the context of children engaging in intimate interactions with adult speakers that are focused on activities or events that interest them. Communication theories assert that children are unlikely to be effective language learners if they are mostly exposed to language stimulation that is not related to their immediate experiences (e.g., listening to adults conversing with each other, listening to the radio, watching TV) or if they are asked to repeat words or phrases that do not have a meaningful relationship to their immediate interests or experiences. Rather, children become effective language learners by being exposed to language that is adjusted to their current level of language functioning and directly related to their activities and interests (Bornstein et al., 1999).

Perhaps one of the most notable characteristics of responsive adults is the way they engage children in joint activities. They interact with children as if they are their social partners. Their goal is not so much to observe what children are doing or to stimulate or instruct children, but rather to encourage children to engage in some type of joint activity in which both they and children play an active role. They do not talk to children from a distance or play by watching or directing them; rather they make special efforts to engage in frequent one-to-one interactions with them.

As indicated in Table 5.4, during these interactions responsive adults *get into their children's world* by physically getting down to their level and joining in their activities. They are active participants in the interaction, but they encourage children to also play an active role. They *wait for children to take a turn* (i.e., do something) and limit the amount that they say or do. By *saying and doing less* (i.e., becoming less dominant interactive partners), they encourage children to do more—to be active participants in the activity. They focus more on sharing activities and experiences with children as opposed to making these activities either exclusively the child's or exclusively their own (Bruner, 1983; Mahoney, 1988a, 1988b).

Table 5.4

Responsive Behaviors Promote Communication Pivotal Behaviors

Responsive Behavior	**Communication Pivotal Behaviors**
Get into children's world	Joint activity
Wait for children to take a turn	
Say and do less so children can do more	
Face-to-face interactions	Joint attention
Balanced, reciprocal interaction	
Follow children's focus of attention	
Treat unintentional behaviors as if they were meaningful	Intentional communication
Respond to nonverbal communication with actions and communication that match the child's feelings, needs, or observations	
Accept incorrect words by responding to children's intentions	
Match children's expressive language	Conversation
Translate vocalizations and word approximations into words that match children's actions or intentions	
Accompany language with nonverbal context cues	
Clarify or rephrase words that are mispronounced or used inappropriately	
Reduce grammatical complexity	
Model more advanced grammatical forms to clarify the child's intention	

Joint Attention

In the context of face-to-face interactions with their parents, children progress from "primary intersubjectivity," in which children's interactions with adults are focused on feelings, needs, and state, to "secondary intersubjectivity," or joint attention, in which children incorporate objects into their interactions with adults. Joint attention involves children's "meeting of minds" with parents and others. It provides the foundation for all subsequent acts of communication involving reference to the outside world. Once capable of engaging in joint attentional interactions, children are able to learn from others about the language that is used to refer to their environment (Carpenter, Nagell, & Tomasello, 1998; Landry & Chapieski, 1989).

Joint attention, which for typically developing children emerges 3 to 4 months prior to the use of words (i.e., 9 to 12 months of age), develops in three stages. The first stage is *shared attention.* This can be characterized by situations in which the parent and child are playing with a toy and the child looks from the toy to the adult's face and then back to the toy. That is, when the child and adult are engaged with a toy, the child is aware of the adult's focus.

The second stage is *following attention.* In this stage, children use the direction of adults' visual gaze, pointing, or gestures as cues for directing their own attention. This behavior is viewed as an indication that children are beginning to understand that the adult is capable of intentional or goal-directed behavior. Among typically developing children, this behavior may begin to emerge at approximately 9 months of age, but it is not well established until approximately 15 months of age.

The final stage is *directing attention.* In this stage, children direct adults' attention to an outside object through an act of intentional communication. This stage of development is viewed as the basis for imperative (telling the adult what do) and declarative communications (showing the adult something) (Carpenter et al., 1998).

The skill with which adults involve children in interactions from early on in their lives is key to promoting joint attention (Morales et al., 2000). As indicated in Table 5.4, there are several responsive interactive behaviors that promote joint attention, including *face-to-face interactions,* balanced and reciprocal interactions, and *following children's focus of attention.*

Parent–child play and caregiving rituals also promote joint attention. As parents *engage in repetitive games or joint action routines,* children begin to learn the role they play in social exchanges and to anticipate actions or communications by the adult. When these routines are well established, adults can modify them to maintain children's interest by changing the timing, language, or role the child is expected to play. These modifications encourage children to participate actively and help them understand the adult as an intentional agent.

Intentional Communication

Intentional communication refers to the ability of children to communicate their observations, needs, feelings, and ideas to others using some type of voluntary behavior. There are at least two basic components to the development of intentional communication. One is children becoming aware of their own feelings, needs, and perceptions. The other is children developing their sense of agency—the sense that they can convey their feelings, needs, and perceptions to others.

Responsive parents repeatedly engage in interactions that are ideally suited to promoting children's intentional communication. When they *treat children's unintentional behavior as if it were meaningful,* they encourage children to play an active role in conversations before children understand that the purpose of these interactions is to exchange information (Bruner, 1983). The more actively children participate in preconversational exchanges, the more opportunities they have to discover the "intentions" of the person with whom they are interacting as well as learn that their own behavior can also convey meaning.

Responsive parents respond to children's nonverbal vocalizations or gestures with actions or communications that match their feelings, needs, or observations (van den Boom, 1994). This interactive feature is highly effective for teaching the fundamentals of intentional communication. For example, in the early days of life, children's cries are automatic or unintentional reactions to internal feelings such as hunger or pain. Responsive parents react promptly to children's cries by picking them up, soothing them, and then responding to their needs through a process of trial and error (e.g., rocking the child, nursing the child). Through these interactions, children begin to discover the relationships between (a) their feelings, needs, or observations; (b) the signals they produce; and (c) the impact these signals have on getting their parents to respond to their needs or feelings. Children discover through this dynamic interactive process that they can use their cries as a means of (a) gaining their parents' attention, (b) getting their needs met, and (c) communicating to parents about their needs and feelings. After children learn these basic intentional skills, they begin to produce different cries for different needs, indicating their increasing awareness of their own feelings and needs.

Even when children have learned the basics of intentional communication and begin to use words to communicate, the tendency of responsive parents to *accept incorrect words by responding to their children's intentions* continues to be critical for children's communication development (Koegel, Koegel, & McNerny, 2001; Nelson, 1973). For example, Nelson reported that typically developing children attain higher levels of language functioning in their third year of life when parents *accept their children's incorrect use of words or language by responding to their intentions* as opposed to correcting their mistakes. Nelson's research indicates that language development is motivated by children's need to communicate their intentions. Parents facilitate this by trying to interpret what their child is communicating rather than by correcting their child's word selection or grammar, which often interferes with children's efforts to communicate.

Conversation

Children learn words and grammar by engaging in frequent and increasingly longer episodes of conversation with adults (Girolametto, Pearce, & Weitzman, 1996). There are a number of features of responsive parents' communication that both enhance children's participation in conversation and make it easier for them to understand and use new words.

The first feature is *matching their children's expressive language.* When responsive parents have conversations with children who are at the initial phases of language development, they tend to use one word and short, grammatical utterances that are only slightly more complex than their children's utterances (MacDonald & Gillette, 1984; Mahoney, 1988a). Children can usually understand language that is more complex than what they can speak. However, by using language that matches children's expressive language functioning, responsive parents are modeling the language their children either currently use, or are in the process of learning. Children are more likely to respond to, imitate, and remember words or actions that are close to their current level of functioning. When adults' language exceeds children's expressive language abilities, children are unlikely to repeat, use, or remember that language (MacDonald, 1985).

Second, responsive parents *translate their children's vocalizations, unintelligible words, and jargon into words or phrases that match their actions or intentions.* They provide children words that match their intention and respond to their intentions. Rather than requesting or demanding that children use the correct word, they focus on keeping their children actively involved in conversation. As this pattern recurs over time, children gradually become aware of the limitations of their own language and strive to use more appropriate or correct words and grammar.

Third, responsive parents *accompany their language with nonverbal context cues.* Children do not learn language by only listening to their parents. Children decipher the meaning of language in the context of the nonverbal cues their parents use, such as visual gaze, pointing, showing, facial displays, and voice intonation. Responsive parents make it easier for children to participate in conversational exchanges by frequently using nonverbal context cues. These include joining children's activities, pointing and gesturing to accompany their language, exaggerating their intonation, and using a play face.

Fourth, responsive parents *clarify or rephrase words that children either mispronounced or used inappropriately.* When children begin to use words intentionally, effective language facilitation must both provide an appropriate model and encourage children's conversational efforts. Language facilitation is effective when it (a) increases children's awareness of appropriate language forms, (b) enhances children's success as conversational partners, and (c) encourages children to sustain their conversational efforts.

Syntax and grammatical structure help children to convey increasingly complex intentions in their conversations with others. Responsive adults facilitate children's syntactic growth in ways that are similar to how they contribute to other aspects of communicative competence. First, they *reduce the grammatical complexity of their communications so that it parallels and at times mimics the child's grammatical forms.* In conversations with children at the one- to two-word stage of language development, responsive adults routinely model interrogative and declarative utterances using the agent–action–object sequence (e.g., "I want milk") that children typically use in their early two- and three-word utterances. In addition, adults use only a few grammatical morphemes, and those that are used contribute minimally to the meaning of the utterance, particularly in the context in which it is used (e.g., "What's that?").

Second, during conversations adults *occasionally model more advanced grammatical forms that clarify the intent or meaning of children's utterances.* When this occurs, children are not only exposed to higher level linguistic forms, but they also learn through these interactions that advanced linguistic forms provide a more effective means of communicating their intent. Thus, the acquisition of higher level linguistic forms, though undoubtedly an outgrowth of advances in children's thinking, is nonetheless motivated by their need to communicate their intentions more clearly and effectively in their conversations with others.

Pivotal Behaviors Promote Social–Emotional Well-Being

In contemporary child development theory and research there is an emerging notion that when young children manifest serious behavior problems such as tantruming, hitting, biting, screaming, and noncompliance, many of these problems result from children's deficiencies or failure to develop one or more critical social–emotional behaviors. From this perspective, aggressive behavior is not something young children learn from their environment; it is the result of children failing to develop critical social–emotional pivotal behaviors, such as self-regulation or coping skills, which help them deal with their intense emotions and fears. This perspective is based upon the observation that all children experience anger and frustration, but not all children act aggressively toward others. Children act aggressively toward others when they lack the self-regulation skills that they need to cope with their feelings of anger and frustration.

Although attachment theory is one of the most common theories used to describe the social–emotional development of young children, it does not provide an adequate explanation for why children who are securely attached to their parents may still exhibit serious behavior problems during the early childhood period. In RT, we acknowledge that attachment is an important social–emotional pivotal behavior, but we maintain that it is only one of several pivotal behaviors that contribute to children's social–emotional well-being. The other pivotal behaviors we have included in this curriculum are manifested by young children, are directly related to behavior problems commonly seen in the early childhood period, and are associated with parental responsiveness. In addition to attachment or trust, these behaviors include empathy, cooperation, self-regulation, feelings of confidence, and feelings of control.

Social–emotional pivotal behaviors are behaviors that children develop gradually and at different ages during the early childhood period. For example, attachment to primary caregivers is a behavior that develops during the first 12 months of most children's lives. In contrast, pivotal behaviors such as self-regulation develop throughout the early childhood period, with major improvements in self-regulation occurring in the 3- to 6-year age range. One of the characteristics of social–emotional pivotal behaviors is that they are most useful for helping children deal with stressful situations such as transitions and close social encounters with unfamiliar people. The following section provides a more detailed description of the six social–emotional pivotal behaviors that are addressed by the RT curriculum.

Trust and Attachment

Attachment refers to the unique and intense social–emotional relationship that develops between children and their parents during the early years of life. As a pivotal behavior, attachment refers to children's ability to trust in their primary caregivers. As early as 12 months of age there are substantial differences in how much children trust or are attached to their mothers (DeWolff & van Ijzendoorn, 1997). Some of these differences are caused by the inherent biological characteristics of children (e.g., activity level, sociability, tolerance for physical contact). This is particularly true for children with neurological disorders that have been caused by genetic conditions such as autism or prenatal exposure to toxic substances, such as alcohol and drugs. Nonetheless, there is a strong relationship between the responsiveness of mothers during children's first year of life with the quality of children's attachment in the second year (Mangelsdorf, McHale, Diener, Heim Goldstein, & Lehn, 2000). Children are more likely to have a secure, trusting relationship when their mothers' interactions are warm, sensitive, and responsive (DeWolff & van Ijzendoorn, 1997).

The interactive qualities of warmth, sensitivity, and responsiveness are major contributors to children's ability to engage in a trusting relationship with their parents. Nonetheless, several other interactive features are also crucial to children's attachment formation. For example, as indicated in Table 5.5, the *frequency that parents interact with their children,* parents' tendency to *be playful with their children,* and the degree to which parents *respond affectionately to their children's cries and needs for attention* are also interactive dimensions that encourage children to have a more trusting relationship with their parents. Thus, attachment is influenced not only by parents' responsiveness but also by other caregiving qualities, including the amount of time they spend with their children and the extent to which they are emotionally and physically available (Kochanska et al., 1999).

Table 5.5

Responsive Behaviors Promote Social–Emotional Functioning

Responsive Behaviors	Social–Emotional Pivotal Behaviors
Interact frequently with children	Trust
Respond to children in playful ways	
Respond affectionately to children's cries and needs for attention	
Face-to-face interactions	Empathy
Respond to nonverbal signals	
Imitate children's emotional expressions	
Balanced, reciprocal interactions	Cooperation
Be nondirective	
Request actions that match children's developmental level	
Match children's interests	
Interpret noncompliance as a choice or lack of ability	
Give children frequent opportunities to make choices	
Help children complete tasks	
Have developmentally appropriate rules and expectations	Self-regulation
Match children's behavioral style	
Respond to children's behavioral state	
Discipline promptly and comfort	
Value what children do	Feelings of confidence
Accept whatever children do	
Treat children's behavior as legitimate and meaningful	
Respond quickly to behaviors children initiate	Feelings of control
Give children frequent opportunities to make choices	

Children's success at establishing a trusting relationship with their primary caregivers contributes to several aspects of their social–emotional functioning during the early childhood years. It is related to children's ability to separate from their mothers and to assert their independence when they are 3 years old. It is also related to how well they adjust to childcare settings and interact with their peers when they are 3 to 5 years of age (Kochanska, 1997).

Although children's attachment is generally thought to be a special bond that is "fixed" during the first year of their lives, evidence to support this view is far from conclusive. Most parents tend to be fairly consistent in how they interact with their children over time, and because of this are as likely to have similar attachment relationships with their children when their children are 5 years of age as when they were 12 months old.

Many parents, however, experience inconsistencies in the manner they relate to their children from one age to another. Some parents of children with developmental problems have difficulty accepting their children's condition and relating to their children in the first year of life. However, most of these parents make dramatic changes in their attitudes and perceptions of their children by the second year. Although their relationships may not have been optimally suited to promoting their children's attachment during the first year, by the second year they have established responsive and supportive relationships with them. In most cases, the ambivalent relationships these parents had during their children's first year of life have no impact on their children's social–emotional adjustment during the remaining early childhood years.

In other cases, parent–child relationships that were optimally suited to promoting children's attachment during the first year of life deteriorate substantially during the second and subsequent years. This can occur if parents are confronted with serious physical, social, or emotional difficulties that they did not have to deal with during the first year of their children's lives. In these cases, children's social–emotional functioning is more apt to reflect the quality of their current relationship with their parents than the quality of the relationship they had during the first year (Kochanska, 1998).

RT maintains that trust or attachment is a pivotal behavior that for some children will need to be monitored continually throughout the early childhood years. Insofar as children's social–emotional behavior is influenced by the way their parents relate to them at the moment (Kochanska, 1998), the quality of children's trust or attachment can improve whenever parents become capable of garnering the physical and psychological resources necessary for engaging in more responsive and nurturing interactions with their children.

Empathy

Children learn to empathize or become attuned to the emotions and feelings of their parents and others through a process referred to as "intersubjectivity." Empathy is critical to children's social–emotional development because it is the process through which children (a) become attuned to their own emotional state; (b) learn how to express the full range of emotions (e.g., sadness, anger, disgust, fear, joy, interest, surprise); and (c) learn how to react emotionally to different people and events.

Empathy is a learned behavior that evolves in the context of the intimate interactions that take place between children and their parents. This process proceeds through the stages of (a) affective matching, to (b) intersubjective sharing, to (c) sharing subjective states toward objects and events. How parents interact with children contributes to children's development of this process (Kochanska et al., 1999).

Affective matching, which facilitates children's emotional expressiveness, occurs through repetitive face-to-face interaction. In the affective matching stage, parents and children imitate the affective displays of each other. Children are not yet fully aware of the link between their own internal state and affective expressions, nor do they recognize the feelings or emotions underlying their parents' affective expressions.

The frequency that children smile in later childhood and socialize with their peers is related to the frequency that their mothers smile during face-to-face interactions. If mothers are either over- or undercontrolling in face-to-face interactions, they may elicit higher levels of gaze aversion from their children, which in turn leads to higher levels of socially avoidant behavior. If mothers appear depressed during interaction, their babies may display facial features and body language that convey feelings of depression (Leadbeater, Bishop, & Raver, 1996).

In the stage of intersubjective sharing, children are able to use affective displays to communicate, or share, their own feelings or emotions with their parents. These emotions are personal or inner directed rather than feelings about external objects and events.

At the stage of sharing subjective states toward objects and events, children and their parents are able to share feelings and emotions about objects that are external to themselves. Through mutual sharing of subjective states with their parents, children learn socially appropriate reactions to people, objects, and events, thus enabling children to react emotionally to social events in a manner that is compatible with conventional norms. As they learn to react appropriately to people and events, they become capable of increasing the range of people and activities that they can tolerate or feel comfortable with (Lay, Waters, & Park, 1989).

Children with severe social–emotional disorders, such as autism, may actively avoid eye contact and face-to-face interaction. As a result, their interactions are often missing the rich range of emotions that typically occur between parents and children. This may cause these children to (a) develop unusual emotional expressions, (b) engage in low rates of emotional sharing with other people, and (c) have inappropriate emotional responses to people, objects, and events.

As outlined on Table 5.5 responsive parents promote empathy by engaging in face-to-face interactions, in which they maintain intermittent eye contact; responding to the child's nonverbal signals, including body movements, facial expressions, and vocalizations; and imitating the child's emotional expressions.

Cooperation

Cooperation refers to the ability of children to participate reciprocally in joint activities with their parents. It is a critical social behavior that children develop by engaging in repeated episodes of cooperation with their adult partners. Children's inability or refusal to cooperate can be a major source of conflict between parents and young children, particularly if parents view their child as being willfully disobedient, defiant, or stubborn. This type of misbehavior is often referred to as noncompliance, but RT uses the term *cooperation* to emphasize the reciprocal parent–child processes involved in children learning this critical pivotal behavior.

How responsive adults are with children is highly predictive of how cooperative children are during their interactions with them (Mahoney et al., 1985). When adults are highly responsive, children are more likely to participate actively in interaction and to comply with what adults ask them to do (van den Boom, 1995). The degree to which children cooperate and comply with adults is not simply a reflection of their biological predispositions or internal states, but is also influenced by how adults interact with them and the kinds of demands they make.

There are seven qualities associated with responsiveness that promote children's cooperation. First, responsive parents engage in *balanced, reciprocal interactions* with their children. They do not sit back and passively monitor or observe what their children are doing; rather, they look for opportunities to insert themselves in their children's play. Although actively involved, their interactions with their children are balanced, not dominating. They make suggestions and provide guidance, but they also give their children equal opportunities to determine the focus of the interaction and express their interests. They make sure their children are aware of their presence while they are playing, thus helping their children learn that interaction is a process of "give and get." This helps children learn that by cooperating with adults they can gain the opportunity to do what they want.

Second, responsive parents tend to be *nondirective.* In a study involving young children with developmental problems (Mahoney et al., 1990), parents who were very directive with their children made 50% more requests than parents who were less directive, yet the number of times children complied did not increase as their parents' rate of requests increased. Children complied the same number of times with parents who made a lot of behavior requests as they did with parents who made few requests. However, because high-directive parents made twice as many requests as low-directive parents, children's relative rate of compliance to their parents was 50% lower than the rate that children complied to low-directive parents. In other words, parents caused their children to become noncompliant by requesting them to respond at a rate that apparently exceeded children's capacity to respond. Because responsive parents are relatively nondirective and only occasionally ask their children to do things, their lower rate of requesting gives children the opportunity to learn how to cooperate while giving them opportunities to take the lead with their parents.

Third, responsive parents routinely *request actions that match their children's developmental level,* which are behaviors that are within children's current range of capabilities. In another study (Mahoney & Neville-Smith, 1996), we found that the likelihood that children complied with their parents' requests was related to whether their requests were within children's current level of developmental functioning. When 2-year-old children who were functioning at a 12-month developmental level were asked to perform a behavior that children normally do not perform until they are at the 24-month stage of development, the difficulty of what they were being asked to do made it impossible for them to comply. However, when these children were asked to perform behaviors that were at or below their current level of developmental functioning, their rate of compliance increased dramatically.

Fourth, responsive parents *match their children's interests.* In the same study (Mahoney & Neville-Smith, 1996), we also examined children's compliance in relation to their current interests. Children's interests are expressed by what they are doing at the moment. If a child is playing with a toy stove, then, at that moment, the child is interested in the stove and not some other nearby toy. Mothers could ask their children to do something that was unrelated, partially related, or completely related to their current interests. Children were two times more likely to comply with requests that were completely related to their current interests compared to requests that were only partially related or unrelated.

Fifth, responsive parents *interpret noncompliance as a choice or lack of ability.* Children's failure to comply to their parents' requests often becomes a source of conflict, particularly when parents interpret it as an act of defiance. When parents view their children as stubborn, belligerent, or otherwise oppositional, they often increase their efforts to coerce them to comply or conform. In turn, children respond by crying and becoming upset, thus aggravating both parents' and children's frustration with each other.

However, when parents interpret noncooperation as (a) an indication their children are unable to do what is asked of them or (b) their children's choice not to do something, the interaction is less likely to escalate into an emotionally charged event. This is the approach responsive parents routinely take. Rather than viewing their children as defiant, they tend to react to their children's lack of cooperation by attempting to find alternatives for gaining their cooperation.

Sixth, responsive parents *give their children frequent opportunities to make choices.* When parents give children choices, children are much more likely to cooperate than when only one option is presented. However, providing choices is only effective at gaining children's cooperation if each of the choices is desirable from the perspective of the child. If the child is given two choices, and only one is desirable, in reality the child has no choice (e.g., eat your dinner or go to bed). However, when children are able to choose from desirable alternatives, the probability they will cooperate increases significantly.

Seventh, responsive parents *help their children complete tasks*. Typically, issues related to cooperation arise in the context of children being asked to complete some type of task (e.g., pick up toys; eat dinner). Often what parents ask their children to do, although within their capabilities, is not something most children can complete independently at their current level of development. Responsive parents handle this situation by joining their child in the task. They scaffold their children's participation by working cooperatively with them rather than demand that their children complete tasks independently. To encourage their children to assume greater responsibility for task completion, over time these parents gradually withdraw their support.

Self-Regulation

Self-regulation refers to children's ability to cope with their emotions and frustrations. It is a competency that evolves slowly throughout the early childhood years. It requires that children develop strategies for reducing stress as well as for delaying their needs for emotional gratification. Children who are unable to regulate their emotions react to stress with negative behaviors such as crying or tantruming.

The term *acting out* refers to tantruming or excessive crying; aggression such as hitting, biting, or screaming; inability to cope with novelty or change; destructive behavior such as throwing and dirtying; excessive motor activity including running away; and fearfulness. These acting-out behaviors are normal occurrences in early childhood. Occasionally, all children display some or all of these behaviors. For example, almost all 9-month-old children make messes when they eat, not only by smearing food over their bodies but also by throwing food at other people or on the table and floor.

Acting-out behaviors are partly the result of children not having the cognitive, language, and emotional skills needed to regulate their emotions. For example, tantruming, which typically begins at about 18 months of age, and which for many children peaks between 2 and 3 years of age, is thought to be triggered by children's limited ability to express their feelings and needs (e.g., immature communication) at a time when their cognitive and emotional behaviors are developing rapidly. Fearfulness increases as children become more perceptive and aware of people and objects, at a time at which they lack the experience needed to understand that these people or events will not harm them.

There are considerable individual differences among children in the degree to which they act out. To a large extent these differences can be related to children's biological predispositions, including their temperament and activity level. Children who have easy temperaments and who prefer low levels of activity may act out only occasionally; children with difficult temperaments, who react strongly to novelty and change, and who require constant and high levels of physical activity are likely to act out frequently (van den Boom, 1995). In addition, biological conditions such as autism and attention-deficit/hyperactivity disorder clearly predispose children to react strongly and negatively to a wide range of situations that usually do not affect most children.

Parents' attitudes about their children's behavior, particularly as manifested in their responsiveness, also contribute to the frequency and intensity with which children act out. The following describes some of the characteristics of responsive parents that reduce the occurrences of acting out.

- *Responsive parents have developmentally appropriate rules and expectations.* A common public scene in stores, restaurants, and churches is that of parents struggling to get their children to sit still, be quiet, or stop grabbing or throwing objects. More often than not, children react to these situations by crying, screaming, tantruming, hitting their siblings, running away, or throwing themselves on the floor. Parents' expectations for how their children should behave in these situations often exceed what children are able to do at early stages of development. Whereas some 2-year-olds may be able to conform to these kinds of social expectations, the majority of 2-year-old children simply cannot be expected to sit still, be quiet, and pay attention for any extended period of time. The way these children behave in stores, restaurants, and churches is the way they behave at home or in any other setting. They have not yet reached a level of social awareness where they are able to conform to the social requirements of these situations.

The more parents try to get their children to do something they are not developmentally ready to do, the more children become frustrated and agitated such that they can no longer control their emotional and physical reactions. By making demands that exceed children's capabilities, parents can actually cause their children to act out. Often these situations are made even worse by parents interpreting their children's behavior as bad and by punishing them rather than recognizing that their reaction to the situation is typical for their stage of developmental functioning.

Responsive parents virtually eliminate these problems by understanding the developmental limitations of their children. They expect their children to react the way children at their developmental age level typically react. They avoid placing their children in situations in which they are not yet capable of conforming to social expectations. When forced to place their children in these situations, they provide them alternative activities that are more appropriate to their current level of developmental functioning (i.e., giving them toys to play with) that help them engage in socially appropriate behavior.

Responsive parents implement rules with which their children can comply. For example, rather than trying to enforce a rule that their child should not touch certain objects, they remove these objects from their children's reach (e.g., remove a vase from a coffee table). If they have a rule that their child should sit with the family at dinner time, they limit this expectation to a few minutes, recognizing that the child will have difficulty staying longer periods of time until they are much older. By implementing rules that are compatible with their children's current level of development, they introduce their children to the idea of rules in the context of behaviors with which they can be reasonably expected to be able to do.

- *Responsive parents also match their child's behavioral style.* In a landmark child development study, Thomas, Chess, and Birch (1968) examined the impact of temperament on children's social–emotional adjustment in the early school years. Temperament is thought to be a biologically determined behavioral predisposition children manifest soon after they are born. Thomas et al. reported that in the first year of life, children could be classified into one of three temperament groups. "Easy" children were children who adapted readily to new situations or change. They tended to enjoy social interaction and were easy to soothe when they cried. "Slow to warm up" children often became distressed or agitated when confronted with change or novelty. However, these children would adjust to such situations after short periods of time, and they were relatively easy to console when they became agitated and upset. "Difficult" children made extremely poor, or slow, adaptations to novelty or change. They reacted strongly to new situations and were extremely difficult to console when they became agitated.

These children were followed through the completion of the second grade. Children who were identified by their teachers as behavior problems during the early school years were children who had been classified as having a difficult temperament in the first year of life. Almost none of the children classified as easy or slow to warm up in their first year of life presented problems in the early school years. These findings underscore the strong association between the biologically determined behavioral predispositions of children and their ability to control and manage their behavior in demanding social situations (Kochanska, 1998).

The most interesting information from the study by Thomas et al. (1968) came from their examination of the developmental consequences of having a difficult temperament. When these researchers examined all of the children who had been classified as difficult, they found that only a portion of them had behavior problems in school. There were several difficult children who did not exhibit behavior problems who adjusted well to the demands of the classroom.

The different outcomes observed for difficult children were associated with the way their parents interacted with them. Difficult children who made poor adjustments to school tended to have parents who had a rigid or demanding child-rearing style. These parents expected their children to conform to socially appropriate behavioral norms, and they reacted to their children's misbehavior with punishment or other disciplinary procedures. In contrast, difficult children who made good adjustments to school had parents who had a flexible child-rearing style. These parents adjusted their parenting style to the biologically influenced behavioral characteristics of the child. They appeared less concerned about enforcing socially appropriate behavioral norms than they were with supporting the unique characteristics of their children. They anticipated how their children would react to new and stressful situations, and they supported their children during difficult transitions by giving them room to react as they seemed predisposed to do.

This study suggests that matching children's behavioral style may be a highly effective strategy for reducing acting out behavior, particularly for children with difficult temperaments. When parents accommodate to children's temperament, they support rather than punish children for behaving in a manner that is consistent with their nature. They provide their children the time, acceptance, support, and nurturance they need to develop their ability to cope with their feelings and manage their behavior more effectively. In contrast, parents who fail to accommodate to their children's temperament risk escalating episodes of acting out into emotionally charged events. These episodes keep children agitated and upset and prevent them from developing the coping skills they need to more effectively manage their feelings and behavior.

• *Responsive parents respond to their children's behavioral state.* State refers to whether a child is alert, happy, and receptive to social interaction or fussy, tired, hungry, and unreceptive to social interaction—characteristics that vary from one time of day to another.

Highly responsive parents are also highly sensitive. Sensitivity refers to being aware not only of children's interests but also of children's state. Responsive parents read children's state and respond appropriately. When children are tired or fussy, these parents respond by comforting them, putting them to sleep, or letting them play alone for short periods of time. When children are alert and receptive to interacting, they engage in reciprocal play and communication with them. In doing this, responsive parents avoid pressuring children to interact at times that they are not ready to interact. Because children often act out when they are tired or irritable, responding to children's state eliminates one of the major contributors to this problem.

• *Responsive parents discipline promptly and comfort.* Parents who are highly responsive are generally effective at gaining their children's cooperation and reducing the frequency of acting out behaviors (Kochanska et al., 1999). Nonetheless, they have occasional needs to discipline their children. Three characteristics of the manner in which responsive parents discipline their children contribute to the effectiveness of their discipline:

1. They limit the range of behaviors that require discipline. In other words, they establish boundaries for their children that are essential for the child's safety and well-being (i.e., the child runs away from the parent; the child touches a hot stove) or are critical to upholding core values of the family (e.g., the child hits the parent intentionally). In all cases, the limits established for the child are based upon a consideration of what are reasonable expectations at the child's current level of developmental functioning.

2. They discipline the child promptly after the child has violated a rule or limit. Parents do not threaten or delay discipline until a later time (e.g., the child is disciplined when the father gets home). In addition, the discipline is severe enough that the child recognizes that he or she is being disciplined but not so severe that it harms the child physically or psychologically.

3. They do not allow the discipline to interfere with their relationship with their child. Discipline is effective because it is administered by someone whom the child trusts and is attached to. Soon after the child is disciplined, parents comfort and reassure the child of their love and affection, which helps the child to recognize that parents are not unhappy with the child, but rather with what the child did.

Feelings of Confidence

Feelings of confidence refer to how children perceive their capability as opposed to how much ability they actually have. Some people view themselves as incompetent, even though they clearly have the ability needed to succeed. Perfectionists or people with unreasonably high expectations develop these self-perceptions. Because of the way they judge themselves, people who have low feelings of confidence over time begin to act incompetent, even though they have the ability to be successful.

Children's self-perception of their own competence is a strong predictor of their school performance. Even among high-ability students, children who perceive themselves as incompetent do more poorly than expected (Miserandino, 1996; Phillips, 1984, 1987; Phillips & Zimmerman, 1990). For example, competent third and fourth graders who doubted their abilities had less curiosity and enjoyment and more anxiety, anger, and boredom in school. In addition, they performed poorly in math and social studies (Miserandino, 1996). Children's perception of their ability also affected the difficulty of tasks they chose and the extent to which they became involved with or persisted at these tasks (Eccles, Wigfield, & Schiefele, 1998).

Responsive parents enhance children's feelings of confidence in two ways. First, they value what their children do. This is reflected by supporting and encouraging their children's initiations and accepting their children's behavior as important and meaningful, even when it is at a lower level than expected at their child's age. These parents take delight in their children's new developmental skills as well as in the novel things they do. This is reflected in their comments to their children as well as in their conversations about their children with other adults.

Second, responsive parents provide their children frequent opportunities for success by engaging in activities that their children can do. In these types of interactions children are highly likely to be successful in meeting their requests or expectations. However, even when their children do not respond appropriately or meet their expectations, these parents still accept whatever their children do and treat their behavior as legitimate and meaningful. This pattern of interaction results in children feeling successful, regardless of how they perform.

Because children with developmental problems are often unable to keep up with their peers, they have a tendency to perceive themselves as incompetent. This pattern can begin to occur in even the early childhood years. However, children with developmental problems can, and often do, experience high degrees of success, particularly when (a) tasks that adults ask them to do are within their range of ability and (b) adults view their performance as successful, even when it does not reach the usual standards of success. Over time these kinds of positive experiences help children perceive themselves as competent, despite their limitations.

Feelings of Control

Control refers to how people view their capacity to impact external events. Children with high feelings of control believe that events are under their control and that they have the power to make changes in their lives (Rotter, 1990). Children with low feelings of control believe that there is little connection between what they do and what happens to them.

The opportunities children have to control their own lives can profoundly influence their perceptions of their ability to control. The more children have opportunities to (a) make their own choices, (b) do what they prefer, and (c) influence their personal outcomes, the more likely they are to have high feelings of control. Conversely, if children (a) have few opportunities to choose what they want to do, (b) participate in activities and daily routines that are dominated by structure and demands imposed by others, and (c) have little experience influencing what happens to them, they are likely to develop low feelings of control.

Feelings of control are strong predictors of young children's performance (Findley & Cooper, 1983; Stipek, 1980; Stipek & Weisz, 1981). Children with high feelings of control tend to initiate action, exert effort, and persist even in the context of challenging tasks. Children with low feelings of control, which is referred to as learned helplessness (Seligman, 1975), tend to be passive, lethargic, and may even appear depressed. These children tend to select easy tasks and seldom impose structure on problems or sequence action steps. "In the face of challenges or failure, children (with low feelings of control) ... become confused; they lose concentration and focus.... Over time, their effort decreases, they experience cognitive demobilization and inhibited generation of ideas, they initiate fewer responses, and they become discouraged, despondent and passive" (Skinner, Zimmer-Gemeck, & Connell, 1998, pp. 10–11).

Children develop feelings of control when they have frequent opportunities to affect what happens to them. Responsive parents promote feelings of control by engaging in two behaviors. First, they respond quickly to behaviors their children initiate. They encourage their children to control the focus of the interaction by making their own behavior contingent on their children's behavior. When adults respond by imitating or acting like their children, children become aware of their ability to influence adults (i.e., control their social environment) and gradually learn to use this skill in appropriate ways.

Second, responsive parents maximize their children's experiences at exerting control by giving them frequent opportunities to make choices. They make sure that their children have desirable alternatives from which to choose throughout their daily routines. They accommodate their children's desires and choices when they change their minds.

Often, children with developmental problems will acquire negative perceptions about themselves. Once established, these can be long lasting and difficult to change. If negative self-perceptions such as low feelings of control take root in the early years of their lives, children can become so paralyzed by these feelings that they avoid engaging in tasks, even though they may be interesting and well within their capabilities. However, the positive self-perceptions children acquire by interacting with responsive parents play a major role in establishing lifelong feelings of control.

Summary

In this chapter, we have presented the theory and research that are the bases for the pivotal behaviors targeted in Responsive Teaching to address children's developmental needs and concerns. We discussed how responsive interaction is a developmental teaching strategy that helps children develop and use the pivotal behaviors or learning processes that are the bases for developmental learning. We described how the apparent impact of responsive interaction on these pivotal behaviors can be understood in the context of contemporary psychological theories.

Chapter 6

The Effectiveness of Responsive Teaching

In this chapter, we present the results from a 1-year evaluation of the children and parents we worked with to develop the Responsive Teaching (RT) curriculum. Results from this evaluation have undergone scientific review and have been published in two professional journals (see Mahoney & Perales, 2003, 2005, for detailed information about some of the technical aspects of this evaluation).

This evaluation provides a rigorous test of the effectiveness of Responsive Teaching. Not only do we examine whether children who received Responsive Teaching made significant developmental and social–emotional improvements, we also examine whether the improvements children achieved in this intervention were related to the causal events, or logic model, of Responsive Teaching, which is described in Chapter 1, Figure 1.1. To do this, this evaluation addressed four questions:

- Do RT strategies actually help parents interact more responsively with their children?
- Do children's pivotal behaviors improve while they participate in RT?
- When children participate in RT, do they make improvements in their developmental and social–emotional functioning that are greater than could be expected at the start of intervention?
- Are the developmental improvements children make in RT related to improvements in their parents' responsiveness or their own use of pivotal behavior?

Participants

The participants for this evaluation were 50 mother–child pairs. The children's ages ranged from 12 to 54 months, with 85% of the children being younger than 36 months when they began. The characteristics of the mothers and children are presented in Table 6.1.

The average age of the mothers was 32.6 years, and most were Caucasian (89.1%) and married (92.7%). Mothers had over 2 years of college education, and half of them worked outside the home, either part or full time.

The sample included 20 children who had been diagnosed by their physicians with an autism spectrum disorder (ASD). As indicated in Table 6.1, these children had delays in cognitive, symbolic, and communication functioning. They also had severe problems in social interaction and self-regulation, as indicated by their scores on the *Temperament and Atypical Behavior Scale* (TABS; Bagnato, Neisworth, Salvia, & Hunt, 1999).

There were also 30 children with developmental disorders (DD). These children had significant developmental delays in cognition or communication (see Table 6.1). Although children with DD (mean age = 23.3 months) were younger than children with ASD (mean

Table 6.1

Demographic Characteristics of Parents and Children at Start of Intervention

	Children with ASD (n = 20)		Children with DD (n = 30)		Total Sample (n = 50)	
Variable	***M***	***SD***	***M***	***SD***	***M***	***SD***
Mother						
Age (years)	32.1	7.1	31.7	5.5	32.6	5.2
Education (years)	15.5	2.6	14.3	1.9	14.8	2.2
Marital status (% married)	100.0	—	88.2	—	92.7	—
Race (% Caucasian)	95.2	—	85.3	—	89.1	—
Employed (%)	52.4	—	44.1	—	47.3	—
Part time (%)	28.6	—	14.7	—	20.0	—
Full time (%)	23.8	—	29.4	—	27.3	—
Father						
Age (years)	35.6	6.0	33.7	5.5	34.5	5.8
Education (years)	15.9	2.6	14.7	2.6	15.2	2.6
Children						
Age (months)	32.4	7.3	23.3	6.1	26.9	7.9
% males	65.0	—	67.0	—	66.0	—
Social–emotional characteristics[a]						
Detached[b]	22.1	21.7	47.3	11.2	37.0	20.4
Hypersensitivity/Hyperactivity[b]	41.0	14.8	46.2	16.4	44.1	15.8
Underreactive[b]	34.3	12.4	47.3	12.4	42.0	13.9
Self-regulation[b]	35.3	16.1	46.8	10.3	42.1	14.1
Overall atypical behavior[c]	58.0	37.0	91.2	24.8	77.6	34.2
Child development[d]						
Object abilities[e]	16.5	6.0	17.8	6.5	17.3	6.3
Symbolic behavior[e]	15.2	5.3	15.1	5.5	15.1	5.4
Expressive language[e]	13.8	6.7	12.6	5.5	13.1	6.0
Receptive language[e]	12.1	7.2	15.3	6.1	14.0	6.7

Note. ASD = autism spectrum disorder; DD = developmental disorders; M = mean; SD = standard deviation. [a] *Temperament and Atypical Behavior Scale* (Bagnato, Neisworth, Salvia, & Hunt, 1999). [b] *T*-score (M = 50, SD = 10). [c] Standard score (M = 100, SD = 15). [d] *Transdisciplinary Play-Based Assessment–Revised Edition* (Linder, 1993). [e] Developmental age (months).

age = 32.4 months), the developmental ages for these two groups were nearly the same. However, children with DD had higher social–emotional scores than children with ASD.

Intervention

Participants received RT during weekly 1-hour parent–child sessions for approximately 1 year that were conducted either at a center-based facility or in parents' homes. Participants were scheduled for one session each week and received an average of 33 sessions during the year. At the completion of intervention, parents reported spending an average of 15 hours each week carrying out intervention activities with their children at home.

Information Used To Evaluate the Effects of Responsive Teaching

A comprehensive child development assessment was conducted at the beginning and end of intervention. Three instruments were used to assess children's development and social–emotional functioning:

The *Transdisciplinary Play-Based Assessment–Revised Edition* (TPBA; Linder, 1993) is a play-based assessment for children up to 6 years of age. Each of the play and social behaviors children produced during a 40-minute observation were transcribed from videotaped recordings and coded according to the child's developmental age level as reported in the *Developmental Rainbow* (Mahoney & Perales, 1996). Developmental ages were computed for two cognitive domains, object abilities use and symbolic behavior, and two language domains, expressive and receptive language. Developmental ages were the highest age level of developmental behaviors children consistently produced (i.e., more than 10 times) during the observation for each of the four developmental domains.

The *Developmental Rainbow* (Mahoney & Perales, 1996) is a child development profile that is designed to guide developmental observations and play-based assessments of children from birth through 5 years of age. This observational tool includes a detailed listing of the skills and behaviors young children are likely to be able to do across five developmental domains: cognition, communication, social–emotional functioning, motor development, and self-help skills. Items included in this profile were compiled from several standardized developmental assessment instruments and preschool curricula, and organized according to developmental age ranges.

The TABS (Bagnato et al., 1999) is a standardized instrument designed to assess problem behavior of children between 1 and 6 years of age. This parent-respondent instrument has 55 items that assess four factors: detachment, hypersensitivity/hyperactivity, underreactivity, and dysregulation. In addition to assessing children's development, we also measured mothers' style of interaction and children's pivotal behavior at the beginning and end of intervention. These assessments were made from a 7-minute videotape of children and mothers playing together with a set of developmentally appropriate toys.

The *Maternal Behavior Rating Scale–Revised* (MBRS; Mahoney, 1999) was used to assess mothers' style of interacting with their children. The MBRS has 12 items that assess four dimensions of interactive style: responsiveness, affect, achievement orientation, and directiveness, with 5-point Likert scales (e.g., 1 = *low;* 5 = *high*).

The *Child Behavior Rating Scale* (CBRS; Mahoney & Wheeden, 1998) was used to assess children's pivotal behavior from the videotapes of parent–child play. The CBRS has seven items that assess children's engagement: attention, persistence, involvement/interest, cooperation, initiation, joint attention, and affect, with 5-point Likert scales (e.g., 1 = *low;* 5 = *high*).

Results

The following provides a summary of the major findings from this evaluation.

Responsive Teaching Enhanced Mothers' Interactions with Their Children

Ratings of mothers' style of interacting with their children are presented in Figure 6.1. These data show that mothers' responsiveness and affect increased by 20% and 13%, respectively, during intervention, whereas their achievement orientation and directiveness declined by approximately 7%. A multivariate analysis of variance (MANOVA) indicated that changes in mothers' interactions with their children were statistically significant, $F(4, 46) = 8.66$, $p < .001$. Compared to preintervention, mothers were significantly higher in responsiveness and affect but significantly lower in achievement orientation. Differences in directiveness were not significant.

Responsive Teaching Enhanced Children's Pivotal Developmental Behaviors

As indicated in Figure 6.2, observations of children's engagement with their parents indicated that children made significant improvements in their use of the pivotal behav-

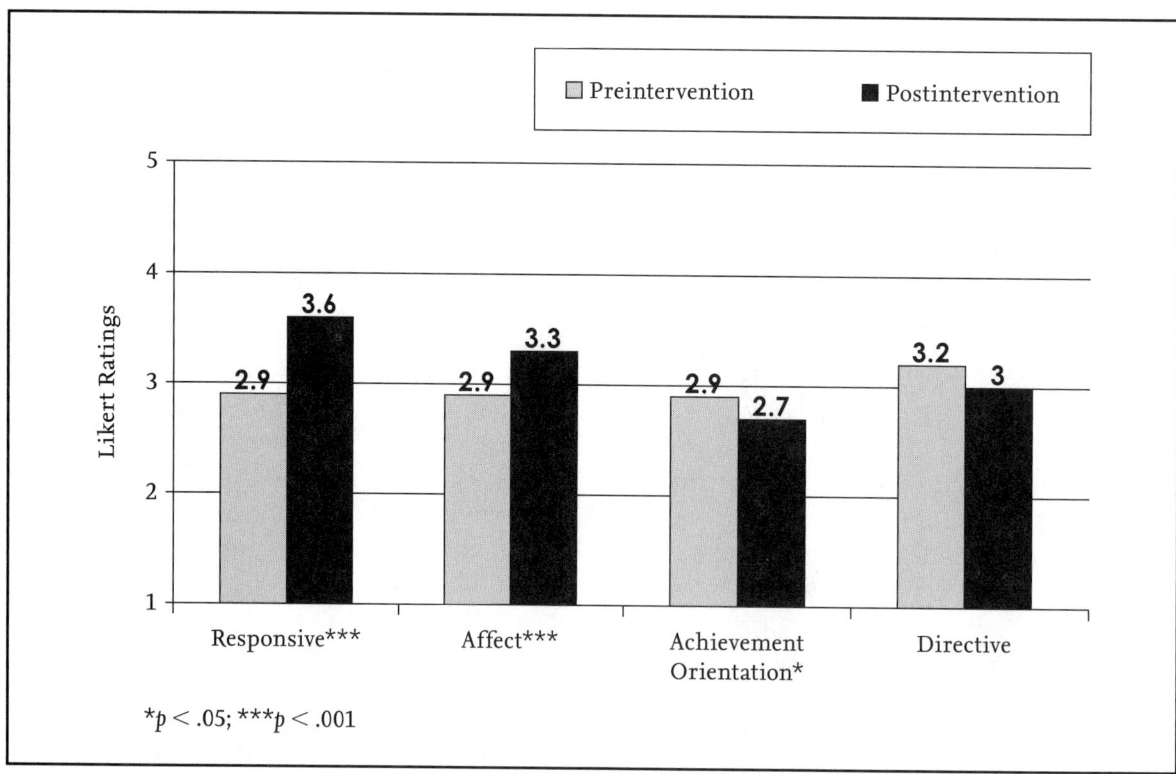

Figure 6.1. The impact of Responsive Teaching on mothers' style of interacting with their children, as measured by the *Maternal Behavior Rating Scale* (MBRS; Mahoney, 1999).

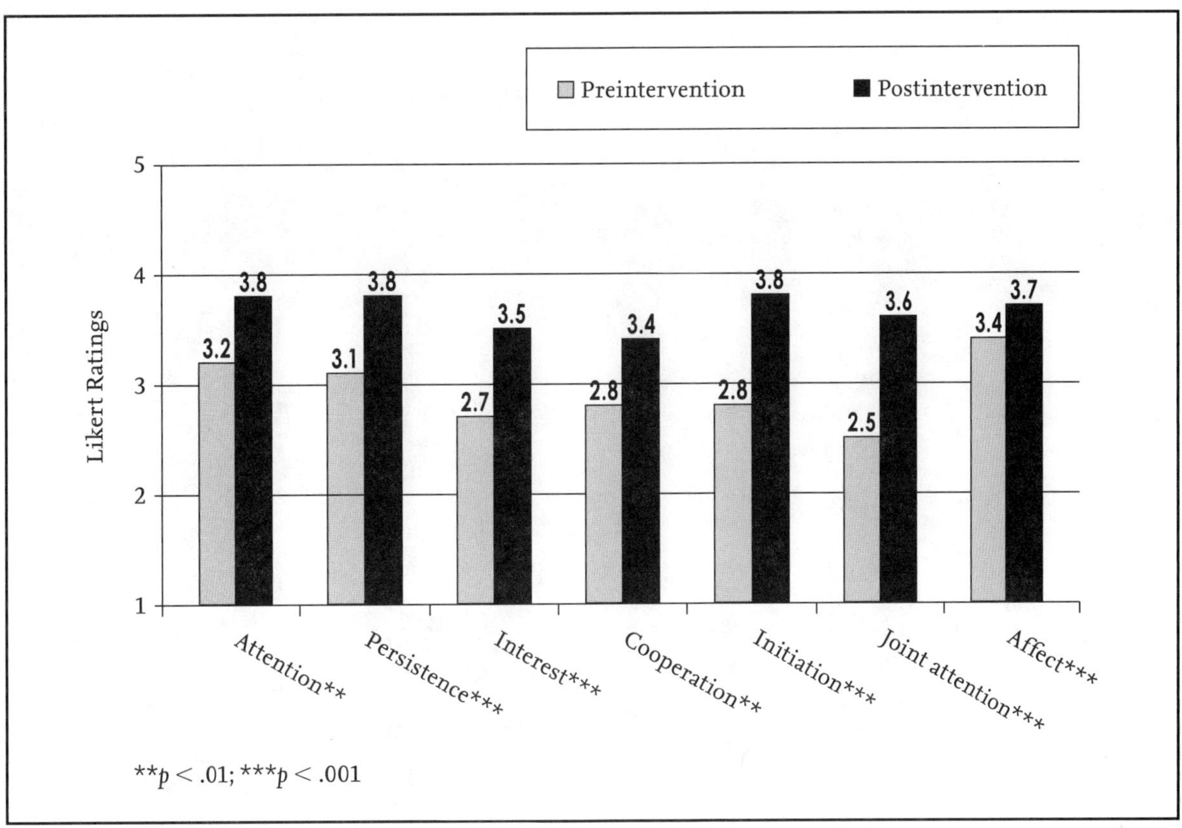

Figure 6.2. The impact of Responsive Teaching on children's use of pivotal developmental behaviors, as measured by the *Childhood Behavior Rating Scale* (CBRS; Mahoney & Wheeden, 1998).

iors during intervention $F(7, 43) = 11.28$, $p < .001$. Across all seven CBRS items, children's pivotal behavior ratings increased by an average of 35% from the beginning to the end of intervention.

Responsive Teaching Promoted Children's Development

Pre–post developmental age scores are reported in Figure 6.3. To assess intervention effects on children's cognitive and language development, we compared the level of developmental functioning observed for children at postintervention with the level they could have been expected to attain had they not received intervention. Expected developmental ages are based upon the assumption that if intervention was not effective, children should develop at the same rate during intervention as they did at the beginning of intervention. Results from the MANOVA indicated that children's developmental age scores observed at the end of intervention were greater than their expected developmental ages. As indicated in Figure 6.3, children made greater developmental improvements in all four developmental domains than they would have been expected to attain had they not received intervention.

We conducted a second set of analyses to estimate the magnitude of the developmental improvements children actually made during intervention. To do this, we computed a statistic called proportional change index (PCI). PCIs compare children's rate of development during intervention to their rate of development before intervention. As reported in Figure 6.4, on average, children's rate of development during intervention was 133% greater

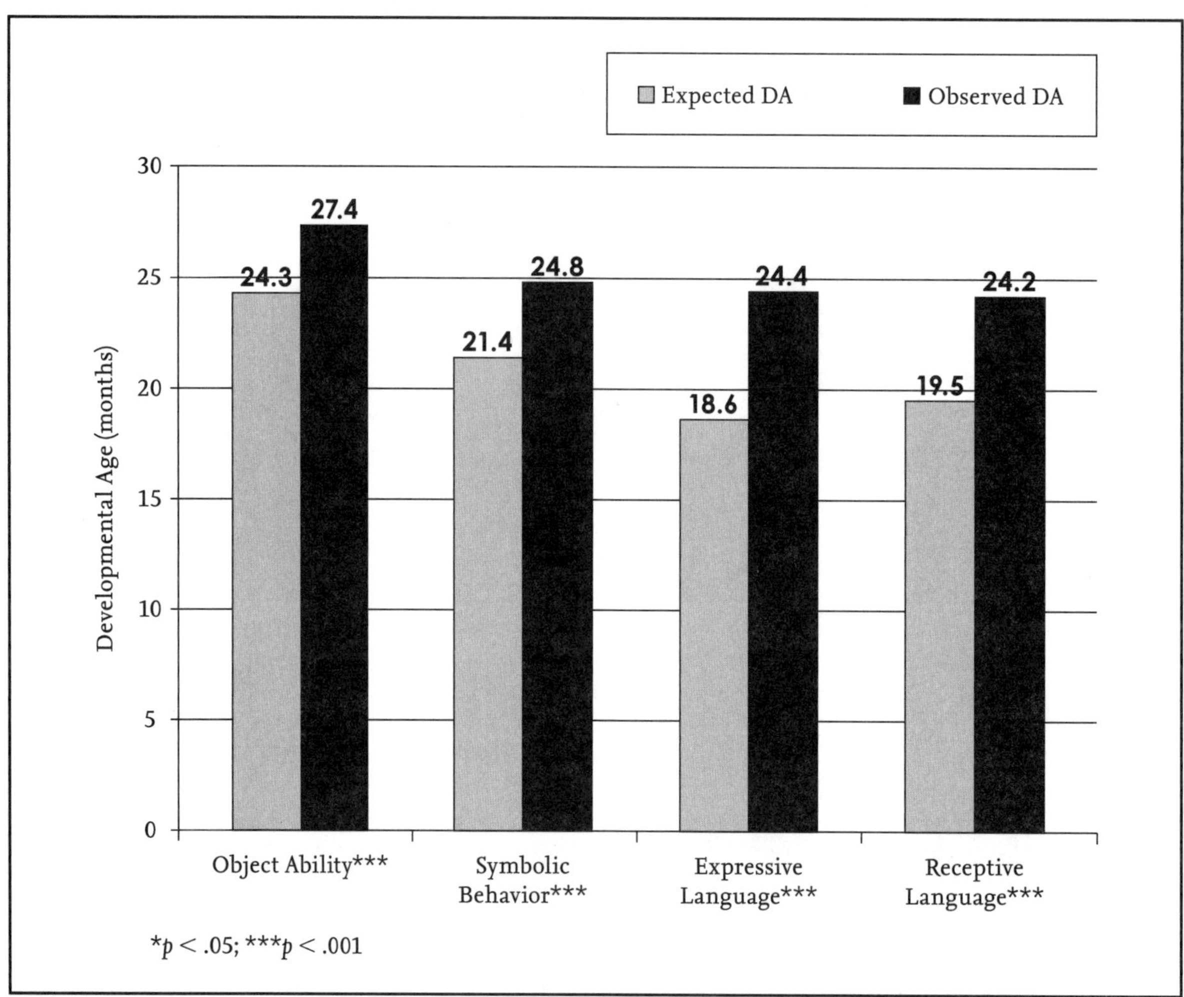

Figure 6.3. The impact of Responsive Teaching on children's developmental age (DA) as assessed by the *Developmental Rainbow* (Mahoney & Perales, 1996) at the end of intervention.

(range = 20% to 259%) than it was before intervention. The data in Figure 6.4 also show that children with autism/PDD made developmental improvements that were more than twice as large as the improvements made by children with DD.

Responsive Teaching Improved Children's Social–Emotional Functioning

Children with DD did not have social–emotional problems at the beginning of intervention, as indicated by their TABS scores. In addition, they made little improvement in this domain during intervention. However, children with ASD who had several social–emotional problems before intervention made dramatic and clinically significant improvements in this domain during the course of intervention, $F(5, 15) = 9.64$, $p < .001$. As indicated in Figure 6.5, this improvement was evident on three TABS subscales—detached, underreactivity, and self-regulation—as well as on their overall scores.

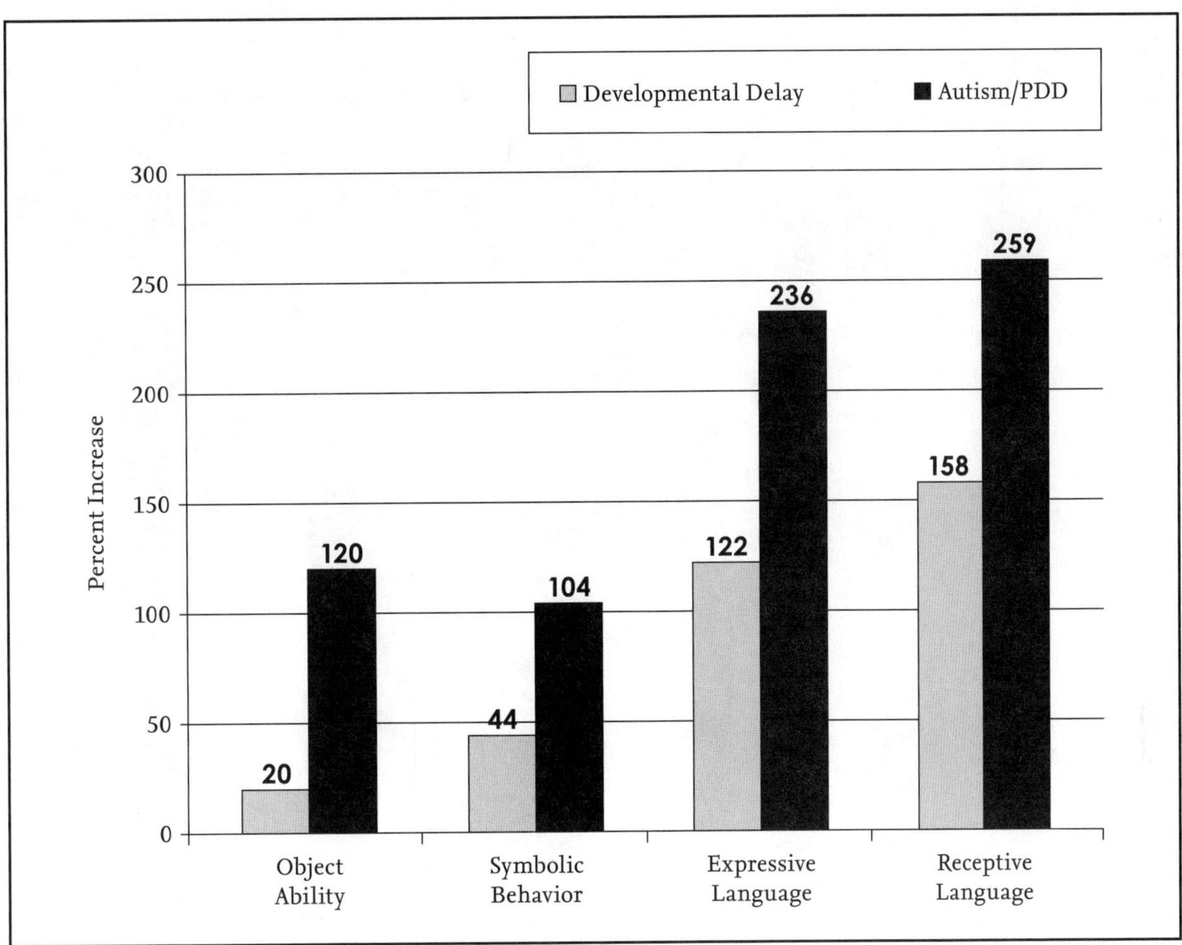

Figure 6.4. Proportional increases in children's rate of development during intervention, as measured by the *Developmental Rainbow* (Mahoney & Perales, 1996).

Improvements Related to Responsive Teaching

One way of establishing that Responsive Teaching was truly responsible for the developmental improvements that were reported is to demonstrate that the changes in mothers' responsiveness and children's pivotal behavior that were promoted through Responsive Teaching were related to the developmental and social–emotional improvements the children made. If the children who made the greatest improvements were the ones whose mothers' changes in responsiveness resulted in the improvements in their pivotal behavior, then there is strong reason to believe that Responsive Teaching is a highly effective developmental intervention curriculum. To do this, we computed several regression analyses and examined (a) how improvements in mothers' responsiveness that were promoted by RT strategies were related to the increases in children's pivotal behavior, and (b) how improvements in children's development and social–emotional functioning were related to improvements in their use of pivotal behaviors. Because these analyses are reported in detail in Mahoney and Perales (2005), in the following we report a summary of the major findings.

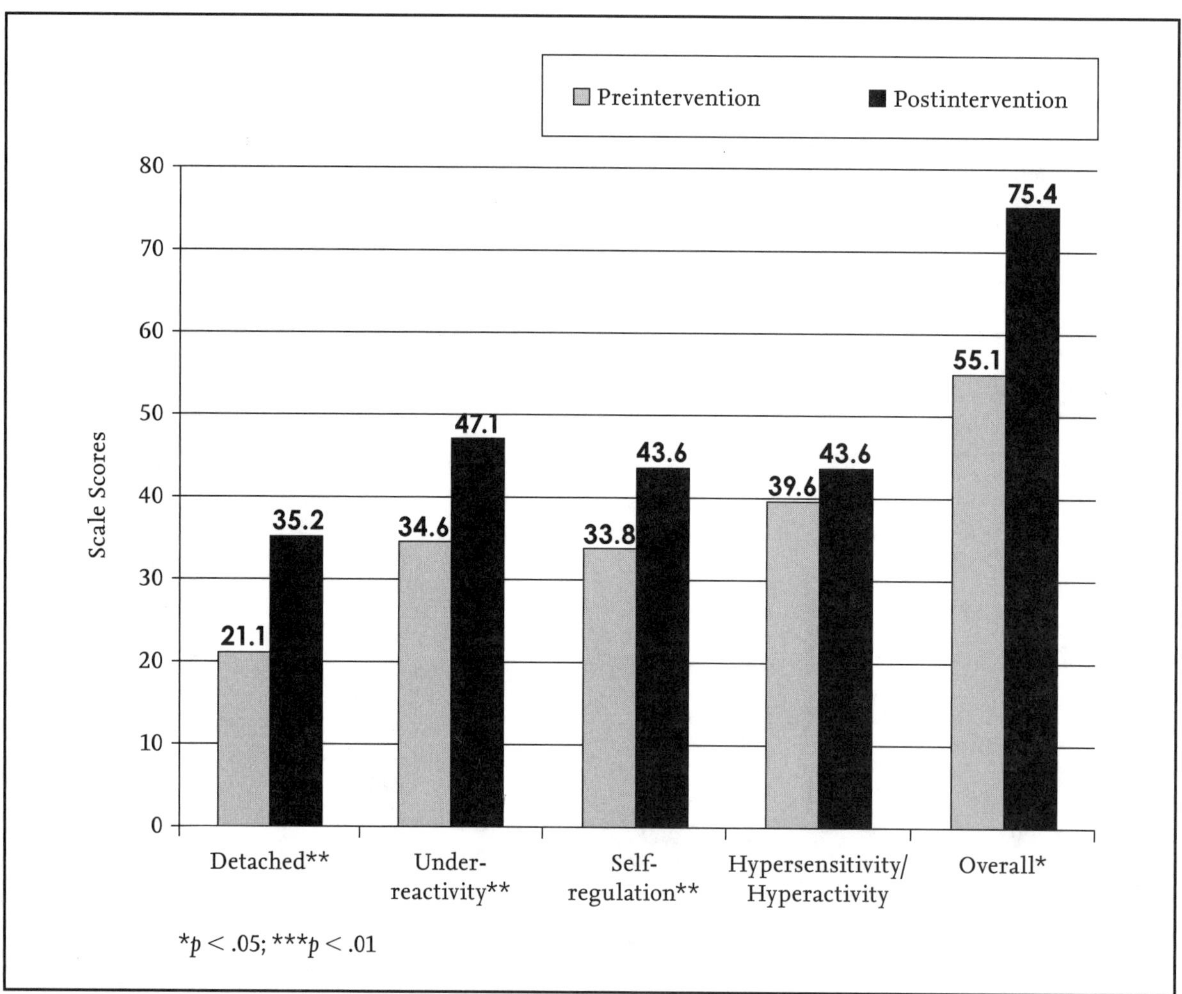

Figure 6.5. The impact of Responsive Teaching on *Temperament and Atypical Behavior Scale* (TABS; Bagnato & Neisworth, 1999) scores for children with autism spectrum disorders.

First, the changes in mothers' responsiveness during intervention accounted for 20% of the variance in changes in children's pivotal behavior. To illustrate this finding, we divided the mothers into three groups based upon how responsive they became during intervention. Level 1 mothers ($n = 16$) made no changes in responsiveness, Level 2 mothers ($n = 12$) made moderate changes, and Level 3 mothers ($n = 22$) made substantial changes. We then plotted the degree to which the children of these three groups of mothers changed their level of pivotal behavior during intervention. As depicted in Figure 6.6, there was a linear relationship between the degree to which mothers changed their level of responsiveness and changes in children's pivotal behavior. When mothers did not change their responsiveness, children made only negligible increases in their pivotal behaviors. However, when mothers became more responsive, the degree to which children increased their pivotal behavior was directly related to the degree to which parents changed their responsiveness. The more responsive mothers became during intervention, the more children increased their pivotal behavior.

Second, changes in children's pivotal behavior accounted for an average of 9.5% of the variance in improvements in children's rate of development for all four developmental

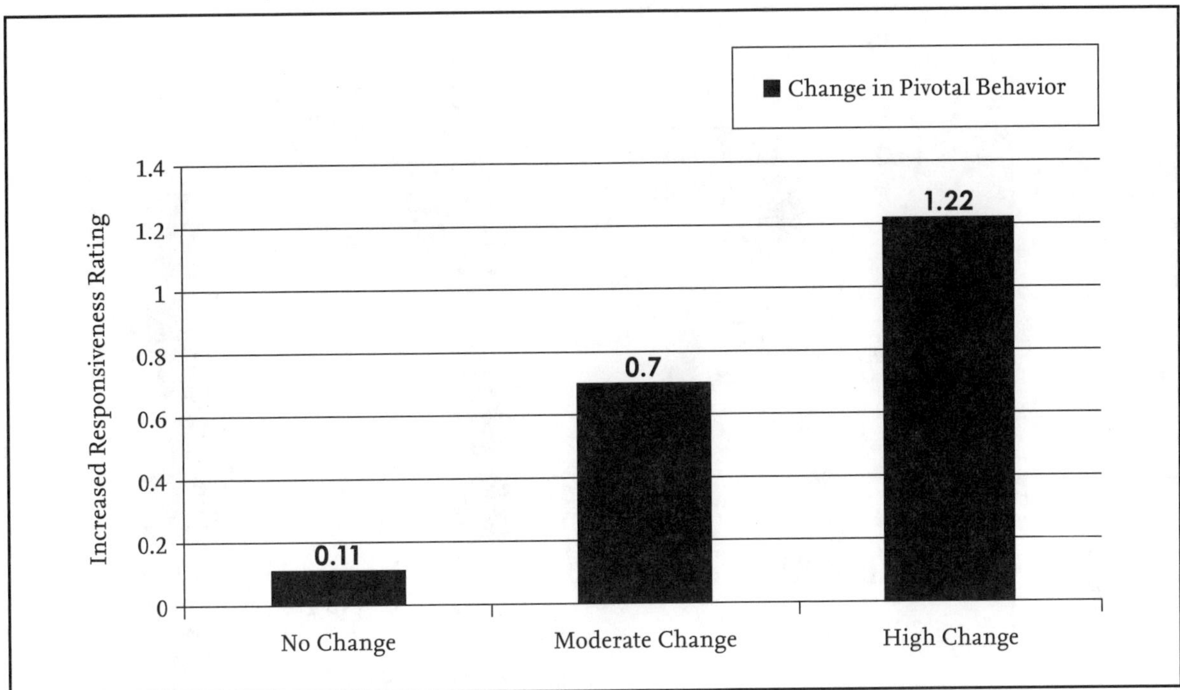

Figure 6.6. The impact of changes in mothers' responsiveness on changes in children's pivotal behavior.

measures, controlling for the effects of children's development at the beginning of intervention. To illustrate this finding, we divided the children into three groups based upon the amount of change in pivotal behavior they made during intervention. Level 1 children (n = 13) made no changes in pivotal behavior; Level 2 children (n = 19) made moderate changes (i.e., less than 1 scale point); and Level 3 children (n = 18) made substantial changes (i.e., more than 1 scale point).

In general there was a "dose response" relationship between changes in children's pivotal behavior to the improvements they made during intervention in their developmental functioning. This relationship was observed for all developmental measures with the exception of receptive language. As indicated in Figure 6.7, if children did not increase their pivotal behaviors during intervention, their rate of developmental improvement was about the same as would be expected based upon their rate of development at the beginning of intervention. However, if children increased their pivotal behaviors during intervention, children's developmental improvements were substantially greater than their expected rate of development. Furthermore, the greater the increases in children's pivotal behavior, the greater were the improvements in their developmental functioning during intervention.

We also conducted regression analyses to examine how changes in children's pivotal behavior contributed to changes in their social–emotional functioning as measured by the TABS. Results indicated that changes in children's pivotal behavior were not related to their social–emotional improvements. Nonetheless, as indicated in Figure 6.8, when we divided the sample into children who did not change their pivotal behaviors during intervention (No Change, n = 13) versus children who made at least some changes (Change, n = 34), children in the change group made improvements on four of the five TABS subscales that were at least 100% greater than improvements made by the no-change group.

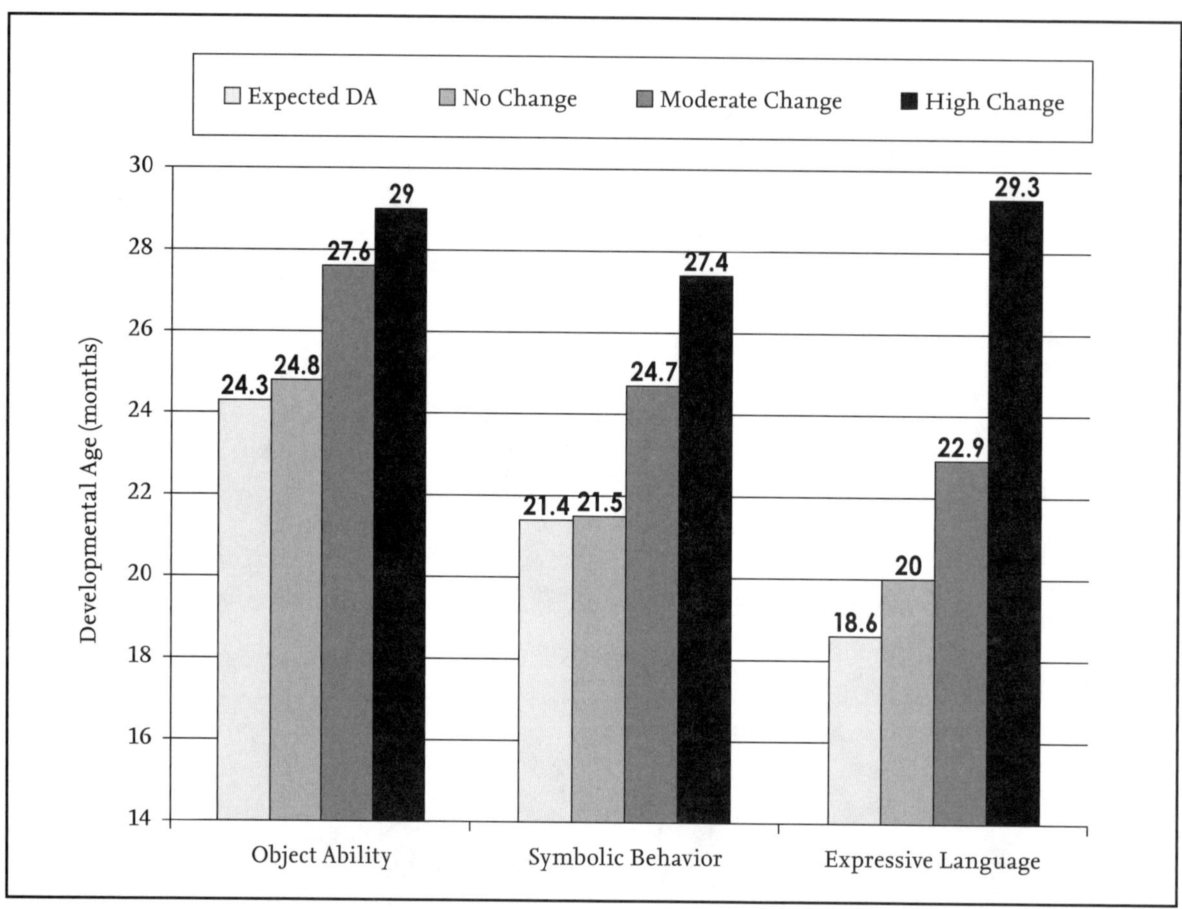

Figure 6.7. The relationship of changes in children's pivotal behavior to their developmental ages (DAs) at post-intervention compared to their expected developmental ages, as measured by the *Developmental Rainbow* (Mahoney & Perales, 1996).

Summary

In this chapter, we have reported results from an evaluation of a sample of 50 children and their parents who received Responsive Teaching for approximately 1 year. We found that even though this intervention involved only modest levels of professional contact with parents and children, Responsive Teaching was effective at encouraging two thirds of the parents to engage in more responsive interactions with their children. Furthermore, there was a strong relationship between how responsive parents became during intervention with how much their children increased their use of pivotal behaviors.

Responsive Teaching was highly effective at promoting children's cognitive and communication development. On average, children's rate of cognitive development during intervention was 60% greater than it was at the start of intervention. Responsive Teaching had an even more dramatic effect on children's communication development. On average children's rate of expressive language development was 167% greater and their receptive language development was 138% greater than it was at the start of intervention.

The size of the effect that Responsive Teaching had on children's development is unparalleled in the intervention research literature. What is more impressive, each of these developmental effects, with the exception of receptive language, was strongly associated

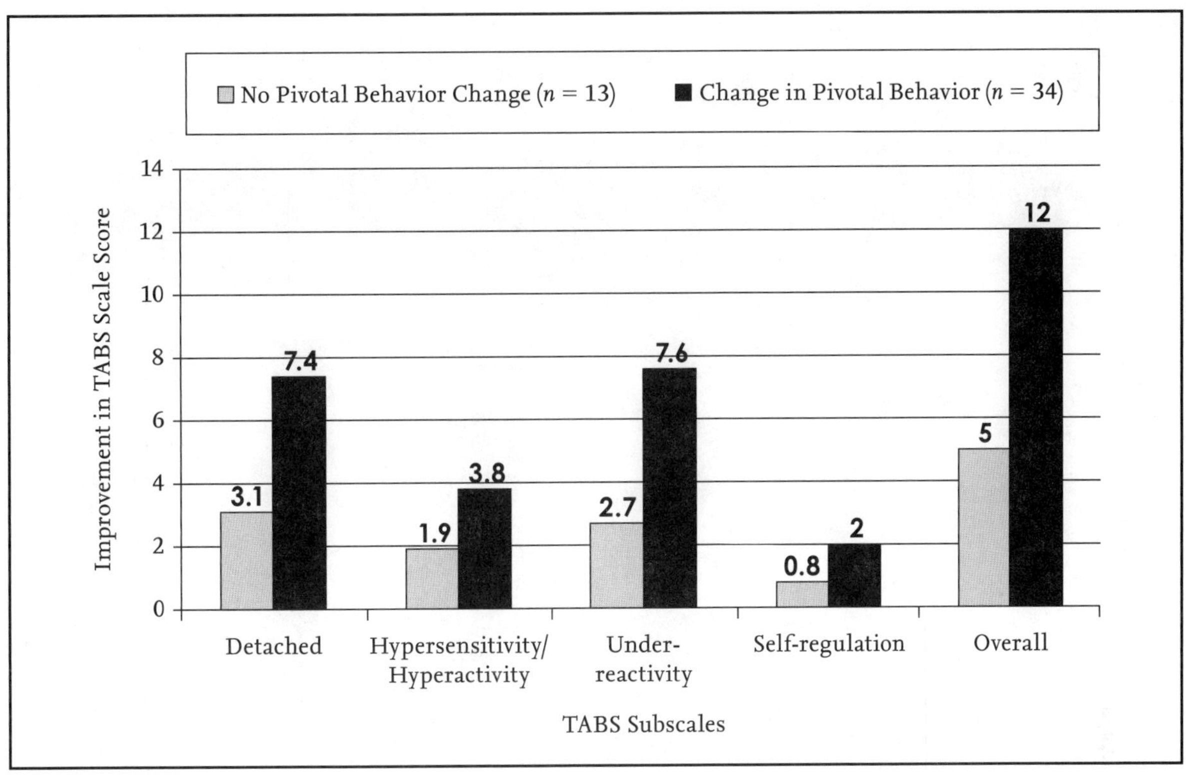

Figure 6.8. The relationship between changes in children's pivotal behavior to changes in their *Temperament and Atypical Behavior Scale* (TABS; Bagnato & Neisworth, 1999) scores.

with the degree to which children increased their use of pivotal developmental behaviors, which is the primary focus of the Responsive Teaching curriculum.

Responsive Teaching was also effective at reducing children's social–emotional problems, but these effects occurred only for children who manifested these problems at the beginning of intervention. Children with DD who did not have social–emotional problems at the beginning of intervention made little improvement in this domain. However, children with ASD who had severe social–emotional problems at the start of intervention made marked improvement in this critical area of functioning. Many professionals have speculated that interventions that encourage parents to become more responsive should be effective at promoting children's social–emotional well-being (cf. Zeanah, 2000). However, this is the first published intervention study to demonstrate this effect.

These data provide extremely strong support for the effectiveness of Responsive Teaching. These results are impressive because of the magnitude of improvement that children made and, what is more important, because of the consistent relationship between the impact of Responsive Teaching on parents' interactive behavior and the developmental outcomes their children attained.

Results from this evaluation should give professionals and the families they work with great confidence. They provide strong evidence that encouraging parents to use Responsive Teaching strategies to promote children's pivotal developmental behaviors is a highly effective intervention for promoting children's development and social–emotional well-being.

Section III

Implementing Responsive Teaching

Chapter 7

Intervention Planning

Responsive Teaching (RT) was designed so that intervention could provide a flexible sequence of activities that are both individualized to the unique needs and learning styles of children and parents and responsive to new problems or concerns that arise. The menu-driven format of RT gives parents and professionals the option of choosing the pivotal behavior objectives, RT strategies, and discussion points on which they want to work. It also allows them to decide how much information to focus on in each session and how long to work on that information.

Because of the flexible nature of this curriculum, parents and professionals need to develop individualized plans for each intervention session. The materials and tools included in this curriculum have been designed so that complete session plans can be developed manually in approximately 10 minutes. The Responsive Teaching Curriculum Planning and Tracking Program, which can be purchased to accompany this curriculum, makes planning even easier. This computer program, which includes the complete Responsive Teaching Curriculum, is compatible with Windows 2000 or later. Once a file has been set up for a client, session plans can be developed and printed in less than 2 minutes.

Figure 7.1 provides an overview of the planning process. All of the tools and information needed for planning are included in Section IV, Curriculum Materials, or in the Responsive Teaching Curriculum Planning and Tracking Program. Each of the steps of this process is described next.

Step 1—Identify Parental Concerns and Classify Them Into One or More Developmental Domains

In most federal- or state-sponsored early intervention programs, parents are asked to identify their concerns about their children's development on the Individualized Family Service Plan (IFSP). In programs where IFSPs are not used, interventionists can identify parents' concerns by simply conducting informal discussions about what they would like to see happen with their child. Parents' concerns typically range from requests for their children to learn how to play; learn colors, numbers, or days of the week; speak, learn words, or be able to communicate their needs; behave or get along with their brothers and sisters (stop screaming, sleep at night, interact with them and be happy); and learn to be assertive and to feel good about themselves. As indicated in Figure 7.2, almost all of these outcomes can be classified into one or more of the Responsive Teaching developmental domains.

Often, intervention must also focus on developmental domains or intervention goals that are not identified as concerns but are directly related to the concerns parents have raised. For example, if parents are primarily concerned about their children's language, intervention may also need to promote other developmental domains, such as cognition and social–emotional functioning, that also affect language development. As interventionists

Steps		Tools
Step 1	Identify parental concerns and classify them into one or more developmental domains.	Figure 7.2, p. 80
Step 2	Target social play as the first pivotal behavior.	Curriculum Outline, p. 163
Step 3	Select the pivotal behaviors most relevant to children's developmental needs.	Pivotal Behavior Wizard, p. 117
Step 4	Assess children's progress on their pivotal behaviors.	Pivotal Behavior Profile, p. 121
Step 5	Select discussion points and Responsive Teaching strategies for intervention sessions.	Planning and Tracking Form, p. 139, or the Responsive Teaching Curriculum Planning and Tracking Program
Step 6	Complete the Intervention Session Plans.	Intervention Session Plan Forms, p. 157, and Curriculum Outline, p. 163
Step 7	Record intervention session activities.	Planning and Tracking Form, p. 139, or the Responsive Teaching Curriculum Planning and Tracking Program

Figure 7.1. Overview of the RT planning process.

Parent Outcome	Developmental Domain
"I want my child to be normal/catch up" "I want my child to learn what he or she needs for school" "I want my child to be more interested in toys" "I want my child to play meaningfully" "I want my child to learn colors, shapes, letters, numbers" "I want my child to learn to share"	Cognition
"I want my child to be more interested in people" "I want my child to recognize me" "I want my child to make his or her needs known to me" "I want my child to talk/learn words" "I want my child to have conversations with me" "I want my child to speak so others can understand him or her"	Communication
"I want my child to stop fussing/crying/tantruming" "I want my child to obey me" "I want my child to go to bed at a decent hour" "I want my child to behave in the restaurant/at church/at my relatives' home" "I want my child not to hit/bite or scream" "I want my child to be more active" "I want my child to act independently"	Social–emotional functioning

Figure 7.2. Responsive Teaching developmental domains that address common parent-identified outcomes for their children.

incorporate content and activities to address these other related goal areas, it is important that they help parents understand why these other goals will help children attain the developmental outcomes desired.

Many children have developmental problems across several domains. As a rule of thumb, we recommend that intervention work on no more than two goals at a time. This keeps intervention sessions focused and clear and makes it easier for parents to follow through with the resulting information. The evaluation data presented in Chapter 6 demonstrates that restricting intervention to a maximum of two developmental domains at a time does not adversely affect children's development in other domains. The RT strategies that parents use for a targeted intervention goal will also help to promote development in the domains that are not the direct focus of intervention.

Step 2—Target Social Play as the First Pivotal Behavior

For all parents and children, regardless of children's developmental needs, intervention begins by addressing the pivotal behavior of social play. Social play helps children learn to engage in frequent, reciprocal interactions with their parents or other caregivers, which are the interactive skills that are foundation for each of the three developmental domains (i.e., Cognition, Communication, Social–Emotional Functioning) addressed in RT. Social play emphasizes the notion that child development is a two-person process that fundamentally depends upon children's ability to engage in sustained episodes of intimate, reciprocal interaction with parents and others.

The amount of time intervention focuses on social play can vary greatly for different parents and children. We recommend that social play continue to be a primary objective of intervention at least until the child achieves a midpoint score of 5 on the Pivotal Behavior Profile (see Curriculum Material 3 in Section IV), or the parent becomes proficient in using the RT strategies "get into my child's world" and "take one turn and wait" (see Curriculum Material 6: Cognition). If it takes longer than four sessions to meet either or both of these conditions, introduce new pivotal behaviors while continuing to focus on social play.

Step 3—Select the Pivotal Behaviors Most Relevant to Children's Developmental Needs

For each of the three developmental domains addressed by RT (i.e., Cognition, Communication, Social–Emotional Functioning), there are five to six pivotal behaviors that contribute to developmental learning in these domains. The order that these behaviors are listed in the Curriculum Outline, in Curriculum Material 6, for each domain corresponds to the general order in which they emerge in young children. It also reflects the fact that some of these behaviors are prerequisites for others. For example, in the communication domain, the pivotal behavior of joint attention cannot occur unless a child is already engaging in the pivotal behavior of joint activity. Similarly, in the cognitive domain, children must engage in exploration before they will encounter situations that require problem solving.

A child's communication needs can be addressed by promoting each of the five pivotal behaviors listed for this domain. The actual pivotal behaviors and order in which they are addressed depends upon the child's current pivotal behavior. This can be assessed through clinical judgment or by using the Pivotal Behavior Wizard in Curriculum Material 2.

The Pivotal Behavior Wizard is a guide for selecting pivotal behaviors that can be used as intervention objectives based upon the pivotal behaviors the child currently displays in the developmental domain of concern. It was developed to help parents and professionals identify pivotal behaviors that are most relevant to a child's current developmental needs. A sample from this Wizard is provided in Figure 7.3.

For example, if a child's developmental needs are related to cognitive development and he seldom varies what he does when he plays with toys or materials, the child's current use of pivotal behavior can be identified on the Wizard. Based on the child's current behavior and developmental needs, the Wizard indicates that "exploration" would be the appropriate pivotal behavior to target as an intervention objective. The complete version of the Wizard provides guides to select intervention objectives for each of the three RT domains. It is presented in this manual in Section IV, Curriculum Material 2, and is also

Pivotal Behavior Wizard

Cognition	
Child's Behavior	**Pivotal Behavior**
• Does not have frequent episodes of one-to-one play with parents and other caregivers • Does not stay engaged long in play and other interactive episodes with parents and caregivers • Engages in play routine with parents and others that are more task oriented than playful and fun	Social Play
• Can sustain reciprocal interactions with adults but usually waits for the adult to decide what to play with or how to play • Chooses what toys to play with or how to play less than half of the time when playing with an adult	Initiation
• Plays with very few toys or materials • Seldom varies what he or she does with toys or materials • Shows little if any interest in any of the features of objects (e.g., shape, texture, parts) • Shows little interest in objects, people, or novel occurrences in the environment	Exploration
• Seeks the assistance of adults whenever he or she has difficulty doing something during play • Tries to solve problems as they arise but becomes quickly frustrated when he or she is unable to solve them • Avoids engaging in activities that may be difficult	Problem Solving
• Seldom repeats developmental skills that are within his or her range of capabilities • Does not have access to toys or materials he or she enjoys • Is often encouraged to produce behaviors that are beyond his or her current level of functioning • Gives up easily whenever he or she encounters an obstacle	Practice

Figure 7.3. Sample section from the Pivotal Behavior Wizard.

incorporated into the Responsive Teaching Curriculum Planning and Tracking Program, available on CD-ROM.

For many children, the Wizard may identify several pivotal behaviors as potential intervention targets. In general, if one developmental domain is being addressed, interventionists should choose no more than two pivotal behaviors to work on at a time. If two developmental domains are being addressed, then only one pivotal behavior should be addressed for each domain. The first pivotal behavior identified for a child on the Wizard should be addressed before those that are listed later.

Step 4—Assess Children's Progress on Their Pivotal Behaviors

As we discovered from our evaluation (see Chapter 6), the developmental improvements children make in RT are related to how much their pivotal behaviors change during intervention. Furthermore, most children increase their use of pivotal behaviors as their parents begin implementing RT strategies with them. As a result, the most important consideration in assessing children's progress in RT is how much their pivotal behaviors have changed. If little or no change occurs, parents will need to learn how to use the RT strategies more accurately (e.g., according to their description) or they will need to use them more often in their routine interactions with their children. Thus, we recommend that the pivotal behaviors that have been selected as the child's intervention objectives be assessed at the following times:

- The first time that an intervention objective is introduced
- At 2- to 4-week intervals during the period that intervention addresses this behavior
- A minimum of every 3 months after this behavior is no longer addressed during intervention

This schedule of assessments helps to establish the child's level of pivotal behavior prior to intervention, how much the child's use of a pivotal behavior improves while it is the focus of intervention, and whether the child sustains improvements in pivotal behavior after intervention. The schedule also provides parents with useful information: It gives them specific examples of the behaviors they are asked to promote, it helps them understand how their child is currently using this behavior, and it provides examples of the ultimate level of pivotal-behavior use their children can attain.

The Pivotal Behavior Profile, which is provided in Curriculum Material 3, was developed to assess children's pivotal behavior. It consists of 16 separate scales that correspond to the 16 pivotal behaviors that can be targeted as intervention objectives in Responsive Teaching. As illustrated in Figure 7.4, each of these scales is written in the voice of the child. They provide a definition of the pivotal behavior and criteria for three levels of pivotal behavior use (1 = *very low*, 5 = *moderate*, 10 = *very high*). These global items are rated on a 10-point scale based upon raters' judgments about where the child's current behavior falls along the continuum defined by the three criteria.

We designed the Pivotal Behavior Profile so that both parents and professionals can use it to evaluate children's behavior. To use this scale, raters must (a) read the definition of the pivotal behavior, (b) review each of the three rating criteria, and (c) rate the child's behavior. (If a rating falls between two criteria, the rater must judge which criteria the child's behavior corresponds more closely with.) Whenever possible, interventionists should encourage parents to be the primary raters and provide parents with a copy of the rating form

Pivotal Behavior Profile

Social Play

Do I play reciprocally with a partner across many situations? Is my play characterized by a "give and take," in which I contribute as much to the activity as my partner? Am I aware of my partner's activity during play?

How am I doing?

10 = Very High I almost always engage in mutual play activities. My play can be characterized as reciprocal interaction, in which I observe the other person's behavior and contribute to the activity when it is my turn.

5 = Moderate Sometimes I am interested in play with other partners, and I engage in reciprocal interaction about half the time with them. I make face-to-face contact and attempt other types of communication at least half of the time I am with them. My partner and I each contribute to a joint activity at least half of the time.

1 = Very Low I never include others in my play. I prefer to play alone or in parallel with my partner. I ignore my partner in parallel play and am usually unaware of my partner's attempts to play with me.

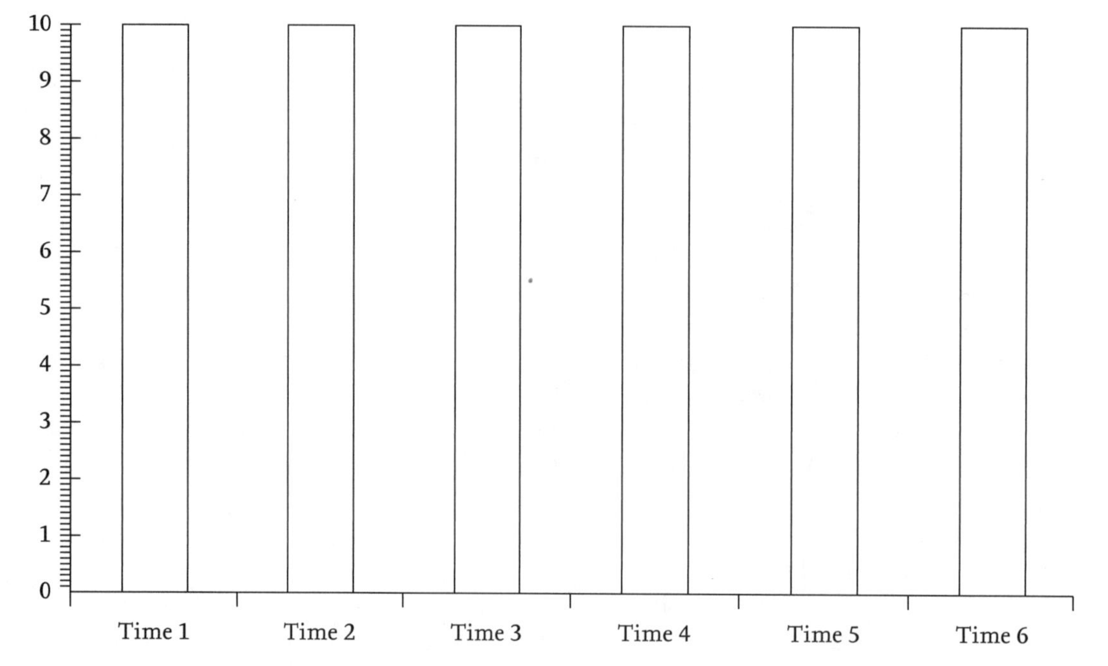

Figure 7.4. Example Pivotal Behavior Profile.

for future reference. If necessary, parents' ratings can be supplemented by independent ratings by professionals.

The following considerations can be used to increase the accuracy or reliability of Pivotal Behavior Ratings:

- Read the item several times to understand the behavior being rated.
- Whenever possible, rate children's behavior based upon their performance in a specific situation (e.g., 5 minutes of parent–child play using toys that are developmentally appropriate in the child's home).
- For behaviors that cannot be observed during intervention sessions (e.g., trust, self-regulation), ask parents to rate their children's behavior over the past 48 hours.
- Rate children's behavior based upon their interactions with the parents who are implementing the RT intervention. (A child may display different levels of pivotal behaviors with other adults.)
- Use the same type of toys and observation to assess how children's behavior changes over time.
- Have the same person (parent or professional) rate the child to obtain an accurate picture of how the child's behavior changes over time.

Step 5—Select Discussion Points and Responsive Teaching Strategies for Intervention Sessions

The Planning and Tracking Form (see Curriculum Material 4) provides a selection or menu of Responsive Teaching strategies and discussion points that are uniquely suited to promoting each of the 16 pivotal behaviors that have been identified as intervention objectives for this program. Figure 7.5 provides a sample of the Planning and Tracking Form for the pivotal behavior social play.

This form can be used to select RT strategies and discussion points for as many as 10 intervention sessions. The computer version of this form provides drop-down menus for each pivotal behavior objective that provide the same information listed on the Planning and Tracking Form.

For each session, as many as two discussion points and two RT strategies may be selected to address the intervention objectives that are being targeted. The strategies and discussion points that are selected should be based upon (a) parents' knowledge and understanding of their child's intervention objectives and (b) the effectiveness with which parents are able to use RT strategies presented in previous sessions. If review would be helpful, strategies and discussion points may be repeated from previous sessions as often as needed.

Issues To Consider When Selecting Intervention Content

There are several things to consider when selecting content for intervention, including the amount of time needed to address each pivotal behavior, the selection of discussion points that reflect parental concerns, and the time needed for parents to adequately learn the RT strategies they will be working with. These issues are discussed in more detail in the following sections.

Domain		**Cognition**										
Pivotal Behavior		**Social Play**—To support and promote children's ability to engage in balanced reciprocal play with others	**Session Date**									
			11/28	**12/04**	**12/11**	**12/18**	**1/04**	**1/11**	**1/18**	**1/25**	**2/05**	**2/12**
Discussion Points	C-101	Social play with parents is critical for promoting children's developmental growth.	X					X				
	C-102	Cognitive learning is a two-person process.		X								
	C-103	By themselves, children can only learn information they discover accidentally.	X									
	C-104	Adults scaffold children's involvement in play.			X	X						
	C-105	Adults enhance children's play by providing new information related to their current activities.					X					
	C-106	Adult responses to children's play activities enable children to learn the social consequences of their actions.							X		X	
	C-107	Adults challenge children's thinking by occasionally mismatching children's expectations or intentions.								X		X
Responsive Teaching Strategies	113	Get into my child's world	X								X	
	114	Use mirroring and parallel play to join an activity	X									
	121	Take one turn and wait			X	X	X	X		X	X	X
	131	Play face-to-face games without toys								X		
	312	Imitate my child's actions and communications		X		X						
	412	Wait with anticipation					X		X			
	421	Act as a playful partner.										
	514	Act in ways my child can act						X	X			X
	535	Match my child's interactive pace										
Rating		Social Play: Pivotal Behavior Rating	3				4			6		7

Figure 7.5. Example Planning and Tracking Form.

Devote Several Sessions To Address Each Pivotal Behavior Objective

The time it takes for children to make meaningful progress in developing and learning to use pivotal behaviors depends upon children's current level or stage of development as well as parents' ability to consistently implement RT strategies to promote these behaviors. If sessions take place weekly, interventionists may devote as many as six sessions or more that focus on the same pivotal behavior objective. By introducing new RT strategies, interventionists can keep their sessions fresh and informative, even though the intervention objective has not changed. If children's progress is slow, interventionists should work on a pivotal objective for several sessions, introduce a new objective for a period of time, and then revisit the original objective.

The goal for all children is to reach the highest level of pivotal behavior use, which is a score of 10 on the Pivotal Behavior Profile. However, as a rule of thumb, intervention should shift to a new intervention objective after approximately four sessions if children's scores on the Pivotal Behavior Profile continue to be rated *moderate,* even when parents use many or all of the RT strategies that have been recommended.

Select Discussion Points That Are Relevant to Parents' Concerns

To promote a pivotal behavior, parents need to understand what the behavior is and how it contributes to their children's developmental learning. Interventionists need to emphasize these themes in every intervention session. The discussion points outline several of the key points presented in the Facts To Consider section provided in the Curriculum Outline for each pivotal behavior. Not all of these discussion points may be relevant to parents' concerns, however. When interventionists select the discussion points for a session, it is important to consider how this information can help parents understand how a pivotal behavior will address their concerns for their children.

Give Parents Time To Learn RT Strategies

The Planning and Tracking Form identifies 5 to 10 RT strategies for each of the 16 pivotal behaviors, and each intervention session should encourage parents to use one or two of the strategies listed. There are two issues to remember regarding the number of strategies that are addressed in a session. First, intervention can be effective even if parents only learn to use one new strategy each session. Second, it is not necessary to address all of the strategies recommended for a pivotal behavior before moving to the next objective. The decision to move to a new objective should be based upon the child's ability to use the targeted pivotal behavior.

Most parents need time (e.g., several sessions) to learn each RT strategy. There are at least two reasons for this. First, parents interact with their children without being aware of how they do it. Their patterns of interaction are automatic habits that they formed as a result of the thousands of interactions they have had with their children. RT asks them to do something that they simply are not used to doing with their children.

Second, the way parents interact with their children reflects their understanding about their children's development and their personal beliefs about the role they play in it. To learn how to use a strategy effectively, many parents must make fundamental changes in their understanding and beliefs about their children's development. In addition, they might need to give up patterns of interaction that have become automatic and learn to interact with their child in a way that, at first, seems unnatural.

Step 6—Complete the Intervention Session Plans

RT session plans can be developed manually by using the Curriculum Outline as a resource for filling in the information requested on an RT Intervention Session Plan form. Alternatively, sessions can be planned on the Responsive Teaching Curriculum Planning and Tracking Program. This program automatically places the discussion points and RT strategies into the session plan after they have been selected from the drop-down menus. The sample Professional Session Plan presented in Figure 7.6 includes each of the components that are needed to conduct an RT session. The Professional Session Plan form is designed for professionals who are working with parents. A slightly different Parent Session Plan form, designed for parents to use with their children at home, is provided in Section IV in Curriculum Material 5. The following is a brief description of the components of a session plan and identifies where the information for each component can be found.

- *Issues/concerns discussed by parents (professional form only).* This blank section of the session plan gives the interventionist space to note any issues or concerns that parents might have.
- *Feedback related to last week's session/Family Action Plan (professional form only).* This blank section is used to record parents' experiences in trying to follow through with RT activities or Family Action Plans from the previous session.
- *Session objectives (definition of pivotal behavior).* This information is used to discuss that the purpose of the session is to provide information and RT strategies that parents can use in their routine interactions to encourage children's use of their pivotal behaviors. Each session can address up to two pivotal behaviors. (Pivotal behavior definitions can be found in the Curriculum Outline.)
- *Discussion points.* This is an outline of the major points that will be used to explain what the pivotal behavior objective is and how it helps to promote children's development. No more than two sets of discussion points should be included on a session plan. If two pivotal behavior objectives are addressed in the session, include one set of discussion points for each objective. (Discussion points for pivotal behavior objectives can be found in the Curriculum Outline.)
- *RT strategies.* This section contains a description of the RT strategies that will be used to promote the pivotal behavior objectives that are the focus of the session. It can also include some, or all, of the suggestions for presenting strategies to parents. No more than two RT strategies should be included on a session plan. If two pivotal behavior objectives are addressed in a session, include one RT strategy for each objective. (RT strategies can be found in the Curriculum Outline.)
- *Pivotal Behavior Profile (optional).* This scale can be used to assess the child's current level of using the pivotal behaviors that are the focus of the intervention session. (Pivotal Behavior Profile can be found in Curriculum Material 3 in Section IV.)

Step 7—Use the Planning and Tracking Form or Program To Record Intervention Session Activities

Both the Responsive Teaching Planning and Tracking Form (see Curriculum Material 4) and the computer-based Responsive Teaching Curriculum Planning and Tracking Program are essential tools for planning. As indicated on the last row of the Planning and Tracking Form (see Figure 7.5), after a session is completed these tools can be used to track children's

Responsive Teaching
Professional Session Plan

Child's name Katie Smith Date 2/15/2006 Location Home

Team members completing form Phyllis Jones

Issues/concerns discussed by parents:

Feedback related to last week's session/Family Action Plan:

Session objectives:

1. Social Play—The purpose of today's session is to enhance your child's ability to play reciprocally with a partner across many situations. Your child's play should be characterized by a "give and take" in which your child contributes as much to the play activity as the partner. Your child should be aware of the partner's activity/experience during play.

2.

(continues)

Figure 7.6. Example Professional Session Plan.

Discussion points related to Social Play :

Discussion point 1

C-102 Cognitive learning is a two-person process

- Child development research indicates that parents play an important collaborative role in children's early cognitive learning.
- The impact parents have on children's development is related more to how they relate with their children than to what they do with them.
- Parents play the same role in children's development, even when children have developmental problems.

Notes:

Discussion point 2

C-104 By themselves, children can only learn information they discover accidentally.

- How children play reflects their current understanding of their world.
- Understanding and insight come from children's repetitive play experiences.
- Children's discovery is slow unless parents/adults are directly involved.

Notes:

RT strategies that can be used to promote Social Play :

Strategy 1

113. Get into my child's world.

Adults must view the world as children do. First, they must establish a mutual physical relationship with their child. The adult and child should have eye contact and be on the same physical level. Second, adults need to interact with their children by playing or communicating like them. Mimicking behaviors such as babbling, cooing, smiling, and using a playful face let the child know that the adult is willing to interact on the child's terms. Third, adults must try to understand the world as the child does. Most experiences do not have the same meaning to children as they do to adults.

Practical Suggestions

- Play with the child in a face-to-face position. Get down to the child's physical level so that the child does not have to look up.
- Make eye contact while playing or interacting with the child.
- Play in the small ways that children do without pressuring children to do anything other than stay involved in the interaction.

Strategy 2

114. Use mirroring and parallel play to join an activity.

Play side by side with a child by using the same or similar toys or acting in ways that the child is acting.

Practical Suggestions

- Many children younger than 15 months developmental age have difficulty exchanging a toy with an adult during interactive play. They do not yet understand the rules of "give and take."
- Notice how children pay attention to adults' actions when parents (a) play with the same object; (b) play in the same manner as the child; and (c) play side by side with the child.
- Show parents how they can take turns in parallel play by doing the same kinds of activities that the child is doing with a toy or object.

Pivotal Behavior Profile (optional) ☐

Figure 7.6. *Continued.*

progress with pivotal behavior objectives. In addition, when planning the next session, the Planning and Tracking Form or computer program can be used to (a) review intervention objectives that have been targeted in a previous session, (b) identify the RT strategies and discussion points that have been used to promote these objectives, and (c) review the child's progress on pivotal behaviors, as indicated from previous ratings using the Pivotal Behavior Profile.

Interventionists who work with 10 to 25 families each week inevitably have difficulty remembering exactly what they covered in previous sessions and even more trouble recalling intervention content over longer periods of time. The Planning and Tracking Form and accompanying computer program provide a convenient system for collecting this information, which can be used to decide whether to review content presented previously or to introduce new strategies and discussion points and to decide what these should be.

Parents who use this program on their own can do the same thing. The information on the Planning and Tracking Form and in the computer program enables them to review the discussion points and strategies they have worked on previously with their child and decide whether to go back and review these again or to move on to different strategies and discussion points.

Summary

In this chapter we have presented the seven steps involved in developing RT session plans. The flexibility provided in the RT curriculum allows intervention to be tailored to the unique needs and learning styles of children and parents. The information and structure provided in this curriculum assure that all session plans provide a comprehensive, systematic approach to promoting the developmental outcomes that parents desire for their children. The planning tools, which include the Curriculum Outline, Pivotal Behavior Wizard, and Planning and Tracking Form or computer program make planning quick and easy.

Chapter 8

Guidelines for Conducting Intervention Sessions

Responsive Teaching (RT) can be implemented with a variety of intervention formats (e.g., group or individual sessions). There are four general principles for conducting sessions that can be applied to any format that is used. We describe these principles, after which we present a format that we recommend for individualized parent–child intervention sessions.

Create an Environment That Is Conducive for Learning

Interventionists must deal with two learners at the same time—the child and the parent—and therefore the intervention environment must be conducive for the child, to engage in developmentally appropriate play activities, and also for the adult, to learn about the child's development as well as how to use RT strategies with the child.

To promote developmental learning, an environment must have sufficient room for the child to move around. There should be enough unobstructed floor space to accommodate the child and at least one (ideally, two) adults. In a home setting, interventionists might need to ask parents if they can move some of the furniture, which they can then replace at the end of the session. If there is insufficient room in a house to meet these criteria, interventionists might explore the possibility of using nearby community facilities (e.g., library, neighborhood school, community center, park) for conducting at least some of the intervention.

A child-friendly environment also requires developmentally appropriate toys and equipment. These can be toys that interventionists bring or children's own toys, so long as the toys afford opportunities to engage in the pivotal behaviors that are the intervention objectives for the session and children can handle them independently.

There are at least three issues to consider for making an environment conducive for adult learning. First, the adult needs to be comfortable. Second, the adult needs to be able to observe the interventionist as he or she models RT strategies with the child. Third, the environment must be designed so that the adult is able to get on the floor to interact with the child.

A major challenge relates to balancing the need for a comfortable environment with encouraging the adult to get on the floor to interact with his or her child. It is difficult (if not impossible) to coach parents on how to use RT strategies to play or interact with their children if they are sitting on a chair during the entire session. Although most parents have little difficulty making the transition from sitting to getting on the floor with their children, it can be a problem for some. We have found that it is easier to get these parents on the floor if sessions begin with everyone on the floor (e.g., remove chairs from the room to encourage parents to sit on the floor). Interventionists can also make it more comfortable to be on the floor by using pillows, bolsters, mats, and so forth.

Focus on the Child and the Child's Development

The primary purpose of Responsive Teaching is to promote children's development and social–emotional functioning—*not* to change the way parents interact with their children. As a result, RT sessions need to be structured to emphasize that the focus is on the child and how well the child is developing. Each session should be organized around helping children acquire and use targeted pivotal behavior objectives. Interventionists need to explain to parents how RT strategies promote children's pivotal behavior and their implications for children's development. While demonstrating strategies or observing parents using strategies, interventionists should point out the effects of these strategies on the child's behavior.

Give Information Through Concrete Experiences

Parents learn to use RT strategies through personal experience rather than through talking about them. As a result, intervention sessions are most effective when substantial amounts of time are used for interventionists to demonstrate and parents to practice using RT strategies. The amount of time needed for this hands-on experience depends on several factors, including how much one-on-one interaction a child can tolerate, how long it takes parents to notice the nuances of a strategy when the interventionist demonstrates it, and the amount of time that parents feel comfortable interacting with their child.

Programs that use RT in parent groups where children are not present will need to rely on other methods for providing concrete information, for example, (a) videotapes of other adults using RT strategies with children, (b) live demonstrations by the interventionist or parent with a child, or (c) simulated experiences where participants role-play strategies with each other.

Invite Feedback

Responsive Teaching sessions should involve balanced conversations between interventionists and parents rather than one-way monologues by professionals. Because the RT curriculum is so structured and prescriptive, there is a danger that professionals can use it to dominate conversations with parents. To prevent this from occurring, professionals need to make sure that parents have frequent opportunities to discuss the topics and RT strategies being presented. Interventionists can encourage parents to participate more actively in sessions by asking questions that encourage parents to express their opinions and feelings. Some examples of these questions include the following:

- Tell me what you think about this idea/strategy.
- How does this compare to the way that you are used to thinking about or doing things with your child?
- Have I presented this information in a way that makes sense to you?
- How does it feel when you try to use this strategy?
- What do your husband/relatives/neighbors think about the information/strategies we have been talking about?
- Is there something that you would like me to do to make it easier for you?

Recommended Session Format

The following describes a format for conducting individual parent–child sessions that can be implemented in center-based schools or clinics as well as at homes. Sessions begin with the interventionist interacting with the child *on the floor* and inviting the parent to join them. Every effort is made to minimize distractions. When sessions are conducted in homes, parents might be asked to put the phone on quiet ring; turn off TVs, radios, or stereos; and ask other adults who are not directly involved in the intervention to move to another side of the room.

This session format consists of five phases: (1) Planning, (2) Rapport and Review, (3) Purpose and Rationale for Intervention, (4) Demonstration and Practice of RT Strategies, and (5) Family Action Planning. The following describes each of these phases. The Intervention Session Guide, located in Curriculum Material 1 in Section IV of this manual, can be used to assess whether the activities identified for each of the five phases described actually occur during a session.

1. Planning

In addition to developing intervention session plans, as described in Chapter 7, three other activities are involved in planning. First, interventionists need to review both the RT content and the issues and concerns parents brought up in the previous session. Second, interventionists can prepare supplementary materials to give to parents. These could include written descriptions of the strategies and discussion points that will be presented (which can be developed using the Responsive Teaching Curriculum Planning and Tracking Program), other print materials such as articles or magazines, and videotapes demonstrating information being presented. Third, interventionists need to arrange the environment before the session begins. This includes making sure that there are adequate toys and materials that are appropriate for the child's level of development and likely to promote behaviors that are relevant to the objective of the session. Make enough toys available so that the child can participate in a variety of activities during the session.

2. Rapport and Review

The interventionist initiates the Responsive Teaching sessions by

- greeting the parent and child warmly and enthusiastically;
- giving the parent the opportunity to talk about him- or herself, the child, or the family; and
- encouraging the parent to talk about how the family was able to follow through with RT content presented in the previous session.

This part of the session is designed to (a) help the parent and child feel comfortable; (b) give parents the opportunity to express their observations, concerns, or needs; (c) determine how well the parents have been able to understand and integrate previous intervention content into their daily routines with their children; and (d) reach closure on topics or issues that were unfinished from the last session. Interventionists must be highly attentive and responsive to parents. They should complement parents about their participation in intervention and their parenting skills and let them know how much their efforts to follow through with recommended activities are critical to their child's intervention.

Occasionally, parents bring up issues or concerns that require interventionists to modify their planned activities. For example, if parents are confused about information or strategies presented in a previous session, the interventionist may ask the parents if they would like to review this information before moving on to new content. If parents bring up family or personal issues that are major concerns that are preventing them from carrying out intervention activities with their children, interventionists may decide to use the session to address these issues rather than proceed with the planned content.

These conversations with parents must be short enough that they do not exceed the child's capacity to remain interested, attentive, and composed. We recommend that this portion of the session last no longer than 10 to 15 minutes. If the parents' issues cannot be addressed during this time, the interventionist can simply suggest that they move on with the intervention plan and revisit the parents' issues at the end of the session.

3. Purpose and Rationale

In this phase of the session, the interventionist describes the purpose and rationale for the session (e.g., "In today's session we are going to talk about strategies that can be used to promote your child's self-initiated play behavior [initiation] as well as to increase your child's rate of practicing his or her existing behaviors [practice]"). Following this, the interventionist should describe the pivotal behaviors being addressed in this session and review at least one set of discussion points related to this behavior. Periodically, this phase of the session should also be used to ask parents to rate their child's current use of this behavior using the Pivotal Behavior Profile. This exercise gives parents a concrete experience of what the pivotal behavior is. The amount of time devoted to this phase should be based upon parents' involvement in the discussion. With parents who are not active, this phase should last no longer than 10 minutes. However, if parents are actively involved, this phase can last up to 15 minutes.

4. Demonstration and Practice of Responsive Teaching Strategies

The following procedures should be used to present RT strategies to parents:

1. The interventionist should explain in detail the RT strategy that she is going to demonstrate and describe how this strategy should affect the child's behavior. For example, if the strategy is to imitate the child, the interventionist can talk about how she is going to implement the strategy (i.e., that she will imitate almost any behavior that the child produces) and that she expects that within a short period of time the child will (a) notice that interventionist is imitating him and (b) begin to produce behaviors to see how the interventionist will respond to or imitate his behavior.

2. The interventionist should demonstrate the strategy. While interacting with the child, the interventionist should use the strategy much more frequently than it would normally be employed. In other words, if the strategy is imitation, the interventionist might imitate almost everything the child does to highlight this behavior, even though this may not be the way that imitation would be used with the child in everyday routines.

While demonstrating the strategy, the interventionist should occasionally ask the parent to notice what she is doing and how her behavior is affecting the child's behavior. Interventionists should not assume that the parent will actually see the strategy being demonstrated unless they explicitly draw the parent's attention to what they are doing, such as by saying, "Did you see the way I use the strategy with your child?"

Interventionists should demonstrate a strategy for 5 to no more than 10 minutes at a time. How long this demonstration lasts depends upon how many opportunities there are to actually use the strategy. In the case of imitation, interventionists can imitate nearly everything the child does. With these types of strategies, 5 minutes provides enough opportunity to demonstrate the strategy and to help parents understand how they can do it with their child.

3. After completing the demonstration, the interventionist should ask whether the parent has any questions about what a strategy is or how to go about doing it.

4. After the parent's questions have been answered, the interventionist should invite the parent to practice the strategy with the child. The interventionist should give the parent a few minutes to become comfortable interacting and trying to use strategies with the child before saying anything to the parent during this phase. The first comments to the parent should complement what the parent is doing. After the parent has had 3 to 4 minutes to practice a strategy, the interventionist can then make one or two suggestions to help the-parent use a strategy more effectively. In the next 3 to 5 minutes, the interventionist should observe how the parent is interacting with the child and if needed make one to two additional comments or suggestions. As the parent begins to implement a strategy correctly, the interventionist should point out how the RT strategy is affecting the child's behavior.

Parents should be given a total of 5 to 10 minutes to practice using a strategy. The actual amount of time should be determined by how involved parents are with their child and how many opportunities they have had to use the strategy. At the end of this phase, the interventionist should reengage the parent and give the child the opportunity to do whatever activity he or she chooses.

If two RT strategies are presented during a session, the sequence of demonstrating and practicing a strategy should be repeated separately for each strategy. When they have the opportunity to focus on one strategy at time, parents are more likely to remember and use a strategy after a session is completed. If the strategies presented in a session are related to two different pivotal behaviors, intervention should focus first on one pivotal behavior and then be repeated for the second pivotal behavior. The entire demonstration and practice phase of intervention sessions should last no longer than 25 minutes.

5. Family Action Planning

Family action planning is that part of a session where the interventionist helps the parents make RT intervention content relevant and meaningful to their own lives. It is where parents and interventionist take time to look at the bigger picture. It is informal with no predetermined solutions and should take between 5 and 10 minutes.

During this phase, interventionists should revisit the issues or concerns parents brought up at the beginning of the session that were not addressed at that time. For example, at the beginning of the session the parent may have indicated that he did not follow through with intervention activities from the past week because he was so exhausted from the other childcare and work responsibilities and that his spouse or another relative raised questions about the intervention that he was unable to answer. The interventionist should explore these issues and help parents develop a Family Action Plan (see Curriculum Material 5 in Section IV) for addressing them.

Coaching and Feedback

Coaching is the process of providing parents suggestions for how to interact with their children and is used in the early stages of parents' learning to use these behaviors. It works best when the interventionist targets one strategy at a time.

Before beginning coaching, interventionists should tell parents the purpose of coaching, which strategy will be targeted during the practice session, and how this process will occur. Parents should be given the opportunity ahead of time to indicate whether or not they would like to be involved in this type of process. Interventionists should let parents who are nervous about being coached know that they will limit themselves to one or two suggestions during the session.

There are two keys to effective coaching. The first is to observe carefully how parents interact with their child. The second is to coach only when there is something the parents can do that will help them become more successful. In most instances, the suggestions will need to be in the form of simple reminders, such as "Make eye-to-eye contact with the child," "Wait for your child to do something," "Be more animated," and so forth. Coaching should never involve elaborate instructions; rather, it should provide suggestions that parents can respond to without disrupting their interaction with their children.

Interventionists should ask parents how they feel about being coached. Did parents feel that the coaching supported them, or did it hinder them from interacting with their children? Parents should also be asked how they would like interventionists to interact with them during coaching.

Interventionists should give parents feedback about the positive things they are doing and also about what they need to do to improve. Most parents require several sessions to work on a strategy before they are able to implement it effectively. Even though most RT strategies seem simple, some parents may have difficulty with them, particularly if the strategy suggested is very different from their normal interactions with their children. Most parents have never had the experience of trying to modify or adjust their natural inclinations for interacting with their children. RT requires a level of self-consciousness and discipline that takes time to learn.

Throughout intervention sessions, interventionists must constantly look for the positive things parents are doing with their children and let parents know how much they appreciate these behaviors. Interventionists must also be direct in letting parents know what they need to do to implement RT strategies more effectively, but this type of information should be given only occasionally. It should be provided in a supportive atmosphere where interventionists have complimented parents repeatedly about the positive interactions they have with their children.

Negative feedback should be limited to no more than two areas and should focus on what parents need to do to support their children's use of the pivotal behaviors that are the focus for the intervention session. The following procedures can be used to provide negative feedback:

- Ask parents what they thought about the session. Encourage parents to identify some of the positive things they did with their children, not just the less-than-optimal interactions.
- Comment on the good interactions that took place between the parent and child during the observation (e.g., "I liked the way you imitated your child's behavior when you were playing together with the nesting blocks").

- Identify and give feedback on one or two problem areas (e.g., "You seemed to do well imitating your child's behavior when you were playing at the sandbox. However, I noticed when he started playing with the dollhouse you began to take the lead in the interaction rather than wait for your child to initiate activities that you could imitate.").
- Encourage parents to believe that they can implement the targeted RT strategy. After identifying the problem areas, discuss some things parents can do to try to prevent problems from recurring.
- Ask the parent if they have any questions.
- Summarize feedback with positive comments and suggestions about what the parent can work on with the child.

Summary

In this chapter, we have discussed several practical considerations for implementing Responsive Teaching, described four general principles for conducting intervention sessions, and described an intervention format that is compatible with these principles and that is highly effective at engaging parents and children in Responsive Teaching sessions. We also outlined several considerations related to coaching parents and providing feedback about their use of RT strategies.

Chapter 9

Family Action Plans

Responsive Teaching (RT) can promote children's development and social–emotional functioning only if there are fundamental changes in the one-to-one interactions parents and other caregivers have with their children. At least two things must happen for this to occur: Parents and primary caregivers must increase their *level of responsiveness* during each interaction they have with their children, and parents and primary caregivers must increase the *number of one-to-one interactions* they have with their children during the course of the daily routine.

Family Action Plans describe what parents and others will do with the information presented during an RT session to bring about these changes. Family Action Plans (FAPs) consist of at least one, but no more than three, follow-through activities to help parents and other family members (a) become proficient with the content and teaching strategies presented during a session and (b) infuse them into the child's daily life. FAPs can be developed by parents who are trying to implement RT on their own or by professionals and parents working together. As indicated in Figure 9.1, FAPs are written on a form that parents can post in the home to remind them what to do. They consist of brief, clear statements that describe

- the activities that parents or other family members should do;
- when or how often they should do these activities;
- where they should do these activities; and when applicable
- how they will address barriers that interfere with carrying out these activities.

Activities

The activities listed on FAPs should not increase the amount of work parents have to do with their children. Rather, they should help parents become aware of how they interact with their children and should remind them to modify their interactions by using RT strategies during routine activities. At first parents will likely find it awkward and difficult to use RT strategies, and it will take an extra effort to use them, but parents who make the effort to use these strategies consistently over time will experience increased enjoyment from interacting with their children.

The kinds of activities listed on FAPs should be directly related to the content and instructional strategies presented in the current early intervention session. They should also be related to the types of changes parents need to make. The most important change for parents who are new to Responsive Teaching is to learn how to use RT strategies to interact more responsively with their children. After becoming relatively proficient using RT strategies, the focus should shift to enhancing children's opportunities for responsive interaction throughout the daily routine. The following sections list different FAP activities that correspond to parents' phase of intervention.

Responsive Teaching
Family Action Plan

Child's name Zack Schwartz Date 2/7/07

What?

1. Practice the strategy "Follow my child's lead" that we talked about today. Notice how your child reacts to you when you do this. Practice only 3 to 5 minutes at a time.

2. Discuss with your husband the role that Initiation plays in your child's development. Give me a call if you need some help about what to talk about.

3. Jot down some notes about any questions your husband has about RT so that we can talk about these questions at our next meeting.

Where/When? Practice RT strategies during bath time or in the mornings after you have completed your chores and have some time to play with your child. Do not try to practice if either you or your child is getting tired.

How to address obstacles? Take some time to talk about RT with your husband. See if there is a time when we can all meet together. We can discuss this at our next session.

Figure 9.1. Example Family Action Plan.

Phase 1—FAP Activities That Enhance the Responsiveness of Primary Caregivers

Figure 9.2 lists FAP activities that are well suited for Phase 1 of intervention followed by a brief description of each activity.

Provide Focused Practice with Responsive Teaching Strategies

One of the best ways to become proficient with RT strategies is to practice them during brief unstructured play activities. An unstructured play activity is one in which the child has the opportunity to choose what he or she wants to do, and the parent plays the role of supporting the child in this activity. Episodes of unstructured play should last no longer than 5 to 7 minutes at a time. This is long enough for parents to practice a strategy, and it is the length of time that infants and toddlers are likely to remain engaged in one-to-one play.

During this 5-minute play period, children may disengage several times from their parents to move to a different toy or activity; parents should continue trying to engage their child until the 5-minute episode is completed. If the child wants to interact longer than 5 minutes, there is no harm in extending the duration of this practice period, but it is more important to have several short periods of practice interaction than to have less frequent but lengthier episodes of interaction.

Review Videotape Recording

Videotapes provide parents the opportunity to see themselves implementing an RT strategy. It is helpful for parents to review videotapes several times to get a better sense of how they actually interact with their child.

Phase 1—Enhance the responsiveness of primary caregivers

- Provide focused practice with RT strategies
- Review videotape recording
- Record and share positive experiences
- Monitor children's developmental and social–emotional progress
- Follow through with at least one strategy that is easy to do
- Observe pivotal behavior in different contexts
- Experiment with contrasting strategies
- Read child development literature and watch videotapes
- Discuss RT with other parents
- Teach RT strategies and discussion points to other caregivers
- Record questions of other caregivers

Phase 2—Increase children's opportunities for responsive interaction

- Increase intentional use of RT strategies in targeted daily routines
- Identify activities or routines in which RT strategies have been useful
- Combine new with previously learned RT strategies
- Practice RT strategies that are difficult to use
- Use self-sticking notes as reminders to use RT strategies in various contexts

Figure 9.2. Suggested Family Action Plan activities.

Record and Share Positive Experiences

One way to focus on the positive effects of RT is by writing a daily log chronicling successes with these strategies. Writing a daily log can take on even greater significance when these experiences are shared with spouses, relatives, or other close friends.

Monitor Children's Developmental and Social–Emotional Progress

Child development profiles or checklists, such as the *Developmental Rainbow* (Mahoney & Perales, 1996) provide detailed lists of the developmental behaviors children typically do during the early childhood years. Writing down the child's current behaviors and finding them on a child development profile is one way of monitoring the day-to-day improvements children are making. Profiles can be especially motivating when children's development is not progressing as quickly as that of children who do not have developmental problems.

Follow Through with at Least One Strategy That Is Easy To Do

If parents are having difficulty learning a new RT strategy, try practicing a strategy that is easier to do at the same time. Avoid becoming discouraged by focusing exclusively on learning RT strategies that are difficult.

Observe Pivotal Behavior in Different Contexts

From time to time use selected items from the Pivotal Behavior Profile (see Curriculum Material 3) to evaluate how children are using a pivotal behavior across a variety of situations.

Experiment with Contrasting Strategies

One way of discovering how an RT strategy affects children is to experiment using contrasting versions of a strategy. For example, while learning the strategy "follow the child's lead," the parent can play for 2 to 3 minutes by following the child's lead followed by 2 to 3 minutes of attempting to get the child to follow the parent's lead. Note how children's behavior changes in response to these contrasting strategies. Observe how children become engaged and responsive when parents use RT strategies and then display lower levels of engagement and are less actively involved when parents use contrasting strategies.

Read Child Development Literature and Watch Videotapes

In the Recommended Materials section at the end of the book, we have listed several books and videos that provide information that supplements the general approach of Responsive Teaching and that will reassure some parents about using RT. These materials can be accessed through the Internet, a library, or a bookstore.

Discuss RT with Other Parents

Some of the most effective teachers of RT are parents who have struggled to use these strategies to deal with the unique problems that arise with their children. Parents who are at different phases of using RT can help each other gain insight by sharing their experiences.

Many parents come up with creative ideas about how to use RT strategies that are practical and effective.

Teach RT Strategies and Discussion Points to Other Caregivers

The involvement of other caregivers should be a FAP focus each time a new discussion point or strategy is introduced. Interventionists can discuss how to present this information to the other caregiver and can also coach the parent about how to help the other caregiver learn to use RT strategies.

Record Questions of Other Caregivers

The success of Responsive Teaching depends on all of a child's primary caregivers agreeing that this is a reasonable and appropriate intervention. To achieve consensus, caregivers need to discuss their views about how to promote their child's development as well as questions they have about the philosophy or procedures of Responsive Teaching.

If Responsive Teaching is provoking intense discussion among caregivers, interventionists might recommend a Family Action Plan activity in which caregivers write down questions they are unable to resolve among each other. Interventionists can review these questions to provide additional information that might be helpful for addressing their concerns.

Phase 2—FAP Activities That Can Help To Increase Children's Opportunities for Responsive Interaction Throughout the Daily Routine

Figure 9.2 also lists FAP activities that are well suited for Phase 2 of intervention. These activities are described here.

Increase Intentional Use of RT Strategies in Targeted Daily Routines

One of the most effective ways of promoting integration of RT strategies into children's daily routines is to use an incremental approach. After parents are successful using RT strategies in planned play activities, they can focus on consciously using strategies in one or two daily activities. This will help parents understand the value of RT strategies at encouraging children to become actively engaged in a variety of situations.

Identify Activities or Routines in Which RT Strategies Have Been Useful

Parents often use Responsive Teaching strategies spontaneously in a variety of interactions with their children. Encourage parents to become more aware of these spontaneous uses so that they become more mindful of interacting in responsive ways. Parents can note these situations in a journal and discuss the effects they had on their children.

Combine New with Previously Learned RT Strategies

Responsive Teaching is a cumulative intervention in which new strategies supplement rather than replace previous strategies. When parents learn new RT strategies, they may forget to continue using strategies they learned previously. Include reminders on Family Action Plans for parents to integrate newly learned strategies with strategies learned previously.

Practice RT Strategies That Are Difficult To Use

At times, RT strategies disappear from parents' repertoires, not just because parents forgot them but because they were difficult to implement. In this case, FAP activities can encourage parents to practice these strategies in structured play situations with their children. Reverting to structured practice with these strategies gives parents additional time to become proficient with them and to understand how they affect their children's pivotal behavior.

Use Self-Sticking Notes as Reminders To Use RT Strategies in Various Contexts

As reminders to use RT strategies throughout the day, place self-sticking notes in locations throughout the home where parents commonly interact with their child. These reminders can be stuck on walls, on doors, or over toy areas as reminders to use Responsive Teaching strategies.

The FAP Planning Process

Interventionists can encourage parents to play an active role in developing their Family Action Plans by summarizing the information and strategies presented during a session and asking parents how they would like to follow through with it. If parents are unable to identify what they want to do, interventionists can suggest alternative activities using the FAP activities previously listed.

There are at least three ingredients of successful FAP activities:

- FAP activities should build on parents' strengths. For each FAP, at least one of the suggested activities should focus on RT strategies that the parents were able to do during the session.
- FAP activities should be simple, not complicated, so that they can be integrated easily into parents' daily routines. If a previously suggested FAP activity was not practical, modify the activity to make it more feasible, or eliminate it altogether.
- There needs to be continuity of FAP activities from one intervention session to the next. FAPs should remind parents to continue working on strategies that were the focus of previous sessions while also recommending practice with strategies introduced in the current session.

Common Barriers to Follow-Through

Many parents are eager to do whatever they can to help their children's development and are willing to follow through with clear and feasible FAP recommendations, but for some parents, there are several legitimate factors that prevent them from doing so. As a result, interventionists must do more than simply recommend activities. They must also identify barriers that prevent parents from following through and help develop plans for addressing these barriers.

In the following we describe several reasons that have interfered with parents following through with their FAP and some of the actions that can be taken to address these issues.

1. *Parents are preoccupied with other stressors in their lives and are psychologically or physically unable to give the attention to their child's intervention that they would like to give.* When conditions in parents' lives become so overwhelming that they are unable to focus on their children's needs, interventionists must take seriously their role as coordinator of services. The FAP needs to focus on helping parents access other agencies and professionals who can provide the assistance they need to deal with their concerns. For example, if parents have financial concerns, interventionists can identify social-service programs that can provide income assistance, job placement, or vocational training. If parents are concerned about their relationships with their spouses or significant others, interventionists can help parents access family counselors or psychologists who are qualified to help them deal with family problems.

2. *Parents are uncomfortable with or are not sure if they believe in the parent-mediated model of intervention.* A fundamental feature of Responsive Teaching is that it promotes children's development primarily by encouraging parents to take on the role of the interventionist. For many parents, this approach raises two concerns that could interfere with their following through with their FAP.

First, some parents begin early intervention with the expectation that professionals will be using their specialized skills to work directly with their children. They do not expect to be active participants in this process. Parents develop these expectations for several reasons: (a) this is what their physician told them to expect; (b) in previous intervention programs, professionals provided services by working directly with their child; or (c) information from articles, videos, or conversations with others indicates that intervention should be professionally driven.

Second, other parents lack confidence that they can truly make a difference in their children's development. Responsive Teaching emphasizes that one of the most critical ingredients for intervention is that parents believe in the unique and critical role they play in their children's development. The less confidence parents have in themselves, the more apt they are to believe that professionals, and not they, hold the keys to their children's future. Interventionists must consistently promote the idea that parents are the most important influences in their children's development and point out how well children respond to their parents or remark on how well parents manage their children. Interventionists should emphasize how the child's progress is related to parents' efforts to use RT.

3. *RT is incompatible with parents' beliefs and child-rearing patterns.* There are a number of parents who faithfully participate in RT sessions, even when they have misgivings about the philosophy of RT and about using RT strategies with their children. These parents perceive Responsive Teaching as asking them to carry out ideas that are incompatible with their own personal beliefs and to interact with their children in a way that is different from their accustomed interactions. When parents' child-rearing beliefs are incompatible with RT, it should not be surprising that they do not follow through with FAP activities. If parents routinely have difficulty following through with their FAPs, interventionists need to explore their personal feelings about RT philosophy and procedures. Interventionists should reassure parents that it is reasonable not to follow through with suggestions and ideas they do not agree with. If parents cannot accept the philosophy and strategies of Responsive Teaching, at some point they should help parents access alternative services that are more compatible with their values and beliefs.

4. *Parents interpret Responsive Teaching as reflecting behaviors and beliefs they already have and, thus, does not require them to change.* If parents already do everything that Responsive Teaching asks them to do with their children, they sometimes feel that there is no reason to follow through with activities listed on their FAPs. In many instances, it is true that parents are highly responsive with their children, and their FAP activities do little more

than reinforce how they already interact with their children. Interventionists therefore need to reassure parents that they are doing a great job with their children and encourage them to continue interacting in that way with their children. These parents need to focus more on the challenge of increasing their children's pivotal behaviors. No matter how responsively parents interact with their children at the start of intervention, children will only increase their pivotal behaviors if their parents interact even more responsively with them.

5. *Parents are too tired or too busy to think about how they interact with their child.* Most parents of young children are tired and busy. The more children and work responsibilities and the fewer supports parents have, the greater the likelihood they will be too tired and busy to devote much effort to their children's intervention. Interventionists need to be sensitive to how tired, busy, or lacking in support parents might be and to let parents know they should not feel guilty about this. At the same time, however, they need to stress how critical it is for parents to follow through with RT to help parents think about what they can realistically do without adding to their burdens, and to emphasize that doing something, no matter how small, is better than not following through.

6. *Parents are receiving suggestions and information from other professionals that are incompatible with the philosophy and procedures of Responsive Teaching.* If parents work with two or more professionals who recommend activities that are based upon contradictory philosophies and instructional procedures, they may become confused about what they should do with their child. For example, the intervention specialist who uses Responsive Teaching may encourage the parent to follow the child's lead and to imitate any actions or sounds the child makes to promote the pivotal behaviors that are the basis for cognitive growth. In contrast, the speech–language pathologist who was trained in behavioral methods of language intervention might encourage the parent to teach a targeted set of words and to refrain from responding to or reinforcing lower level communicative behaviors.

To avoid this problem, interventionists should ask parents what other interventionists are targeting as the goals for their child and what they are being asked to do to achieve these goals. Interventionists can then either show parents how Responsive Teaching methods can be used for attaining the goals recommended by others or point out the impossibility of following through with competing recommendations. Parents must ultimately decide the direction they want to pursue; however, interventionists need to make sure they have sufficient information to make informed choices.

Summary

In this chapter, we discussed how the FAP is one of the most important components of Responsive Teaching. FAPs are necessary for parents who work with professionals and also for parents who try to implement RT on their own. FAPs are the plans for encouraging caregivers to make the kinds of changes in developmental stimulation necessary for their children to achieve higher levels of competence. The two phases to these changes—which require different types of FAP activities—include caregivers (a) learning to interact responsively and (b) attempting to integrate Responsive Teaching into their children's daily routines. We have also described several FAP activities that can be used to bring about these changes.

In the final portion of this chapter, we addressed two issues that are critical to the implementation of Family Action Plans. The first is related to the process of developing Family Action Plans. We suggested that a critical principle is that parents play an active role in developing their FAPs. The role of the interventionist in developing an FAP is to support the activities parents want to follow through, and to suggest options that parents can use for their FAP. The second issue is related to the barriers that commonly prevent parents from following through with FAP activities. To ensure that their children have the opportunity to benefit from Responsive Teaching, interventionists need to identify these barriers and help parents develop plans to overcome them.

Section IV

Curriculum Materials

Curriculum Materials

Introduction

In the following section, we provide all the intervention tools and curriculum materials that are needed to implement Responsive Teaching (RT) intervention sessions. All of the materials in this section may be photocopied for individual use. These materials are also available on the Responsive Teaching Planning and Tracking computer program.

Curriculum Material 1. Intervention Session Guide—Assesses whether the activities identified for each phase of an intervention session occur during a particular session

Curriculum Material 2. Pivotal Behavior Wizard—Identifies appropriate intervention objectives based on a child's current behavior in the intervention's target domain

Curriculum Material 3. Pivotal Behavior Profile—Assesses a child's current level of using each of the 16 pivotal behaviors targeted by Responsive Teaching

Curriculum Material 4. Planning and Tracking Form—Selects and tracks the discussion points, RT strategies, and pivotal behavior assessments implemented in each intervention session

Curriculum Material 5. Intervention Session Plan Forms

- Professional Session Plan—Professionals use to develop an intervention session plan
- Parent Session Plan—Parents use to develop their own child development session plan
- Family Action Plan—Parents and professionals use to develop a Family Action Plan

Curriculum Material 6. Curriculum Outline—Provides information needed to develop intervention session plans for each of the three developmental domains addressed in Responsive Teaching (i.e., cognition, communication, and social–emotional functioning) and provides descriptions of the rationale, discussion points, and RT strategies for each of the pivotal behaviors related to them.

Curriculum Material 1

Intervention Session Guide

Intervention Session Guide

Name ______________________ Date ______________ Observer ______________________

Phases and Activities	NA	No (a)	Partly (b)	Yes (c)
A. Planning				
1. Arrange environment in advance • Have toys and materials appropriate for child's level of development • Have sufficient materials to allow child to make choices • Select materials to promote behaviors related to the day's topic				
2. Have handouts and videotape materials available				
3. Review information from previous session				
B. Rapport and Review				
4. Greet parents and child warmly				
5. Encourage parents to talk about information from previous session				
6. Be attentive to parents				
7. Compliment parents on their participation or parenting skills				
C. Purpose and Rationale				
8. Describe purpose and focus of today's session				
9. Discuss rationale for strategy being presented				
10. Assess or describe the child's current use of the pivotal behavior objective				
11. Speak at parents' level of understanding				
12. Assess parents' understanding of information				
13. Invite parents' comments, questions, and concerns				
D. Demonstration and Practice of Responsive Teaching Strategies				
14. Engage in responsive, balanced interactions with the child throughout session				
15. Model RT strategy that is the focus of today's session				
16. Explain strategy during and after it is modeled				
17. Demonstrate and explain the impact of RT strategy on child's behavior				
18. Involve the parents in interactions with their child				
19. Coach parents while they interact with their child				
20. Give parents feedback regarding their use of a strategy				
E. Family Action Planning				
21. Develop with parents a written plan for follow-through activities				
22. Develop a plan to address barriers or obstacles to follow-through activities				
23. Address concerns parents have raised that are not directly related to RT				
24. Summarize discussion points, strategies, and plans that were covered during the session				
Total Score			Total × 2	Total × 3
Criterion Score (b + c)	60			

Curriculum Material 2

Pivotal Behavior Wizard

Pivotal Behavior Wizard

Cognition	
Child's Behavior	**Pivotal Behavior**
• Does not have frequent episodes of one-to-one play with parents and other caregivers • Does not stay engaged long in play and other interactive episodes with parents and caregivers • Engages in play routine with parents and others that are more task oriented than playful and fun	Social Play
• Can sustain reciprocal interactions with adults but usually waits for the adult to decide what to play with or how to play • Chooses what toys to play with or how to play less than half of the time when playing with an adult	Initiation
• Plays with very few toys or materials • Seldom varies what he or she does with toys or materials • Shows little if any interest in any of the features of objects (e.g., shape, texture, parts) • Shows little interest in objects, people, or novel occurrences in the environment	Exploration
• Seeks the assistance of adults whenever he or she has difficulty doing something during play • Tries to solve problems as they arise but becomes quickly frustrated when he or she is unable to solve them • Avoids engaging in activities that may be difficult	Problem Solving
• Seldom repeats developmental skills that are within his or her range of capabilities • Does not have access to toys or materials he or she enjoys • Is often encouraged to produce behaviors that are beyond his or her current level of functioning • Gives up easily whenever he or she encounters an obstacle	Practice

Communication	
Child's Behavior	**Pivotal Behavior**
• Does not engage in frequent one-to-one social interactions throughout the day • Does not stay engaged in social interaction with parents and caregivers more than briefly • Has few opportunities to engage in interactive routines with parents that are playful, fun, and predictable	Joint Activity
• Engages in joint activities but seldom directs parents' attention other than to get his or her needs met • Maintains eye contact with a parent or other adult for longer than a few seconds at a time • Is unable to follow parents' nonverbal and verbal directional cues (e.g., eye gaze, pointing, gesturing) • Is capable of directing and following the parent's focus of attention but seldom does it	Joint Attention

(continues)

Pivotal Behavior Wizard

Communication *Continued.*

Child's Behavior	Pivotal Behavior
• Seldom uses vocalizations or language to interact • Makes his or her own special sounds but few conventional speech sounds • Is extremely quiet most of the time • Is difficult to understand	Vocalization
• Uses nonverbal cues to express feelings or needs • Jargons, babbles, or uses words by him- or herself but not with others • Jargons and babbles while interacting with others • Vocalizes but only occasionally uses vocalizations to communicate intentions to others • Understands a considerable amount of language but primarily uses nonverbal communication rather than words to communicate • Knows several words but either seldom uses them to communicate his or her intentions or uses them only in a restricted way • Uses a combination of words and jargon to communicate	Intentional Communication
• Uses words and jargon to interact with people • Is rapidly acquiring new words • Is starting to put words together to form longer than two-word utterances • Has several words but seldom stays engaged with adults for more than a few conversational turns • Communicates to get his or her needs met but seldom for other reasons • Actively attempts to involve parents and others in his or her play, even though his or her language is limited • Is interested in communicating elaborate sequences or observations but lacks the language to do it	Conversation

Social–Emotional Functioning

Child's Behavior	Pivotal Behavior
• Is not responsive to his or her primary caregivers • Seldom initiates contact with his or her primary caregivers • Avoids interacting with his or her primary caregivers • Appears tense and anxious when with his or her primary caregivers • Does not respond to parents' discipline	Trust
• Seems unaware of or unaffected by the emotions of people around him or her • Has unusual emotional reactions • Generally has a flat affect • Seems quiet, depressed, or withdrawn • Seldom expresses his or her feelings whether by crying, smiling, or laughing	Empathy

(continues)

Pivotal Behavior Wizard

Social–Emotional Functioning *Continued.*

Child's Behavior	Pivotal Behavior
• Does not actively participate in routine childcare activities (dressing, eating) with parents • Does not allow primary caregivers to become involved in his or her play • Leaves interactions whenever primary caregivers ask him or her to do something • Has difficulty conforming to his or her parents' expectations • Reacts negatively to many of his or her caregivers' requests to do something • Has difficulty playing with other children	Cooperation
• Cries with minimal provocation • Cries frequently and for long time periods • Has difficulty with transitions from one activity to another • Has difficulty adjusting to new people • Tantrums frequently • Acts aggressively toward others by hitting, biting, screaming, or spitting • Destroys things in his or her environment	Self-Regulation
• Is often described by parents in terms of what he or she cannot do rather than what he or she can do • Is hesitant and uncertain • Is dissatisfied with his or her efforts and accomplishments • Seldom asks others to notice what he or she is doing • Gives up in the face of challenge	Feelings of Confidence
• Seldom chooses what to do • Usually looks to adults for guidance or direction • Seems hesitant to initiate activities with others • Remains quiet or unoccupied unless someone tells or shows him or her what to do	Feelings of Control

Curriculum Material 3

Pivotal Behavior Profile

Pivotal Behavior Profile

Social Play

Do I play reciprocally with a partner across many situations? Is my play characterized by "give and take," in which I contribute as much to the activity as my partner? Am I aware of my partner's activity during play?

How am I doing?

10 = Very High I almost always engage in mutual play activities. My play can be characterized as reciprocal interaction, in which I observe the other person's behavior and contribute to the activity when it is my turn.

5 = Moderate Sometimes I am interested in play with other partners, and I engage in reciprocal interaction about half the time with them. I make face-to-face contact and attempt other types of communication at least half of the time I am with them. My partner and I each contribute to a joint activity at least half of the time.

1 = Very Low I never include others in my play. I prefer to play alone or in parallel with my partner. I ignore my partner in parallel play and am usually unaware of my partner's attempts to play with me.

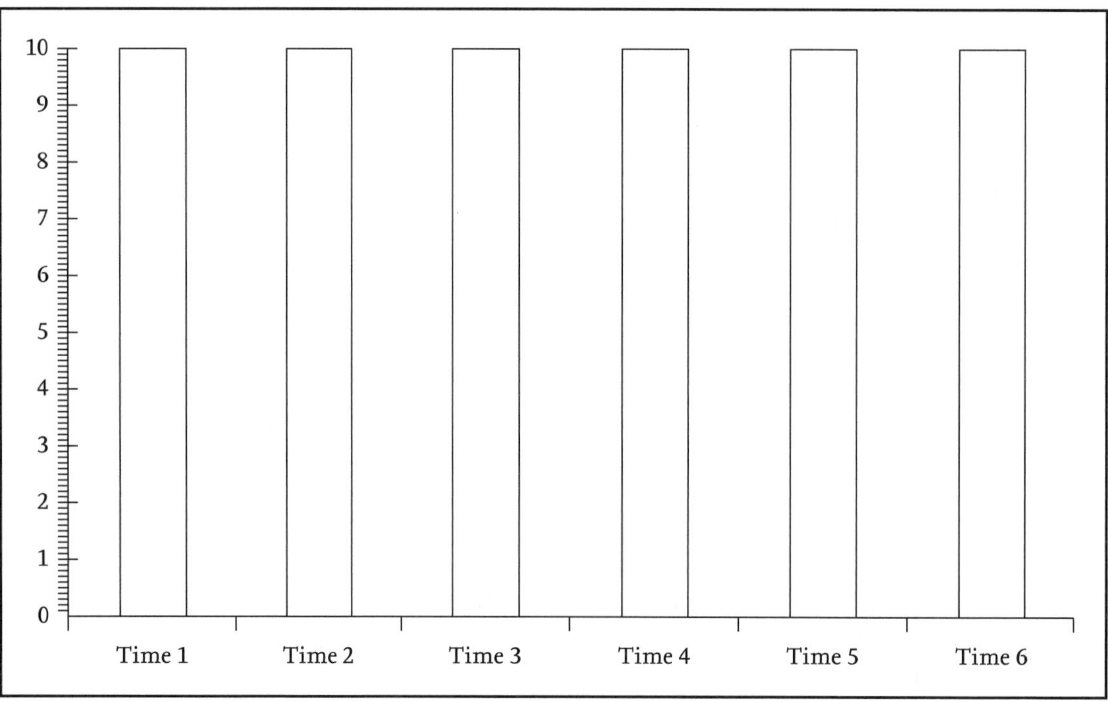

Initiation

Do I start activities on my own, or do I always follow others' leads? Am I active in choosing the nature and direction of an activity? Do I initiate communications, start new games, and change my activities with the same toys? Do I attempt new activities without being prompted by my partner?

How am I doing?

10 = Very High I continually initiate activities when I am playing. I have my own agenda and I usually insist on following it. I rarely play a passive role while playing with others.

5 = Moderate About half of the time I try to initiate activities. However, there are periods of time during which I am passive, am uninvolved, or play primarily by responding to my partner's suggestions, requests, or play agenda.

1 = Very Low I never begin an activity on my own. I tend to be passive and inactive during social play, or I engage in activities only when others take the lead and tell me what to do.

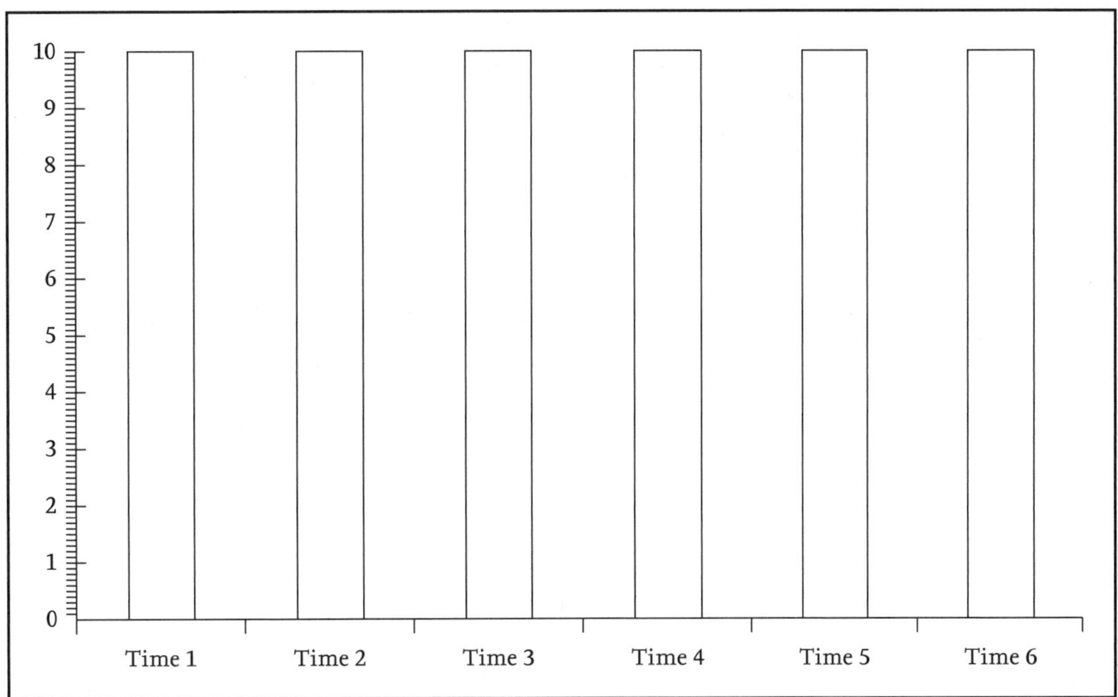

Pivotal Behavior Profile

Exploration

Do I investigate or handle objects and events rather than only observe or come in brief contact with them? Do I explore by using my senses—by mouthing, throwing, handling, looking, or listening? Do I participate actively in the environment by experimenting as well as observing people and things?

How am I doing?

10 = Very High I frequently explore my environment either physically or visually. I may examine multiple objects or respond quickly to novel stimuli. I like to feel, taste, shake, listen to, and view objects and to manipulate them to see what they can do. I continually investigate my surroundings.

5 = Moderate I actively participate in the environment by occasionally exploring and manipulating it in novel ways. Although I experiment with some things, I only engage in these behaviors about half of the time that I have the opportunity to do them.

1 = Very Low I am mostly nonresponsive to my environment. I am not very interested in the external world, and I am often withdrawn, passive, or focused on playing with the same objects in the same ways.

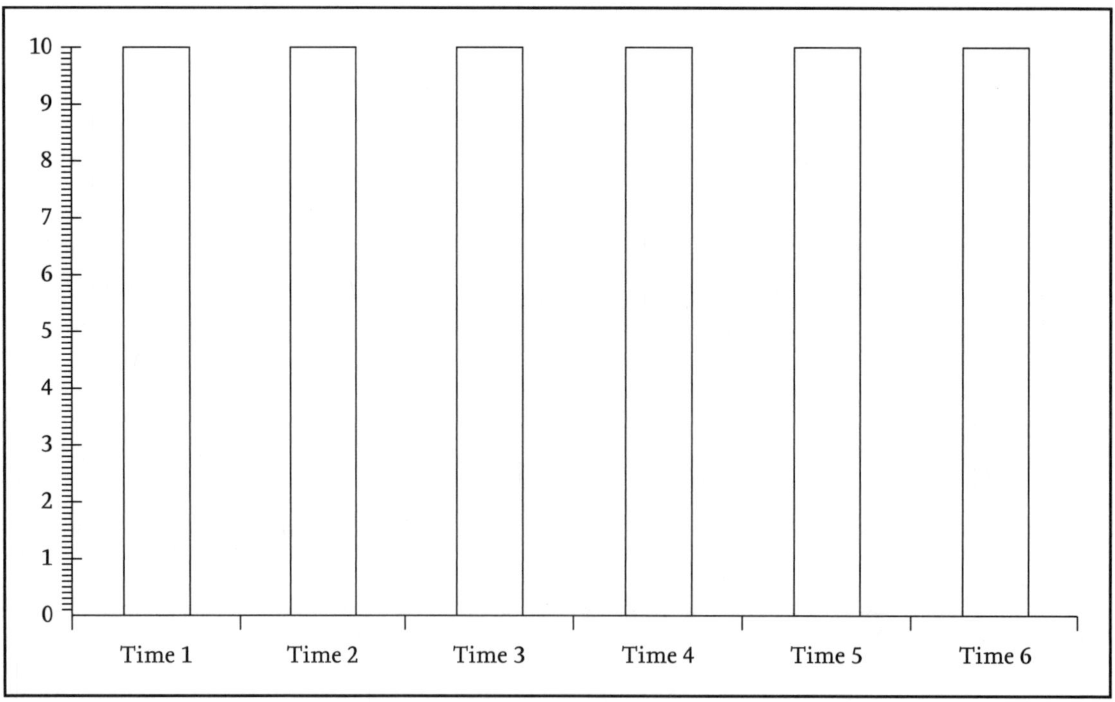

Pivotal Behavior Profile

Problem Solving

Do I persist with tasks that pose some challenge or difficulty? Do I make several attempts and continue to experiment with different solutions even though I am not successful? Do I frequently assess my impact on the environment? Am I creative in attempting to deal with new or challenging situations?

How am I doing?

10 = Very High I almost always make repeated attempts to solve problems, often trying a variety of solutions. I continue to persist at succeeding in challenging situations, even after several efforts have failed. Persistence at problem solving is the highlight of my play behavior.

5 = Moderate I make some attempts to solve problems, but I tend to give up after a few tries. I often fail to vary my attempts to find a solution, or I quickly seek an adult partner's assistance to solve it for me.

1 = Very Low I never attempt a second try when I encounter difficulty. I become frustrated easily when I encounter a problem, and I leave tasks quickly rather than making attempts to overcome obstacles.

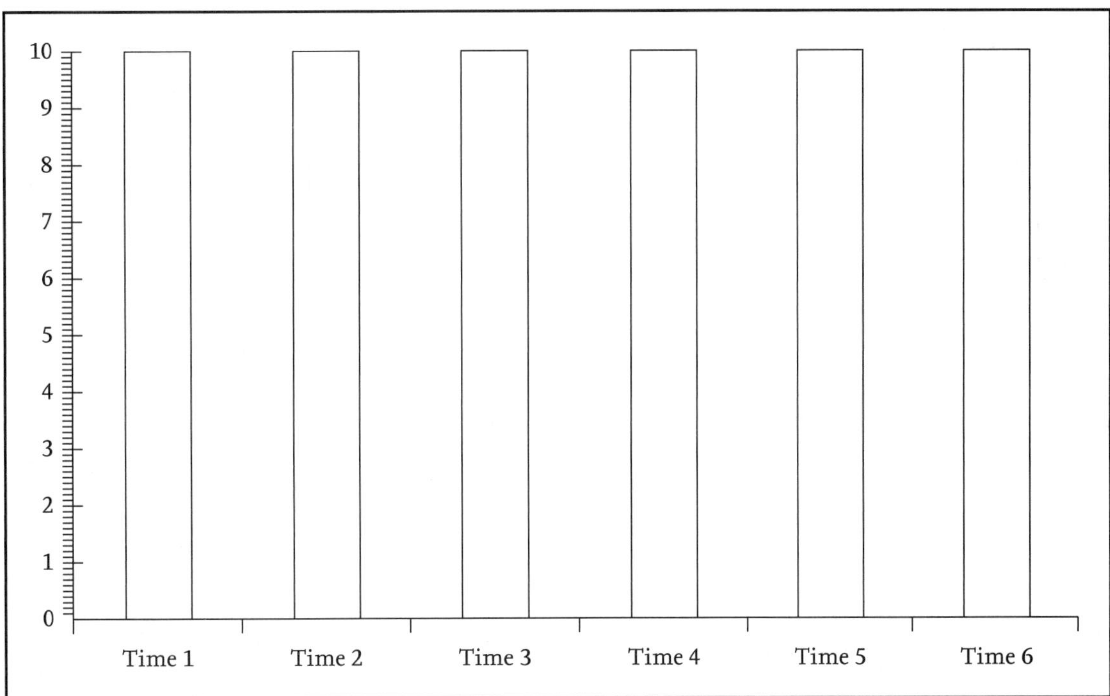

Pivotal Behavior Profile

Practice

Do I repeat behaviors and activities in the same way or by varying them? Do I practice these behaviors by myself and with other people? Are my episodes of practice prolonged in duration, and do they occur with several objects and people?

How am I doing?

10 = Very High I almost always spend considerable time repeating vocal or behavioral sequences. I may frequently change activities, trying a variety of behaviors in a short period of time. Episodes of practice are a constant feature of my play, both alone and with others.

5 = Moderate I have several episodes in which I spend considerable time repeating vocal or behavioral sequences. I frequently change activities, trying a variety of behaviors in a short period of time. My episodes of practice occur about as often as my play episodes that do not involve repeating of behaviors.

1 = Very Low I never engage in sustained repetition of any behavior. I tend to engage in activities haphazardly, moving quickly from one behavior to the next.

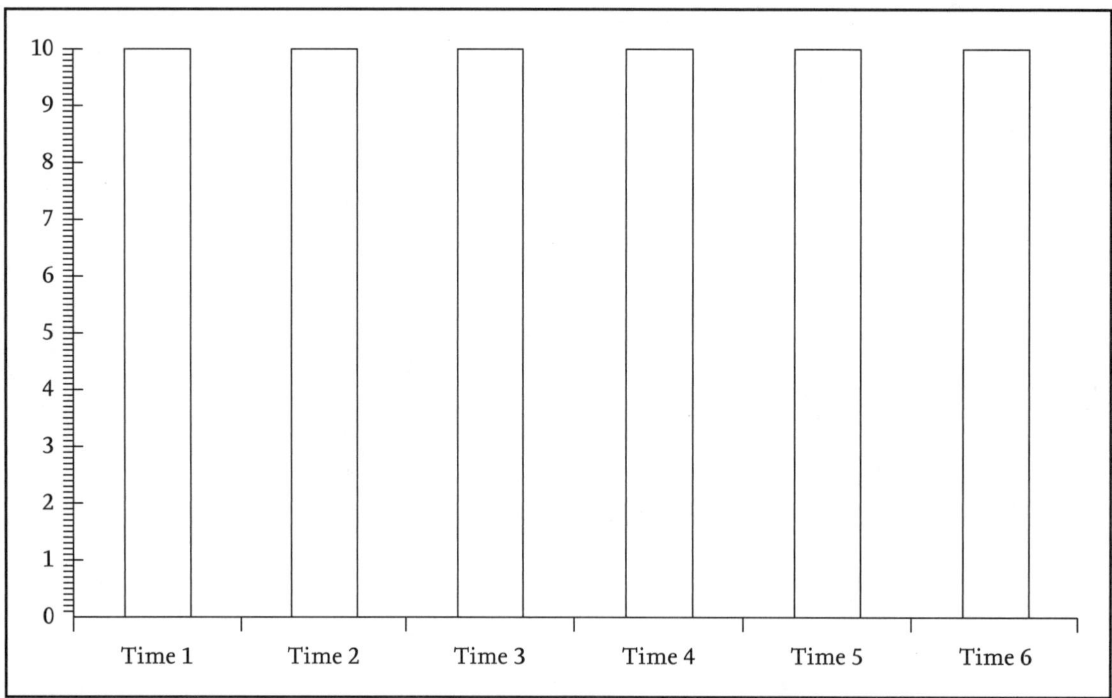

Pivotal Behavior Profile

Joint Activity

Do I engage in active, reciprocal interactions with my partner? Do my partner and I direct our interactions toward each other? Do we respond to each others' behaviors and cues? Are my interactions with my partner characterized by collaboration and exchange?

How am I doing?

10 = Very High I consistently seek out partners, initiate play, and actively keep others in play with me. I make an effort to engage others in my play. I remain engaged with others on a common activity for significant periods of time. My behavior is affected by what my partner does in the interaction.

5 = Moderate I occasionally engage in activities with others for a mutual purpose. Most of my interactions with others are brief sequences of joint activity (e.g., less than 20 seconds at a time). My episodes of joint activity occur about half of the time that I am with adult partners.

1 = Very Low I rarely engage in activities with my partner that focus on a common purpose. I seldom notice my partner, and I use my partner only to get my needs met. If I use a partner to facilitate play, there is no shared activity or purpose. I generally act independently of my partner, except when I need help.

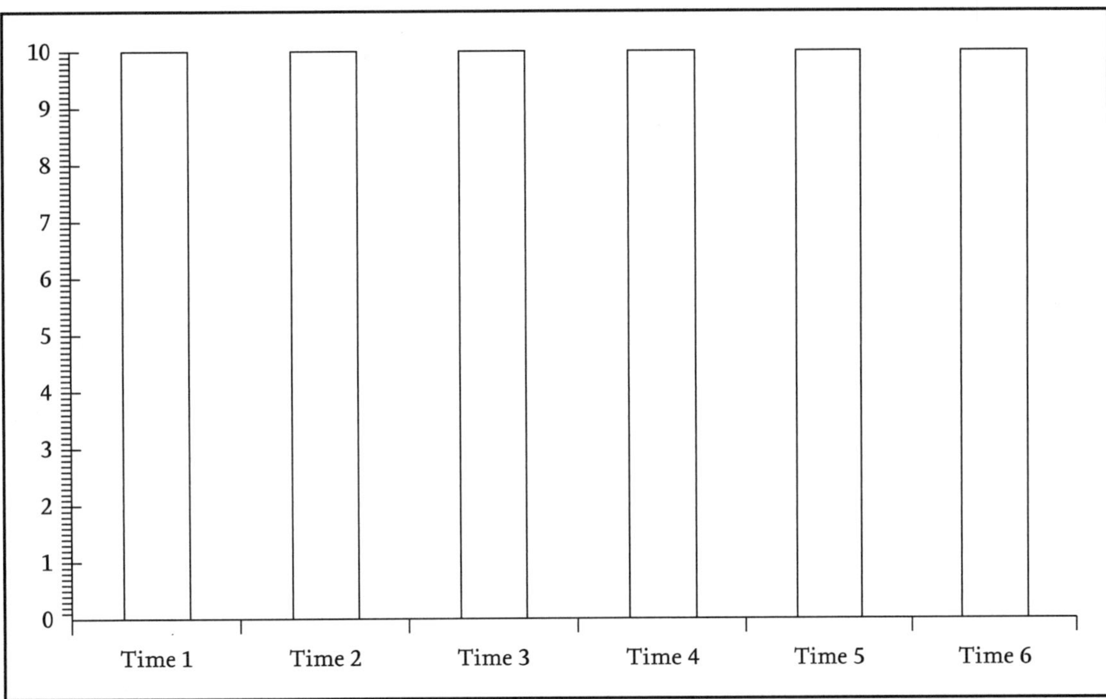

Joint Attention

Do I have frequent bouts of eye contact and other sharing behaviors such as vocalizations with my partner? Do I try to show my partner what I want or what I am interested in by using words, vocalizations, gestures, or looking? Do I follow the gestures, facial displays, eye gaze, or other communications my partner uses to direct my attention?

How am I doing?

10 = Very High I have frequent and lengthy bouts of joint attention with my partners. I make frequent eye contact, and I respond to the cues they use to guide or direct my attention. I also frequently share my experiences by showing or offering toys or objects or by using nonverbal signals or words to direct my partner's attention.

5 = Moderate About half of the time, I make eye contact with my partner, referencing him or her for affirmation, cues, or information. I have periods in which I engage in eye contact or other sharing behaviors, but I am equally likely to have periods of inattention.

1 = Very Low I rarely make eye contact or attempt to gain the attention of my partner. I usually focus only on my own behavior without referencing my partner to gauge reactions or to read cues. I generally do not respond to my partner's attempts to direct my attention. I may physically bring things to get my partner to understand my needs or interests.

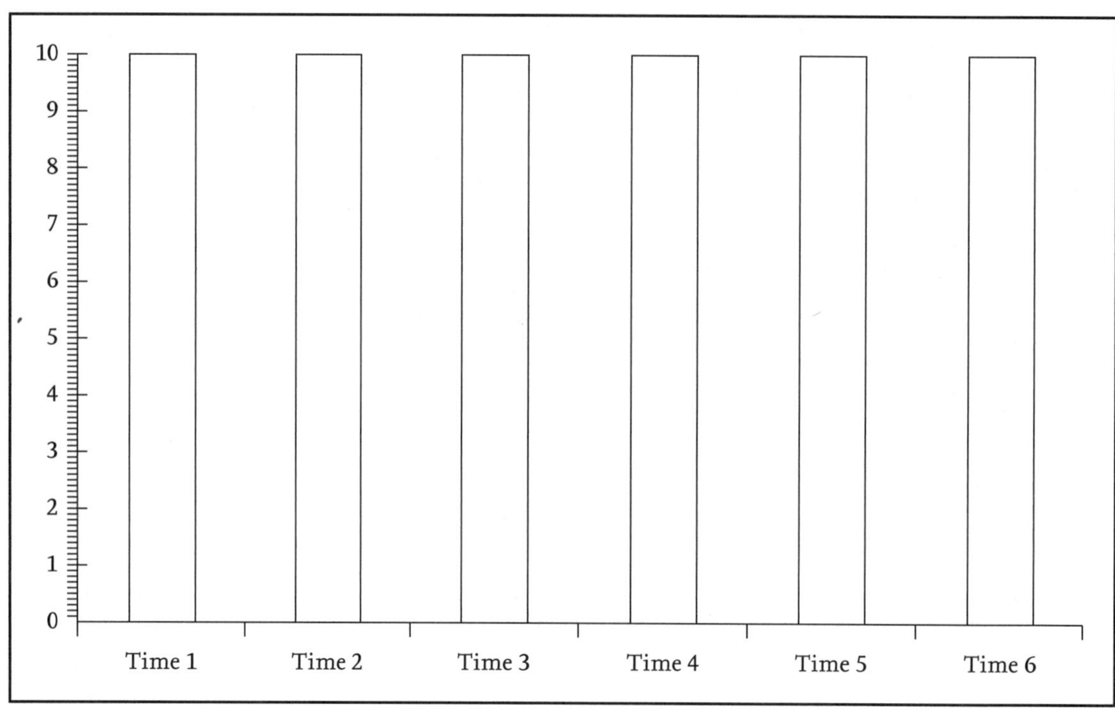

Pivotal Behavior Profile

Vocalization

Do I practice or repeat sounds including grunting, vocalization, singing, or words? Do I make sounds frequently, both by myself and with others?

How am I doing?

10 = Very High I frequently make sounds using my voice, both while playing alone and with others. I vocalize all of the time, both for personal stimulation as well as for communication. I frequently experiment and produce a wide range of sounds.

5 = Moderate I occasionally make sounds when I play by myself and with others. Sometimes I have long periods of quiet, and other times I have episodes in which I produce a high frequency of sounds. I may have inconsistencies in my pattern of vocalizing, such as vocalizing a great deal with people but hardly at all when I am alone.

1 = Very Low I rarely make sounds with my voice. I may be silent much of the time. If I do make sounds, they are restricted to a narrow range.

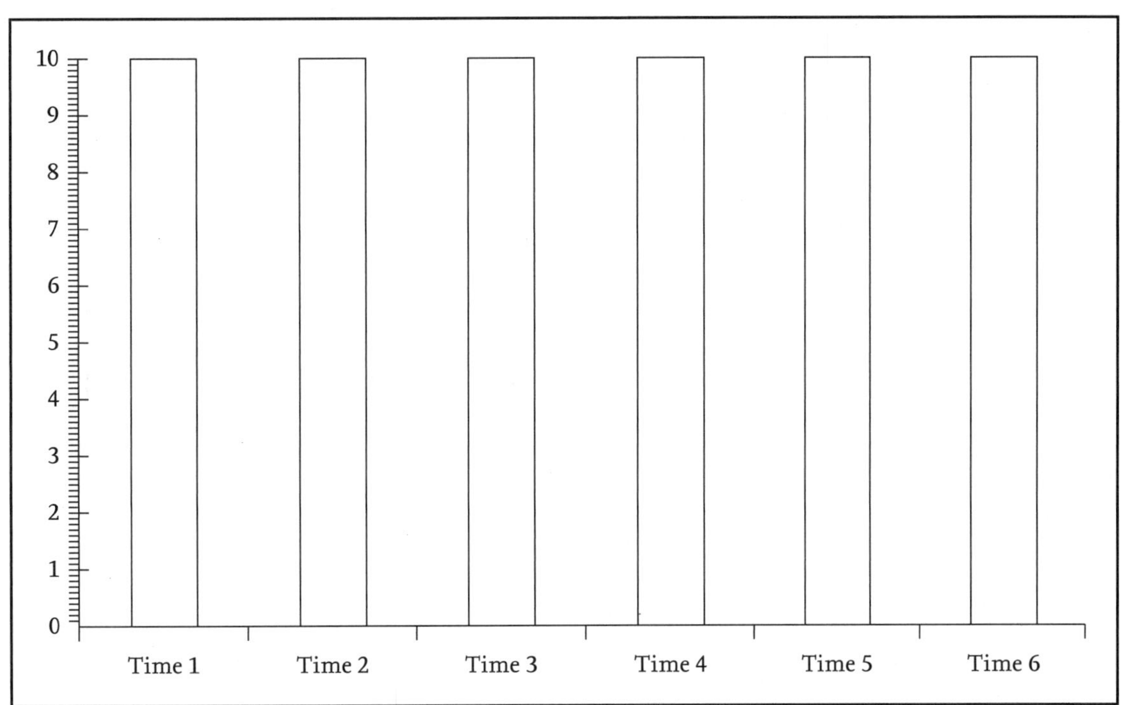

Pivotal Behavior Profile

Intentional Communication

Do I frequently attempt to make my intentions known to my partner? Am I effective at using nonverbal communication, words, or both to make my needs, feelings, and observations known to others? Do I use the words and language I know to communicate my intentions?

How am I doing?

10 = Very High Most of the time I attempt to communicate my intentions to others. I am very effective at communicating a wide range of communicative functions, including greeting, socializing, sharing feelings and observations, noticing and directing attention, and requesting.

5 = Moderate About half of the time, I attempt to communicate my intentions to others. I do not yet express the full range of communicative functions, such as greeting, socializing, sharing feelings and observations, directing attention, and requesting. I tend to communicate mainly to get my needs met.

1 = Very Low I make very few attempts to communicate, and I am usually not effective at communicating my intentions to others. I may know several words and nonverbal signals that could be used to communicate, but I seldom use them to make my intentions known to others.

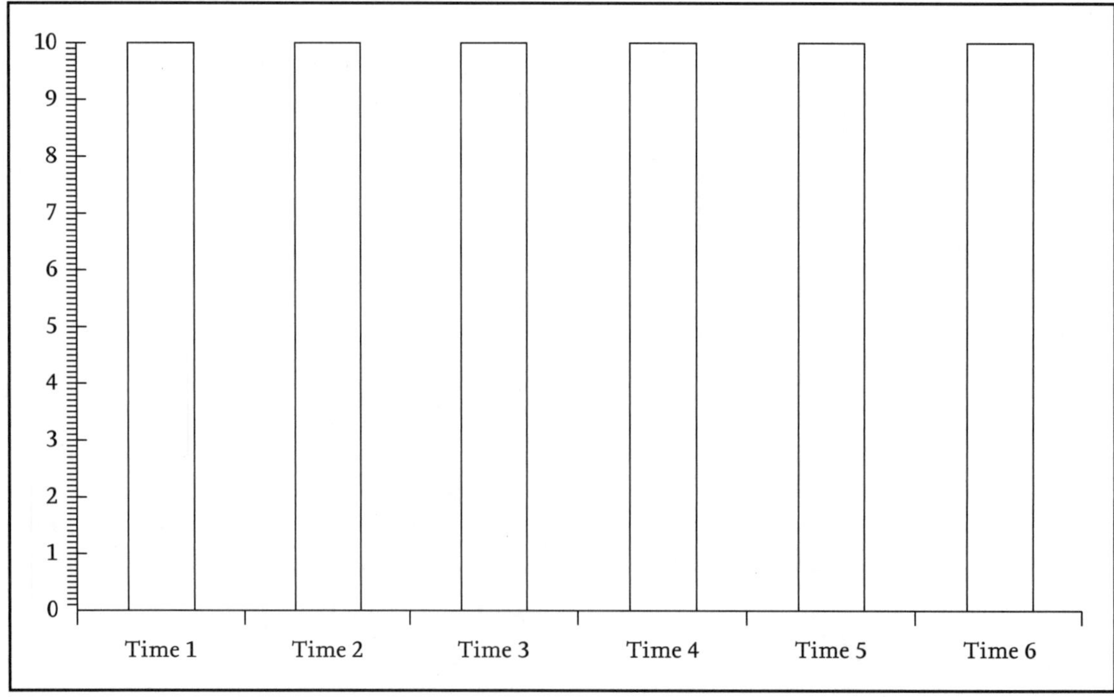

Pivotal Behavior Profile

Conversation

Do I engage in conversations on a variety of topics with multiple people? Do I use both nonverbal communication and verbal language? Do I lead and follow conversations in a give-and-take style? Do I sustain and follow changes in topics? Do I communicate for many purposes, such as companionship, persuasion, information exchange, feelings, and needs?

How am I doing?

10* = *Very High I initiate and sustain conversations frequently with many people. I have conversations for many purposes, including enjoyment, information, joint activity, and to be with people. I participate in the give and take of a conversation, spending equal time listening and contributing to the exchange. I can converse about my partners' topic as well as my own.

5* = *Moderate I occasionally engage in conversation, but only with certain people (e.g., mother) and not others. Conversations are often brief and focus mostly on topics of my choice. I have difficulty changing topics. I often terminate conversations when my partner changes the topic.

1* = *Very Low I rarely initiate or sustain conversations. Most of my conversations are short, nonverbal communications or utterances involving less than two interactive turns. My conversation partner bears the burden for conversation. I do not contribute to conversation exchanges and frequently leave the situation.

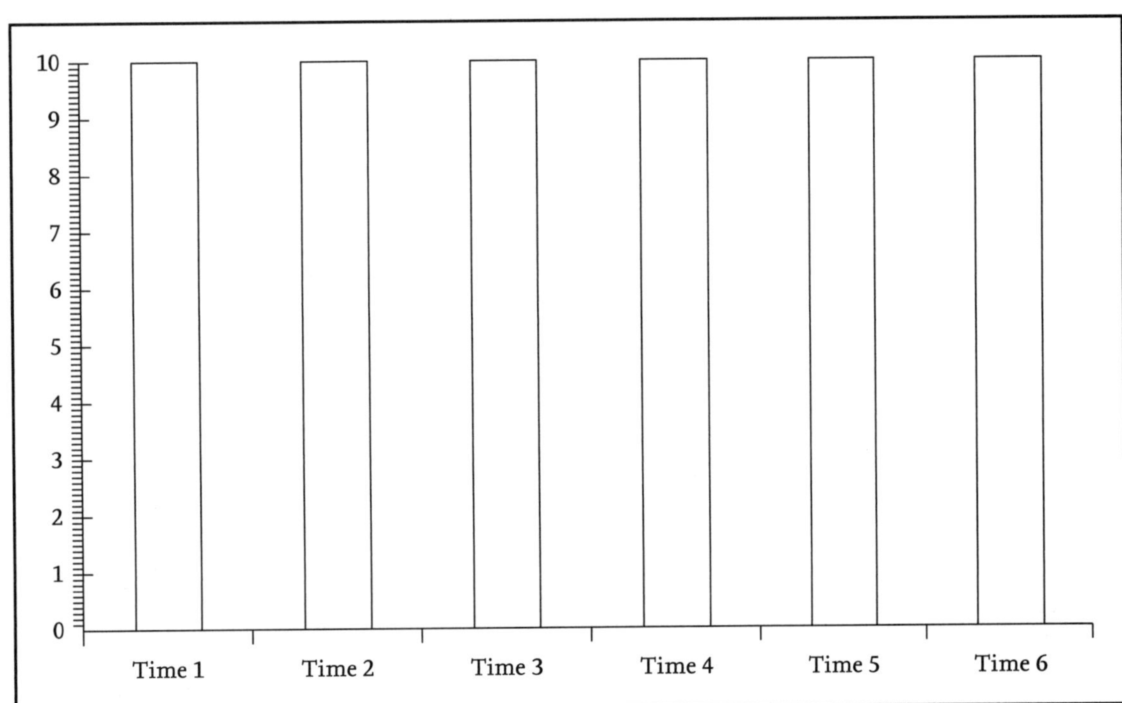

Trust

Do I have a trusting and warm relationship with my primary caregiver? Do I seek out or touch base with my caregiver for comfort or security? Do I take pleasure in being with my caregiver? Do I frequently share information or objects, and do I give my caregiver eye contact, smiles, or hugs?

How am I doing?

10* = *Very High I frequently touch base with my caregiver for playful hugs, teasing, and so forth. I often make eye contact and smile at my caregiver. I am comfortable sitting on my caregiver's lap. I frequently seek my caregiver's attention, and I enjoy showing him or her the things that interest or excite me.

5* = *Moderate I occasionally display trust in my caregiver. About half of the time I am with my caregiver I show pleasure and comfort, as indicated by smiling, eye contact, and seeking physical contact. However, I am more likely to seek out my caregiver to get my needs met rather than to be with him or her.

1* = *Very Low I avoid or I am uncomfortable with my caregiver. I rarely make eye contact or smile at my caregiver. Often I withdraw or physically stiffen when I am with my caregiver. I frequently try to move away when my caregiver approaches me.

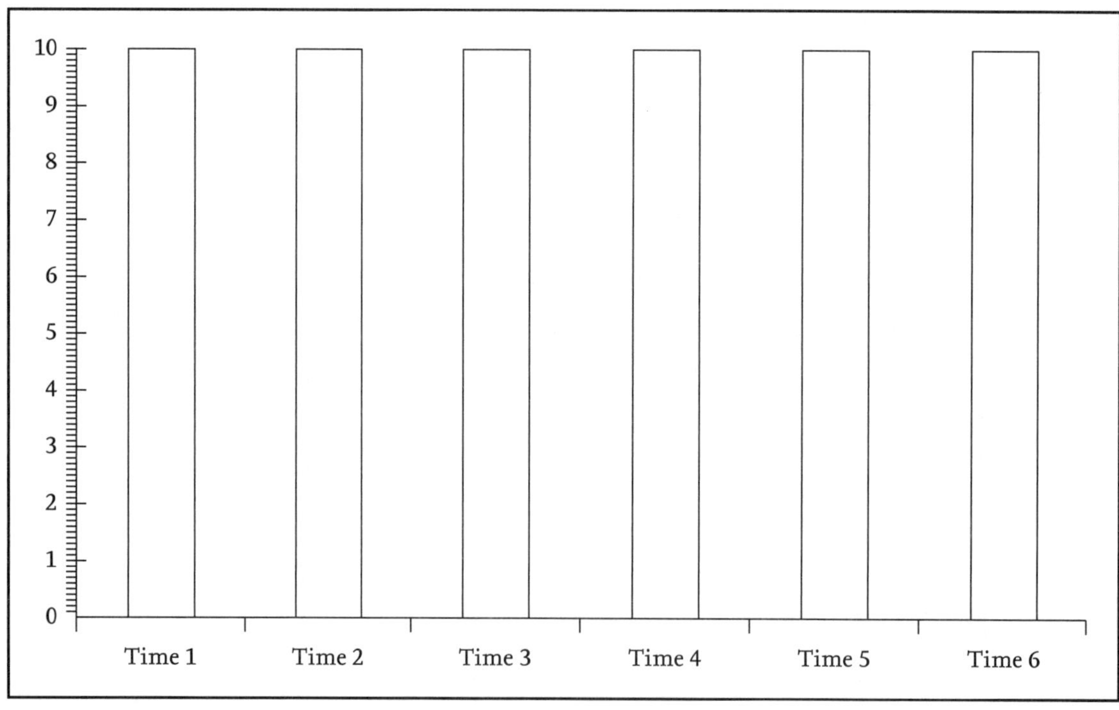

Pivotal Behavior Profile

Empathy

Am I sensitive to others' feelings and emotions and able to adjust my own emotional state according to the emotions of others? Do I care about how others feel, and am I affected by the emotions of others? Do I use my caregivers' reactions to gauge the safety and friendliness of the situation and to regulate how I react?

How am I doing?

10* = *Very High I frequently respond appropriately to several emotional states such as joy, sadness, anger, or fear. I am emotionally expressive and display appropriate levels of positive and negative emotions. I reciprocate to others' emotions. I usually assess my parents' responses to decide whether to avoid or explore the object, person, or situation.

5* = *Moderate I occasionally respond to the moods of others, particularly if they are high in intensity, such as crying or scolding. I often ignore emotions of lower intensity. I generally display moderate levels of emotional intensity, including positive as well as negative emotions. Occasionally, I alter my emotional behavior to match the emotional responses of others.

1* = *Very Low I show little awareness of others' moods or emotions. I do not respond to others being angry or agitated. I seldom alter my emotional state in response to the emotions of others. I also display few appropriate emotional reactions of my own. I appear to be in my own world with little concern for others.

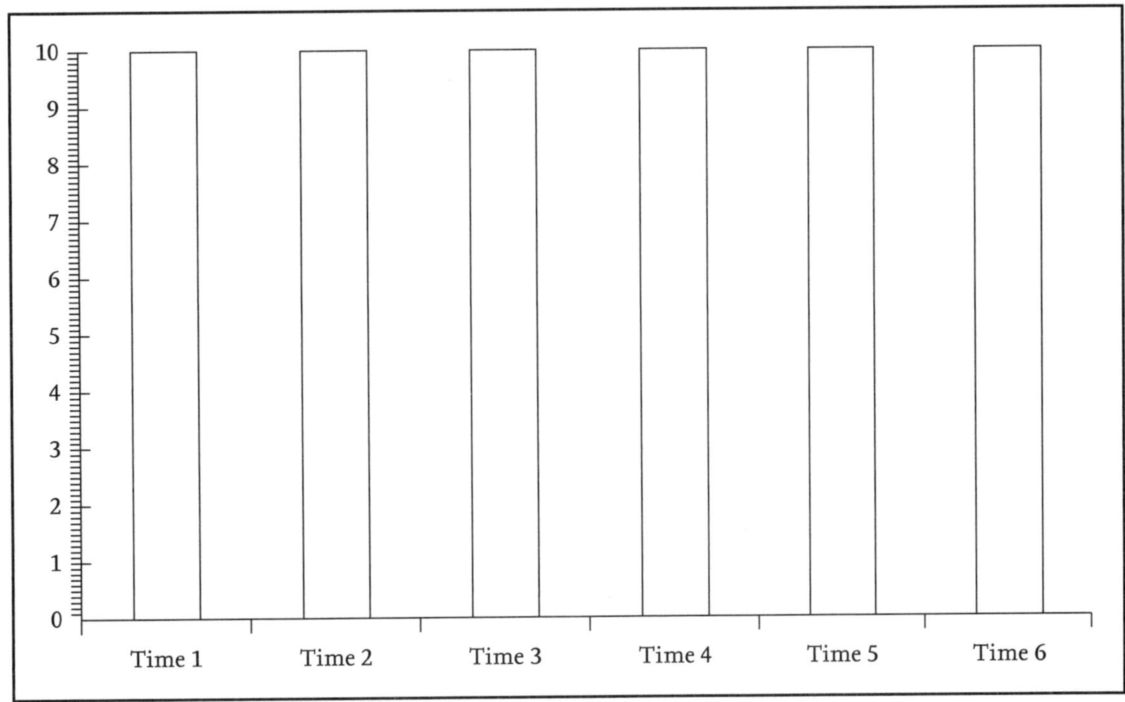

Pivotal Behavior Profile

Cooperation

Do I comply with my partners' requests or suggestions and collaborate in working together with them for definite purposes? Do I consistently make an effort to do what my partners ask? Do I respond quickly to my partners' suggestions?

How am I doing?

10 = Very High I consistently attempt to comply with my partners' requests or suggestions. I understand what is expected of me, and I rarely refuse to do the desired behavior. I am happy and enjoy myself when I am able to do what is asked or expected of me. I rarely resist my partners' requests, and when I do, it is caused by circumstances such as tiredness or an unfamiliar environment.

5 = Moderate I cooperate with my partners' requests or suggestions about as often as I do not cooperate. I may be resistant to an activity at first and then cooperate when my partners become more insistent.

1 = Very Low I almost never follow the requests or wishes of my partners. I often ignore my partners' requests. I leave or turn away when my partners ask me to do something. If my partners pressure me to comply, I usually refuse by saying no or by tantruming.

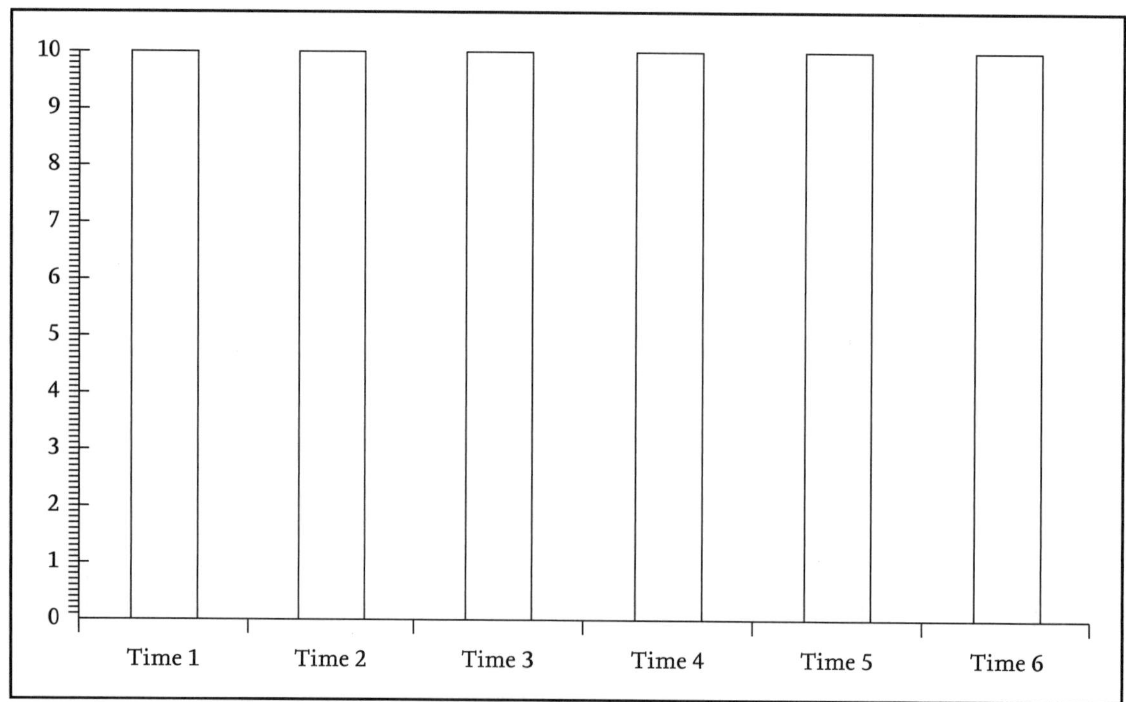

Pivotal Behavior Profile

Self-Regulation

Can I soothe myself when I am upset or frustrated? Are my periods of tantruming and crying infrequent and short in duration? Do I comfort myself by holding a favorite toy or by becoming engaged in a different play activity? Can I make transitions easily and adapt quickly to changes in my environment or routine?

How am I doing?

10 = Very High I am usually very easygoing and tolerate frustration and change well. My periods of crying or frustration are rare and happen primarily when I am very tired or ill. I quickly find relief on my own. I can calm down quickly when comforted by a caregiver, and I can be distracted easily from my distress when presented with a new toy or activity.

5 = Moderate I have periods of difficulty tolerating frustration or change, depending on how I am feeling or whether I am stressed. I need extra comfort and support from caregivers during these times. With some effort, I can be comforted by my caregivers. Occasionally, I can comfort myself either by holding my favorite toy or becoming involved in a new activity.

1 = Very Low I am easily frustrated and I cry and tantrum frequently. I have little tolerance for changes in routine. When upset, I am difficult to comfort, and I do not have self-comforting behaviors. When I cry, I remain upset for a long time, despite my caregiver's attempts to comfort me.

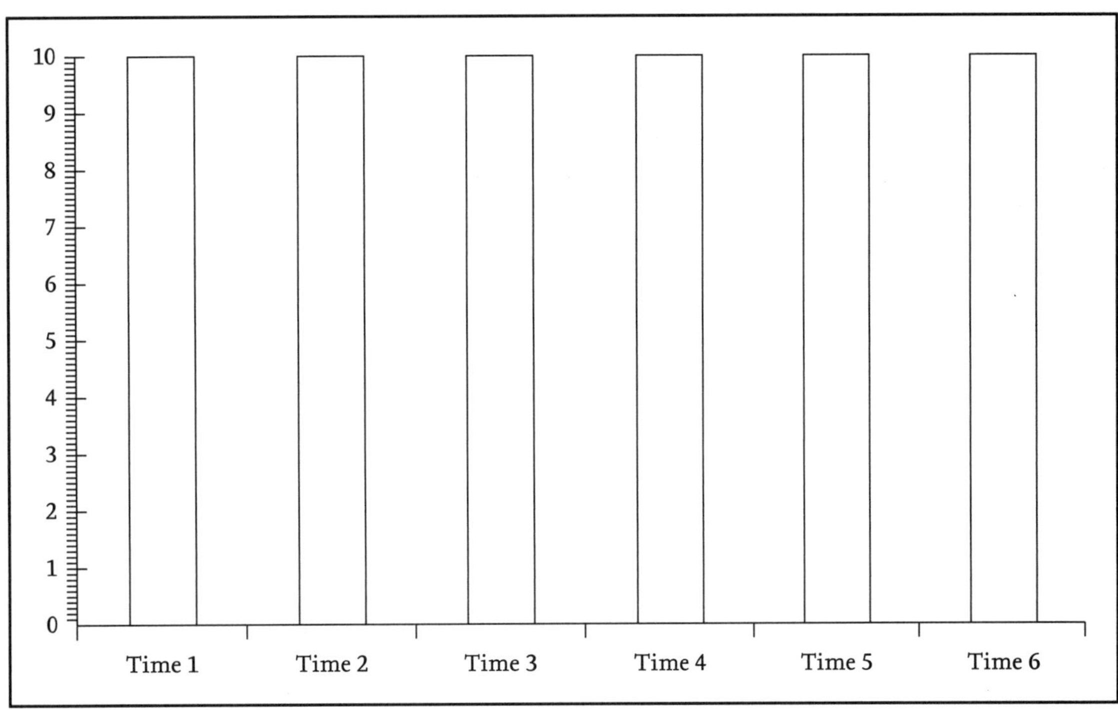

Pivotal Behavior Profile

Feelings of Confidence

Do I have positive feelings about my own abilities to carry out both social and nonsocial tasks? Do I have a positive view of myself, and am I motivated by this to interact with people and to try new things? Do I take pride in what I can do, and am I willing to try new behaviors or activities?

How am I doing?

10 = Very High I am direct and forthright in engaging people and activities. I readily engage with the environment and easily interact with new activities and people. I am outgoing and capable of handling new situations. I rarely hesitate to try new things, and I am reluctant only if the activity is entirely unfamiliar.

5 = Moderate I can be characterized as approach/avoidant. Although I am interested in attempting new activities or situations, I seem unsure of myself. Occasionally, when I am hesitant to try new activities, I may engage by slowly easing into them. I usually withdraw from activities when I encounter any type of obstacle.

1 = Very Low I rarely seem self-assured and often act as though I cannot do things that I am capable of doing. I am usually fearful and hesitant to engage in activities. I am shy and timid and I seldom draw attention to myself by asking adults to look at me or by showing adults what I am doing.

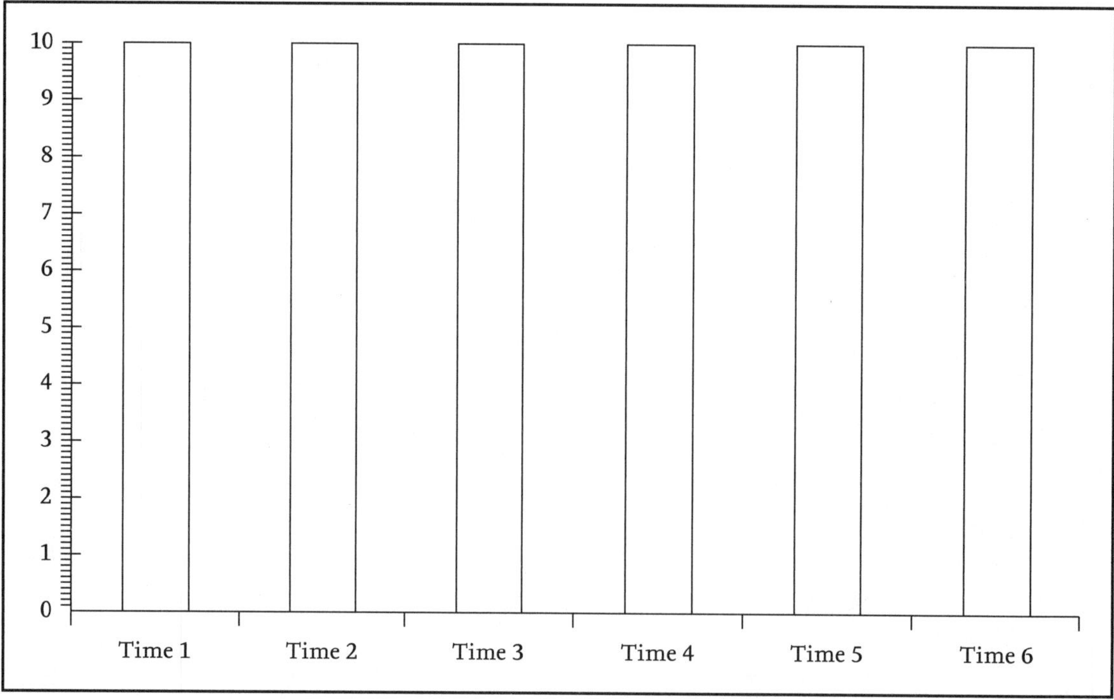

Pivotal Behavior Profile

Feelings of Control

Do I demonstrate mastery of activities and am I aware that I can control their outcomes? Am I highly self-reliant rather than dependent upon others? Do I make frequent choices, seldom looking to an adult partner for direction? Do I purposefully do things to influence what others do? Do I prefer to control rather than be controlled?

How am I doing?

10* = *Very High I routinely use my ability to affect objects and people. I am rarely passive with others, and I behave passively only when I am not familiar with the object, activity, or person. I am highly motivated to engage in activities in which I can directly affect what people do or the actions and sounds toys make. I do not hesitate to make choices both in play and in interacting with others.

5* = *Moderate I enjoy activities in which I can directly affect what people do or the actions or sounds made by a toy. Nonetheless, I am somewhat tentative about the choices I make and frequently look to adults for direction. More than half of the time that I interact with an adult partner, the adult partner leads the activity and keeps me engaged and entertained.

1* = *Very Low I seldom exert control over objects, activities, or people. I seldom call or demand adult partners to respond to me. I usually look to adult partners for guidance and direction. When left alone, I tend to engage in passive activities, such as staring or looking as opposed to physical exploration or manipulation.

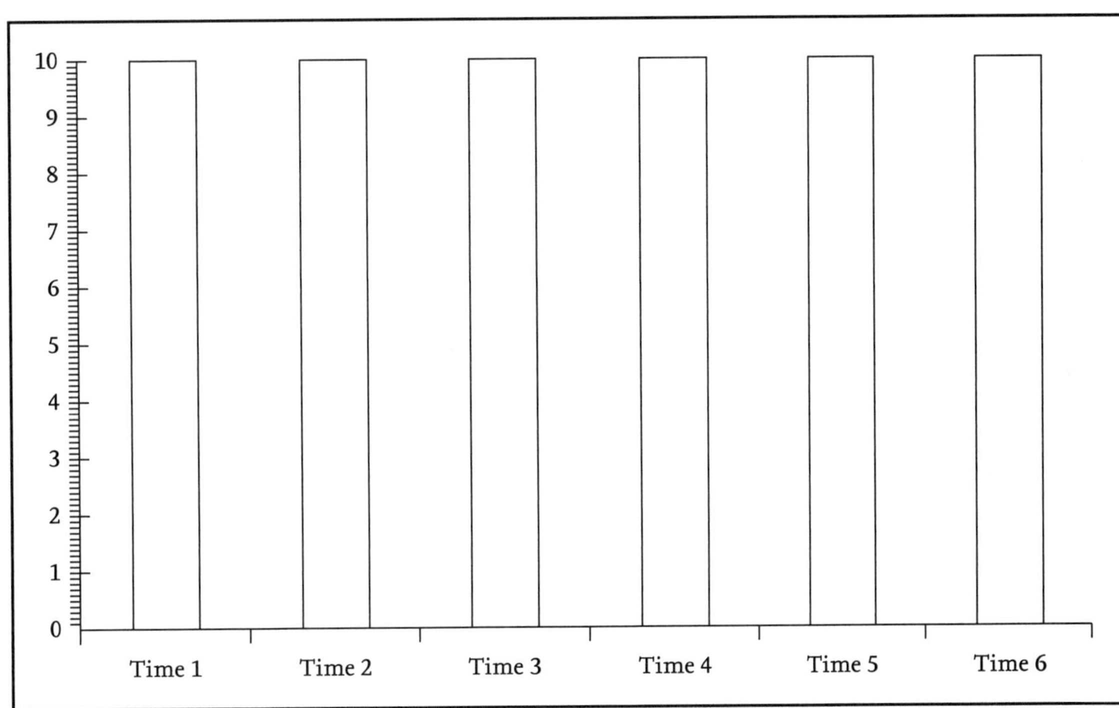

Curriculum Material 4

Planning and Tracking Form

Planning and Tracking Form

			Session Date									
Domain		**Cognition**										
Pivotal Behavior		**Social Play**—To support and promote children's ability to engage in balanced reciprocal play with others										
Discussion Points	C-101	Social play with parents is critical for promoting children's developmental growth.										
	C-102	Cognitive learning is a two-person process.										
	C-103	Cognitive learning occurs whenever children are active and alert.										
	C-104	By themselves, children can only learn information they discover accidentally.										
	C-105	Parents scaffold children's involvement in social play.										
	C-106	Parents enhance children's play by providing new information related to their current activities.										
	C-107	Parents' responses to children's social play activities help children learn the social consequences of their actions.										
Responsive Teaching Strategies	113	Get into my child's world										
	114	Use mirroring and parallel play to join an activity										
	121	Take one turn and wait										
	131	Play face-to-face games without toys										
	312	Imitate my child's actions and communications										
	412	Wait with anticipation										
	421	Act as a playful partner										
	514	Act in ways my child can act										
	535	Match my child's interactive pace										
Rating		Social Play: Pivotal Behavior Rating										

Planning and Tracking Form

Domain	Cognition										
Pivotal Behavior	**Initiation**—To enhance the frequency of child-initiated activity	Session Date									
Discussion Points	C-201 Child-initiated behavior is the hallmark of active learning.										
	C-202 The play behaviors children initiate on their own are generally reflective of their current thinking, understanding, and reasoning.										
	C-203 All children initiate developmentally meaningful behaviors.										
	C-204 The idea that children learn through their routine, self-initiated activities contrasts with many developmental and therapeutic activities.										
	C-205 The types of toys that are available and the ways that adults ask children to use them can affect children's use of active learning strategies.										
	C-206 Children are likely to respond to information, guidance, or direction related to activities they initiate.										
	C-207 Children are likely to attend longer when adult interactions focus on actions or activities that the children themselves have initiated.										
Responsive Teaching Strategies	113 Get into my child's world										
	115 Expect my child to interact										
	125 Communicate less so my child communicates more										
	134 Play with my child with toys										
	231 Respond to unintentional vocalizations, facial displays, and gestures as if they were meaningful conversations										
	311 Communicate without asking questions										
	523 Follow my child's lead										
Rating	Initiation: Pivotal Behavior Rating										

Planning and Tracking Form

Domain	Cognition										
Pivotal Behavior	**Exploration**—To promote children's exploration and manipulation in play	Session Date									
Discussion Points	C-301 Exploration is the basis for discovery learning.										
	C-302 Knowing and understanding are multidimensional–multimodal tasks.										
	C-303 As children's cognitions change, they rediscover new possibilities.										
	C-304 Similar concepts can be learned through a variety of experiences.										
	C-305 Exploration is child initiated, not a guided tour.										
	C-306 Curiosity is a critical tool for learning.										
	C-307 Play provides children opportunities to explore.										
Responsive Teaching Strategies	132 Sustain repetitive play or action sequences										
	211 Observe my child's behavior										
	321 Expand to show my child the next developmental step										
	325 Change the environment										
	441 Value what my child is doing										
	511 Interpret my child's behavior developmentally										
	513 Request actions that match my child's developmental level										
	523 Follow my child's lead										
Rating	Exploration: Pivotal Behavior Rating										

Planning and Tracking Form

		Session Date									
Domain	**Cognition**										
Pivotal Behavior	**Problem Solving**—To promote children's use of experimentation and problem solving in play										
Discussion Points	C-401 Problem solving: persisting in the face of challenge.										
	C-402 Problem solving means learning what does not work as well as what does work.										
	C-403 Situations become problems when they obstruct children from doing what they want.										
	C-404 Obstructions: The bigger they are, the faster they quit.										
	C-405 Collaborate in children's problem solving by following their reasoning.										
	C-406 Interact with children to generate solutions.										
	C-407 Become children's partner, not the solution for their problems.										
Responsive Teaching Strategies	312 Imitate my child's actions and communications										
	321 Expand to show my child the next developmental step										
	322 Expand to clarify my child's intentions or to develop my child's topic										
	323 Wait silently for a more mature response										
	324 Play for a purpose										
	512 Know the developmental skills my child seems ready to learn										
	522 Follow my child's focus of attention										
Rating	Problem Solving: Pivotal Behavior Rating										

Planning and Tracking Form

		Session Date									
Domain	**Cognition**										
Pivotal Behavior	**Practice**—To promote children's frequency of practice or repetition during play										
Discussion Points	C-501 Practice provides children the opportunity to master and determine the uses of behaviors.										
	C-502 To acquire new developmental behaviors or ways of thinking, children must give up old behaviors and ways of thinking.										
	C-503 Repetition and practice are the most common features of children's play.										
	C-504 Children with developmental problems do not practice or repeat deficient behaviors.										
	C-505 Children cannot be stopped from practicing or repeating the developmental behaviors they naturally want to do.										
	C-506 Children do not spontaneously practice and rehearse behaviors that they learn through direct instruction.										
Responsive Teaching Strategies	122 Keep my child for one more turn than usual										
	132 Sustain repetitive play or action sequences										
	133 Join perseverative play (make it interactive)										
	241 Explore how RT strategies can be used to enhance my child's participation throughout daily routines										
	422 Interact for fun										
	424 Repeat activities my child enjoys										
	513 Request actions that match my child's developmental level										
	514 Act in ways my child can act										
Rating	Practice: Pivotal Behavior Rating										

Planning and Tracking Form

Domain	Communication											
Pivotal Behavior	**Joint Activity**—To promote children's frequency of participating in reciprocal action, gestural, and vocal interactions with adults		Session Date									
Discussion Points	CM-101	Children's social interactions are their first conversations.										
	CM-102	Children with language delays are often delayed in nonverbal communication.										
	CM-103	Communication is an advanced level of social interaction: Children must be actively involved in joint activity to learn how to communicate.										
	CM-104	Joint activities occur when children and adults (a) interact equally and (b) have a common focus of attention.										
	CM-105	Joint activities do not always need to involve toys; parents can be children's most effective toy.										
	CM-106	Joint activity is a persistent lifestyle—not just occasional participation in games or activities.										
	CM-107	The longer children remain engaged in joint activities with people, the more sophisticated their communication will become.										
	CM-108	Children must learn to give in order to get.										
Responsive Teaching Strategies	111	Be physically available and interactive										
	115	Expect my child to interact										
	123	Play back and forth with sounds										
	124	Get from my child as much as I give										
	125	Communicate less so my child communicates more										
	131	Play face-to-face games without toys										
	414	Be more interesting than my child's distractions										
	422	Interact for fun										
Rating	Joint Activity: Pivotal Behavior Rating											

Planning and Tracking Form

			Session Date									
Domain		**Communication**										
Pivotal Behavior		**Joint Attention**—To enhance children's effectiveness at directing the attention of adults and following adults' attempts to gain and direct children's attention										
Discussion Points	CM-201	Children learn the meaning of language by using context and nonverbal clues to decipher the relationship to the feelings, observations, objects, or actions these words refer to.										
	CM-202	Children make eye contact with parents when parents persist in making eye contact with them.										
	CM-203	Children attend to their parents when parents are attentive to their children.										
	CM-204	Children learn to follow their parents' focus of attention when parents use multiple cues to direct their attention.										
	CM-205	Children learn to direct their parents' attention by controlling their parents' behavior.										
	CM-206	It takes time for children to learn to develop joint attention.										
Responsive Teaching Strategies	113	Get into my child's world										
	211	Observe my child's behavior										
	222	Respond immediately to little behaviors										
	312	Imitate my child's actions and communications										
	411	Be animated										
	415	Accompany my communications with intonation, pointing, and nonverbal gestures										
	424	Repeat activities my child enjoys										
	522	Follow my child's focus of attention										
Rating		Joint Attention: Pivotal Behavior Rating										

Planning and Tracking Form

Domain	Communication										
Pivotal Behavior	**Vocalization**—To enhance the frequency that children vocalize alone and with others	Session Date									
Discussion Points	CM-301 Children learn to produce sounds by practicing their vocalizations.										
	CM-302 Children must make sounds before they will speak.										
	CM-303 Quiet babies make quiet adults, who make quieter children.										
	CM-304 Children may be quiet when they have motor impairments that impede their ability to make sounds.										
	CM-305 Vocalization (vocal play) leads to more conventional sound production.										
	CM-306 Children develop oral–motor skills most effectively in social communicative contexts, not in rote, repetitive drills.										
Responsive Teaching Strategies	123 Play back and forth with sounds										
	125 Communicate less so my child communicates more										
	222 Respond immediately to little behaviors										
	312 Imitate my child's actions and communications										
	515 Communicate the way my child communicates										
Rating	Vocalization: Pivotal Behavior Rating										

Planning and Tracking Form

Domain		Communication										
Pivotal Behavior		**Intentional Communication**—To enhance the ability of children to express feelings, needs, or observations through nonverbal gestures, vocalizations, and words	Session Date									
Discussion Points	CM-401	Intentional communication occurs when children get others to understand their feelings, needs, and observations.										
	CM-402	The first step toward becoming an intentional communicator is understanding that gestures and vocalizations can be used to express feelings and needs.										
	CM-403	Children become intentional communicators to the degree that their early nonverbal behaviors have effects on others.										
	CM-404	Children's early communications do not have to be understood, only responded to.										
	CM-405	Children's first words describe their actions, experiences, and nonverbal communications.										
	CM-406	Children learn words and language rapidly as they discover how these help them communicate more effectively.										
Responsive Teaching Strategies	221	Respond quickly to my child's signals, cries, or nonverbal requests										
	222	Respond immediately to little behaviors										
	231	Respond to unintentional vocalizations, facial displays, and gestures as if they were meaningful conversations										
	232	Accept incorrect word choice, pronunciation, or word approximations by responding to my child's intention										
	233	Translate my child's actions, feelings, and intentions into words										
	312	Imitate my child's actions and communications										
	415	Accompany my communications with intonation, pointing, and nonverbal gestures										
	521	Read my child's behavior as an indicator of interest										
Rating		Intentional Communication: Pivotal Behavior Rating										

Planning and Tracking Form

			Session Date									
Domain	**Communication**											
Pivotal Behavior	**Conversation**—To enhance the child's ability to use language and other forms of communication in reciprocal conversations with adults and peers											
Discussion Points	CM-501	Children who have language but rarely use it in conversations need to have frequent interactions to learn to converse.										
	CM-502	Children converse longer and more frequently when adults respond to their intentions rather than correct their speech or language.										
	CM-503	Children are more likely to have conversations in situations that are enjoyable, interesting, and related to what they know.										
	CM-504	Communicating for needs is not sufficient to build a habit of conversation.										
	CM-505	Every interaction is an opportunity to practice and learn how to have conversations.										
	CM-506	Children will become conversational when others speak to them in ways they can speak rather than in ways they can only understand.										
	CM-507	Children practice language by talking to themselves; joining children's self-talk is a good way to help them learn.										
	CM-508	Asking children to imitate and then testing them with questions can interfere with their becoming conversational.										
Responsive Teaching Strategies	135	Make a habit of communicating during joint activity routines										
	231	Respond to unintentional vocalizations, facial displays, and gestures as if they were meaningful conversations										
	311	Communicate without asking questions										
	321	Expand to show my child the next developmental step										
	322	Expand to clarify my child's intention or to develop my child's topic										
	323	Wait silently for a more mature response										
	413	Respond to my child in playful ways										
	515	Communicate the way my child communicates										
	523	Follow my child's lead										
Rating	Conversation: Pivotal Behavior Rating											

Planning and Tracking Form

Domain	Social–Emotional Functioning		Session Date									
Pivotal Behavior	**Trust**—To help children develop a trusting, secure, and comfortable relationship with their primary caregivers.											
Discussion Points	SE-101	Attachment refers to children's trust and dependency on their mothers, fathers, and other primary caregivers.										
	SE-102	Children's attachment is manifested by their seeking out and trusting their parents and other primary caregivers.										
	SE-103	Children's attachment relationships with their parents or primary caregivers predict their social–emotional functioning later in life.										
	SE-104	Disrupted attachment relationships will affect children's social–emotional behavior.										
	SE-105	Fathers and other primary caregivers play a critical role in the formation of children's ability to trust.										
	SE-106	Children's attachment relationships with adults depend upon how much adults engage in warm and responsive interactions with them.										
	SE-107	Children who are attached to highly responsive adults learn to function independently in later childhood.										
	SE-108	Children's attachment behaviors progress through predictable developmental stages.										
	SE-109	Parents promote children's independence by comforting them at times of separation distress.										
	SE-110	Attachment is prerequisite to effective discipline.										
Responsive Teaching Strategies	111	Be physically available and interactive										
	112	Play frequently together										
	212	Take my child's perspective										
	221	Respond quickly to my child's signals, cries, or nonverbal requests										
	223	Discipline promptly and comfort										
	421	Act as a playful partner										
	431	By physical but gentle										
	432	Respond affectionately to my child's cries and needs for attention										
Rating	Trust: Pivotal Behavior Rating											

Planning and Tracking Form

Section	Code	Item	Session Date									
Domain		**Social–Emotional Functioning**										
Pivotal Behavior		**Empathy**—To help children express and react emotionally in a manner that is appropriate to the situation or context										
Discussion Points	SE-201	Effective social relationships occur when children become capable of sharing emotional states with others.										
	SE-202	Children learn how to react emotionally from their parents or caregivers.										
	SE-203	Eyes, facial displays, and body gestures are windows to children's feelings and emotions.										
	SE-204	Intersubjectivity: setting the stage for children's emotional reactions.										
	SE-205	The more sensitive adults are to children's affective cues, the more reactive children become to adults' emotions.										
	SE-206	Depressed mothers have depressed babies; animated mothers have animated babies.										
Responsive Teaching Strategies	113	Get into my child's world										
	131	Play face-to-face games without toys										
	213	Be sensitive to my child's state										
	222	Respond immediately to little behaviors										
	233	Translate my child's actions, feelings, and intentions into words										
	433	Comfort my child when he or she is fussy, irritable, or angry										
	442	Treat my child's fears as meaningful and legitimate										
Rating		Empathy: Pivotal Behavior Rating										

Planning and Tracking Form

Domain	Social–Emotional Functioning											
Pivotal Behavior	**Cooperation**—To enhance children's ability to cooperate with others		Session Date									
Discussion Points	SE-301	Children learn to be cooperative when they are successful at complying with requests made by their parents or others.										
	SE-302	Failure to cooperate: one of the major forms of misbehavior.										
	SE-303	Children will comply with their parents' requests when parents ask them to do things that are within their current range of ability.										
	SE-304	Children are more likely to comply with their parents' requests when parents ask them to do things which are related to children's immediate interests.										
	SE-305	Children will comply more often to their parents' requests when parents reduce the number of requests they ask their children to do.										
	SE-306	Children are more likely to comply with their parents' requests when adults engage in frequent, reciprocal interactions with them.										
	SE-307	Parents can gain children's cooperation by giving them frequent opportunities to make choices.										
	SE-308	Transitions are often difficult for children to cooperate with.										
	SE-309	Parents can reduce the stress of children's transitions.										
Responsive Teaching Strategies	112	Play frequently together										
	235	Interpret noncompliance as a choice or lack of ability										
	313	Give my child frequent opportunities to make choices										
	423	Turn routines into games										
	443	Accept whatever my child does										
	513	Request actions that match my child's developmental level										
	516	Have developmentally appropriate rules and expectations										
Rating	Cooperation: Pivotal Behavior Rating											

Planning and Tracking Form

			Session Date									
Domain	**Social–Emotional Functioning**											
Pivotal Behavior	**Self-Regulation**—To enhance children's ability to control their emtions during transitions and other times of stress											
Discussion Points	SE-401	Self-regulation—learning to cope with emotions.										
	SE-402	Children develop their coping skills with time.										
	SE-403	Children's behavioral style or temperament plays a major role in the ease with which they learn to self-regulate.										
	SE-404	Tantruming—children's reaction to stress or frustration.										
	SE-405	Children do not tantrum just to get their way.										
	SE-406	Comfort and acceptance help children learn to soothe themselves.										
	SE-407	Parental anger aggravates children's frustration.										
	SE-408	Parents are most successful at managing their children's behavior when they expect them to react according to their temperament or behavioral style.										
	SE-409	Give children room to react.										
Responsive Teaching Strategies	133	Join perseverative play (make it interactive)										
	223	Discipline promptly and comfort										
	516	Have developmentally appropriate rules and expectations										
	521	Read my child's behavior as an indicator of interest										
	523	Follow my child's lead										
	532	Observe how my child ordinarily engages in interaction										
	533	Respond to my child's behavioral state										
	534	Have expectations that conform to my child's behavioral style										
	535	Match my child's interactive pace										
Rating	Self-Regulation: Pivotal Behavior Rating											

Planning and Tracking Form

			Session Date									
Domain	**Social–Emotional Functioning**											
Pivotal Behavior	**Feelings of Confidence**—To enhance children's feelings of competence											
Discussion Points	SE-501	Children's ability does not determine how they feel about themselves.										
	SE-502	Even at early ages, children form internal models of who they are.										
	SE-503	Children feel good about themselves when adults express pleasure or take delight in what the children do.										
	SE-504	Success breeds self-confidence; failure breeds lack of confidence.										
	SE-505	Children fail when they are unable to do what they are asked to do.										
	SE-506	Long-term learning is more dependent on how children feel about themselves than on the specific skills and behaviors that are taught to them.										
	SE-507	Children who feel self-confident confront challenges and assert themselves in cognitive and social tasks.										
Responsive Teaching Strategies	134	Play with my child with toys										
	231	Respond to unintentional vocalizations, facial displays, and gestures as if they were meaningful conversations										
	441	Value what my child is doing										
	442	Treat my child's fears as meaningful and legitimate										
	443	Accept whatever my child does										
	444	Talk about the novel, funny, and good things my child is doing										
	513	Request actions that match my child's developmental level										
	514	Act in ways my child can act										
Rating	Feelings of Confidence: Pivotal Behavior Rating											

Planning and Tracking Form

Domain	Social–Emotional Functioning											
Pivotal Behavior	**Feelings of Control**—To enhance children's feelings of control		Session Date									
Discussion Points	SE-601	Children have a basic need to control their environment.										
	SE-602	Children learn to control by controlling others.										
	SE-603	Children have no choice if parents always tell them what to do.										
	SE-604	How young children make choices.										
	SE-605	Activities that children choose are just as important as those that parents choose.										
	SE-606	Learned helplessness—not feeling able to control.										
	SE-607	Children with high feelings of control confront challenges.										
Responsive Teaching Strategies	221	Respond quickly to my child's signals, cries, or nonverbal requests										
	222	Respond immediately to little behaviors										
	235	Interpret noncompliance as a choice or lack of ability										
	313	Give my child frequent opportunities to make choices										
	424	Repeat activities my child enjoys										
	523	Follow my child's lead										
Rating	Feelings of Control: Pivotal Behavior Rating											

Curriculum Material 5

Intervention Session Plan Forms

Responsive Teaching
Professional Session Plan

Child's name ______________________ Date ____________ Location ____________

Team members completing form ____

Issues/concerns discussed by parents:

Feedback related to last week's session/Family Action Plan:

Session objectives:

1.

2.

Discussion points related to ____________ :
Discussion Point 1

Notes:

Discussion Point 2

Notes:

RT strategies that can be used to promote ____________ :
Strategy 1

Strategy 2

Pivotal Behavior Profile (optional) □

Responsive Teaching
Parent Session Plan

Child's name ______________________ Date ____________ Location ___________

Session objectives:

1.

2.

Discussion points related to ____________ :

1.

2.

RT strategies that can be used to promote ____________ :

1.

2.

Pivotal Behavior Profile (optional) ☐

Responsive Teaching
Family Action Plan

Child's name ______________________ Date ____________

What?

1.

2.

3.

Where/When?

How to address obstacles?

Curriculum Material 6

Curriculum Outline

Introduction

The Curriculum Outline provides all the information needed to develop Intervention Session Plans and is divided into three sections that correspond to the three developmental domains that can be addressed with Responsive Teaching: Cognition, Communication, and Social–Emotional Functioning. Within each section, the Curriculum Outline is organized around each of the pivotal behaviors targeted by Responsive Teaching to promote children's functioning. The Cognition section provides information related to the pivotal behaviors of social play, initiation, exploration, problem solving, and practice. The Communication section provides information related to the pivotal behaviors of joint activity, joint attention, vocalization, intentional communication, and conversation. The Social–Emotional section provides information related to the pivotal behaviors of trust, empathy, cooperation, self-regulation, feelings of confidence, and feelings of control.

For each pivotal behavior, the Curriculum Outline provides the following information:

1. **Definition**—A brief description of the pivotal behavior, which corresponds to the definition that is used in the Pivotal Behavior Profile. (This information can be used to describe the session objective in the Responsive Teaching Session Plan.)
2. **Facts To Consider**—A narrative description of several topics that can be used to discuss with parents or to reflect about the role that each pivotal behavior plays in contributing to children's development and social–emotional well-being. Before service providers or parents begin to target a pivotal behavior as the intervention objective for a child, they must first become familiar with all of the Facts To Consider for that pivotal behavior. (Additional information about each pivotal behavior can also be found in Chapter 5 of this manual.)
3. **Discussion Points**—Outlines each of the Facts To Consider that are provided for a pivotal behavior. Service providers can use one or two sets of discussion points to guide their conversations with parents about what pivotal behaviors are and how they contribute to children's learning and development. Parents who use this manual on their own can use discussion points as issues to consider as they attempt to use Responsive Teaching strategies to promote their children's pivotal behavior. (Two sets of discussion points can be inserted into the Session Plan under the heading "Discussion points related to ____________.")

   Each discussion point has a unique identifying code. The prefix letters for this code identify the developmental domain that the pivotal behavior is most likely to impact (e.g., C = Cognition; CM = Communication; SE = Social–Emotional Functioning). Following this prefix is a 3-digit number. As indicated in the following tables, the first digit identifies the pivotal behavior. The next two digits indicate the specific discussion point for each pivotal behavior. This same numbering system is used on the RT Planning and Tracking Form and is the identifying code for discussion points in the Responsive Teaching Curriculum Planning and Tracking Program.
4. **Responsive Teaching Strategies**—Complete description of 5 to 10 Responsive Teaching strategies that can be used to promote each pivotal behavior. (This information can be inserted into the Session Plan under the heading "RT strategies that can be used to promote ____________.")

As described in Chapter 4, each RT strategy is designed to promote a specific component and dimension of responsive interactive behavior. We have assigned a 3-digit code to each strategy, which identifies the component and dimension of responsive behavior that the strategy is most likely to promote. The first number identifies the component of responsiveness the strategy promotes (1 = Reciprocity, 2 = Contingency, 3 = Shared Control, 4 = Affect, 5 = Match). The second number refers to the dimension of responsiveness within each component. The third number refers to the number of this strategy in this series of strategies. For example, as indicated in the "Responsive Teaching Strategies" table below, RT Strategy 113 is "Get into my child's world." This strategy promotes the responsive interactive component of Reciprocity, represents the dimension of Engagement, and is the third strategy in this series. This same numbering system is used on the RT Planning and Tracking Form and is the identifying code for RT strategies in the RT Planning and Tracking Computer Program.

Coding System for Discussion Points

Developmental Domains	**Cognition (C)**	**Communication (CM)**	**Social–Emotional Functioning (SE)**
1XX	Social play	Joint activity	Trust
2XX	Initiation	Joint attention	Empathy
3XX	Exploration	Vocalization	Cooperation
4XX	Problem solving	Intentional communication	Self-regulation
5XX	Practice	Conversation	Feelings of confidence
6XX			Feelings of control

Responsive Teaching Strategies

Reciprocity		
Engagement	111	Be physically available and interactive
	112	Play frequently together
	113	Get into my child's world
	114	Use mirroring and parallel play to join an activity
	115	Expect my child to interact
Balance	121	Take one turn and wait
	122	Keep my child for one more turn than usual
	123	Play back and forth with sounds
	124	Get from my child as much as I give
	125	Communicate less so my child communicates more
Joint Activity Routines	131	Play face-to-face games without toys
	132	Sustain repetitive play or action sequences
	133	Join perseverative play (make it interactive)
	134	Play with my child with toys
	135	Make a habit of communicating during joint activity routines

(continues)

Responsive Teaching Strategies *Continued.*

Contingency		
Awareness	211	Observe my child's behavior
	212	Take my child's perspective
	213	Be sensitive to my child's state
Timing	221	Respond quickly to my child's signals, cries, or nonverbal requests
	222	Respond immediately to little behaviors
	223	Discipline promptly and comfort
Intent	231	Respond to unintentional vocalizations, facial displays, and gestures as if they were meaningful conversations
	232	Accept incorrect word choice, pronunciation, or word approximations by responding to my child's intention
	233	Translate my child's actions, feelings, and intentions into words
	234	Rephrase unclear vocalizations and word approximations with words that match my child's actions or intentions
	235	Interpret noncompliance as a choice or lack of ability
Frequency	241	Explore how RT strategies can be used to enhance my child's participation throughout daily routines
	242	Encourage multiple caregivers to use RT strategies
Shared Control		
Moderate Direction	311	Communicate without asking questions
	312	Imitate my child's actions and communications
	313	Give my child frequent opportunities to make choices
Facilitation	321	Expand to show my child the next developmental step
	322	Expand to clarify my child's intention or to develop my child's topic
	323	Wait silently for a more mature response
	324	Play for a purpose
	325	Change the environment
Affect		
Animation	411	Be animated
	412	Wait with anticipation
	413	Respond to my child in playful ways
	414	Be more interesting than my child's distractions
	415	Accompany my communications with intonation, pointing, and nonverbal gestures
Enjoyment	421	Act as a playful partner
	422	Interact for fun
	423	Turn routines into games
	424	Repeat activities my child enjoys
Warmth	431	Be physical but gentle
	432	Respond affectionately to my child's cries and needs for attention
	433	Comfort my child when he or she is fussy, irritable, or angry

(continues)

Responsive Teaching Strategies *Continued.*

Affect *(continued)*		
Acceptance	441	Value what my child is doing
	442	Treat my child's fears as meaningful and legitimate
	443	Accept whatever my child does
	444	Talk about the novel, funny, and good things my child is doing
Match		
Developmental Match	511	Interpret my child's behavior developmentally
	512	Know the developmental skills my child seems ready to learn
	513	Request actions that match my child's developmental level
	514	Act in ways my child can act
	515	Communicate the way my child communicates
	516	Have developmentally appropriate rules and expectations
Interest Match	521	Read my child's behavior as an indicator of interest
	522	Follow my child's focus of attention
	523	Follow my child's lead
Behavioral Style Match	531	Be sensitive to my child's sensations
	532	Observe how my child ordinarily engages in interaction
	533	Respond to my child's behavioral state
	534	Have expectations that conform to my child's behavioral style
	535	Match my child's interactive pace

Developmental Domain: Cognition

Cognition refers to children's ability to perceive, know, understand, reason, and make judgments in their everyday interactions and routines.

Pivotal Behavior: Social Play

C-1 Social Play refers to children's ability to play with their parents and other adults across many situations. Social play is characterized by a "give and take" in which children contribute as much to the play activity as their adult partners. Children are actively involved with the play activity, but they are also aware of their partners' activity and experience.

Facts To Consider About Social Play

C-101 Social play with parents is critical for promoting children's developmental growth.

Children acquire the information and understanding that are needed to promote cognitive growth by engaging in play. Piaget is the child psychologist who helped us to understand how *play is children's work.* He observed that the simple acts children do while playing, such as mouthing, banging, putting objects in and out of containers, lining up objects, and pretend, help children learn about their own behavior and understand their world. Play is children's work because children engage in the activities that are necessary for learning cognitive skills while playing, such as manipulating and exploring objects.

Since cognitive learning occurs primarily through play, *the best way parents can help their children learn and develop is by joining them in social play.* This helps in two ways. First, parents encourage their children to play for longer periods of time and more frequently, thus increasing children's opportunities to learn. Second, parents enhance the quality of their children's play. *The information and guidance parents provide children makes their play a richer learning experience.*

C-102 Cognitive learning is a two-person process.

Numerous research studies have reported that *how well children develop is related to how their parents play and communicate with them.* In fact, parents' social play with their children can account for as much as 25% of children's learning and development. The influence that parents have on their children's development far exceeds the developmental influences of preschool, childcare, special education, therapy, or even special learning toys and equipment. These research findings underscore the statement that child development is a two-person process. How well children develop does not depend solely upon their own learning capabilities. It also depends on the support and guidance parents provide them, especially during play and other social interactions.

Parents who play several times each day are much more likely to have a positive impact on their children's learning and development than parents who play only once or twice each day. These play episodes do not have to be long—in fact it is probably best if they last less than 5 minutes at a time. Furthermore, these play activities do not have to involve toys. They can be any type of playful activity, so long as it is fun and enjoyable. Routine activities such as feeding a child, changing a child's clothes, giving the child a bath, or just communicating back and forth with sounds or gestures are excellent opportunities for social play.

The impact parents have on children's cognitive development is related more to how much they respond to their children than to what they do when they play. Responsive social play means that parents engage in balanced give-and-take activities in which the child contributes as much to playing as the parent. Parents have two roles to play with their child. One is to provide guidance, suggestions, and information related to what their child is doing. The other is to support and encourage their child to initiate and continue activities that the child finds interesting. Both of these roles are important, but the most critical is being a responsive and supportive play partner.

Parents play the same role in children's development, even when children have developmental problems such as Down syndrome or autism. Disabilities can have a profound impact on children's ability to learn and develop, but their learning and development still depends upon how much they play with their parents. However, when children's disability affects their interest in playing with their parents, parents need to make a special effort not only to engage in social play as often as possible, but to also be highly responsive and supportive of their children's play activities and interests.

C-103 Cognitive learning occurs whenever children are active and alert.

Children's learning takes place throughout the day during their routine activities and experiences. *Any activity or experience can provide opportunities for cognitive learning.* These experiences can be a source of new information and insights that add to or challenge children's current ways of thinking. No matter how subtle or trivial, information children gain through their routine experiences can gradually enhance their knowledge and reasoning.

Whether children learn depends more upon how actively they are involved than on the nature of their learning experiences. If children are attentive and physically involved, if they try to make sense out of their experiences, and if they compare their experiences with their previous knowledge, then they will learn something from the activity. However, if children are not participating actively in an activity, the likelihood is very low that they will learn something from it.

Parents and other adults are the key to encouraging children to be alert and active. *Children are much more likely to be active and alert when they engage in reciprocal social play with a responsive adult.*

C-104 By themselves, children can only learn information they discover accidentally.

During the early stages of development, *children's play reflects their current understanding of the world.* Because young children have such limited means of gathering information and making sense out of their world, the way they understand or perceive objects and activities is based upon their experiences with them. For example, children who mouth objects perceive and think about objects in terms of their sensory attributes: their appearance, color, weight, taste, and texture.

Children's understanding and insight evolve from their repetitive play activities. As children repeat the same play activities with different toys and materials and with different play partners, these diverse experiences challenge children's thinking and understanding, and motivate them to acquire a more adultlike knowledge and understanding. Children develop new understandings and cognitive skills by discovering new information and insights while they play. But *children's discoveries are slow unless parents become involved in their play.*

Parents can enhance children's understanding and ability to think by engaging in frequent episodes of social play with them. During these play episodes, parents can help their children discover new information by providing guidance and suggestions directly related to their children's play activities and intentions. When parents coordinate the information they provide with their children's desire to discover new information or develop new ways of thinking, it can have a profound impact on promoting children's knowledge and understanding.

C-105 Parents scaffold children's involvement in social play.

Scaffolding is a term used frequently to describe the role parents play in children's development. *Scaffolds are temporary supports that are used to construct new buildings.* They provide workers the support they need to engage in the next phase of construction. Normally, a scaffold is slightly larger than the structure that is being built.

One of the most important developmental psychologists of the 20th century was L. S. Vygotsky. Vygotsky described the role of parents in children's development as serving as a scaffold for children's learning. Vygotsky believed that, like a scaffold, parents support their children's development by providing stimulation that is slightly more advanced than the behaviors or language children currently use. In fact, parents who are effective at promoting their children's learning provide stimulation that is slightly more complex than their children's own behavior. Although this is an important ingredient of effective parenting, it is not the only way the parents serve as a scaffold for their children's development.

Because *cognitive learning occurs primarily through children's engagement in social play,* the most important thing parents can do to help their children develop is to encourage them to participate actively in social play. *Effective parents act as a scaffold by supporting their children's participation in social play.* They do this by becoming their children's responsive play partner, accepting and approving whatever their children do, making interactions fun, and keeping interactions interesting by introducing new ideas or information.

C-106 Parents enhance children's social play by providing new information related to their current activities.

Whatever information parents provide children during social play must be coordinated with children's actions, intentions, and feelings. This can be accomplished in a number of different ways:

First, when parents "take their turn," they can *draw children's attention to elements of an activity that children may be overlooking.* For example, if a child attempts to put stacking rings on a peg without appearing to notice that the rings are different sizes and different colors, during his or her turn the parent might identify the color of the rings or help the child notice that one ring is larger or smaller than another.

Second, parents can *help children consider alternative activities they can do with objects* by demonstrating slight variations of what the child is doing. For example, if the child repeatedly lines up toy trucks in a rigid pattern from front to back, during their turn parents could alter this pattern slightly by inserting objects other than trucks into the lineup or by reversing the direction of half of the trucks. Parents should do this only occasionally so that they do not interfere with their child doing what interests him or her most.

Third, parents *can demonstrate solutions to problems that children cannot solve on their own.* For example, if a child is unsuccessful at trying to put a plastic object into a shape sorter, parents could try to draw their child's attention to another opening in which the object would fit, or perhaps they could take turns with the child and demonstrate how the object can be rotated so that it fits easily into the shape sorter.

Parents' role in providing information does not so much instruct their children as it helps them discover new information on their own. The information parents provide will have a positive impact on children's thinking and cognitive learning if it is provided when children are active participants in social play.

C-107 Parents' responses to children's social play activities help children learn the social consequences of their actions.

Cognitive learning not only concerns children's knowledge and understanding about their environment, but also involves *children learning how their actions and behaviors affect others.* Even the simplest acts, such as putting a toy in their mouth, can have social consequences if children produce these behaviors in the company of other people. For example, as a child puts a toy figure in her mouth, a mother could respond by saying, "That tastes good!" or "That's disgusting!"

The more parents respond expressively to children's behavior, the quicker children become aware of the effects their behaviors have on others. Parents can promote children's understanding of the social effects of their behavior by using exaggerated facial features (e.g., surprise face), reacting with visible emotions to children's activities (e.g., pretend crying), or role-playing the feelings of dolls, figures, and inanimate objects with which the child is playing (e.g., speaking for a doll, say, "I don't like it when you hit me with the block").

However, it is also important that *parents' reactions to their children's behavior be matched to children's current level of developmental functioning.* If children are at the phase of development where they routinely throw and bang objects together, parents should respond by letting them know that these behaviors can hurt others or are socially inappropriate. At the same time, they must also recognize that their children's play is a reflection of their current level of developmental functioning. Their children may be doing something that is dangerous or inappropriate, not because they are bad or intend to hurt others, but because they are at a stage of development where they are fascinated by the noises that objects make or what happens when they throw things.

Discussion Points

C-101 Social play with parents is critical for promoting children's developmental growth.

- Children acquire the information and understanding needed to promote cognitive growth by engaging in play.
- The best way parents can help their children learn is by joining them in social play.
- The information and guidance parents provide children make their play a richer learning experience.

C-102 Cognitive learning is a two-person process.

- How well children develop is related to how their parents play and communicate with them.
- The impact parents have on children's development is related more to how they respond to their children than to what they do when they play.
- Parents play the same role in children's development, even when children have developmental problems.

C-103 Cognitive learning occurs whenever children are active and alert.

- Any activity or experience can provide opportunities for cognitive learning to occur.
- Whether children learn is more a function of how actively they are involved than on the nature of their learning experiences.
- Children are more likely to be active and alert when they engage in reciprocal social play with a responsive adult.

C-104 By themselves, children can only learn information they discover accidentally.

- Children's play reflects their current understanding of their world.
- Children's understanding and insight evolve from their repetitive play activities.
- Children's discoveries are slow unless parents become involved in their play.

C-105 Parents scaffold children's involvement in social play.

- Scaffolds are temporary supports that are used to construct new buildings.
- Cognitive learning occurs primarily through children's active engagement in social play.
- Effective parents act as a scaffold by supporting children's participation in social play.

C-106 Parents enhance children's play by providing new information related to their current activities.
Parents can

- Draw children's attention to elements of an activity they may be overlooking,
- Help children consider alternative activities they can do with objects, and
- Demonstrate solutions to problems children cannot solve on their own.

C-107 Parents' responses to children's social play activities help children learn the social consequences of their actions.

- Children must learn how their actions and behaviors affect others.
- The more parents respond expressively to children's behavior, the quicker children become aware of the effects their behaviors have on others.
- Parents' reactions to children's behavior should be matched to their current level of developmental functioning.

RT Strategies That Promote Social Play

113 ***Get into my child's world.*** Make three adjustments to view the world as your child does. First, establish a mutual physical relationship with your child. Make eye contact and interact on the same physical level as your child. Second, interact by playing or communicating like your child. Mimicking behaviors such as babbling, cooing, smiling, and using a playful face let your child know that you are willing to interact on the child's terms. Third, consciously strive to understand the world as your child does. Remember that most experiences do not have the same meaning to your child as they do to you.

Practical Suggestions

- Play with your child in a face-to-face position. Interact with your child on his or her physical level so that he or she does not have to look up to see you.
- Make eye contact with your child when you are playing or interacting with him or her.
- Consider that as your child begins to experience the world, he or she must make sense of his or her experiences. Your child sees and understands the world very differently than you do.
- Consider that, as your child matures, he or she will continually rediscover his or her world. The world as your child understood it at the 3-month stage of development takes on a new meaning at the 9-month stage. The changes in thinking and understanding that occur in the early years of development lead your child to perceive and experience objects or events he or she was familiar with from a dramatically new perspective.
- Play in the small ways your child does without pressuring him or her to do anything other than stay involved in the interaction.

114 ***Use mirroring and parallel play to join an activity.*** Play side by side with your child using the same or similar toys or acting the same way that he or she acts.

Practical Suggestions

- Consider that most children under 15 months developmental age have difficulty exchanging toys with an adult during interactive play. They do not yet understand the rules of "give and take."
- Observe how your child notices your actions when you play (a) with the same object, (b) in the same way, and (c) side by side with your child.
- Professionals can demonstrate how to take turns in parallel play by doing the same kinds of activities that the child is doing.

121 ***Take one turn and wait.*** *Take one turn* means to reduce the length of each of your interactive turns so that each interaction with your child consists of *a simple, discrete action or communication,* whether verbal or nonverbal. After you produce your turn, *wait* 5 to 7 seconds for your child to take a turn. When you are waiting, *do not* do anything except give a clear visible look of anticipation for your child to take a turn (e.g., raise your eyebrows, open your mouth, extend your hands).

Practical Suggestions

- Your child's turns can be nonverbal communications and actions as well as verbal communications. Do or say *one* thing, then wait for your child to communicate in any way he or she can.
- Experiment waiting for periods as long as 5 to 7 seconds to identify the amount of time it typically takes your child to produce a turn.
- Do not wait so long that it disrupts or ends the interaction.
- If your child does not wait for you to take a turn, gently hold or restrain him or her until you have completed your turn.
- Consider that when you "wait" you give your child time to process the situation and come up with a creative response.
- Practice playing with your child in two ways: first by dominating play by doing all the actions and communications, and second by waiting for your child to interact. Notice the effects of the two styles. Children are more likely to stay interacting in the second situation than they are in the first.

131 ***Play face-to-face games without toys.*** Use simple games with your child such as songs, nursery rhymes, hand games, and games with other parts of the body that require simple sequences in which your child can play an active role.

Practical Suggestions

- Consider the kinds of games that you have seen your own parents or other parents play with young children.

- Find books that describe simple games that parents can do with young children.
- Professionals can show parents how to modify games to make them balanced interactive routines. It is especially important to simplify games that are difficult for children who are developmentally young.

312 ***Imitate my child's actions and communications.*** You can imitate any behavior that your child produces. If your child has little interest in interacting with you, you can get your child's attention by imitating behaviors that may even be inappropriate or bizarre (e.g., rocking, thumb-sucking, loud shrieking or crying, throwing objects). Imitation has two functions. First, it helps to establish an interactive relationship with your child that is based upon what your child is doing. Second, imitation gives your child an immediate opportunity to control what you do.

Practical Suggestions

- Notice how imitation encourages your child to increase the variety and scope of his or her behavior and does not reinforce undesirable behavior.
- Consider that one important outcome of imitation is that your child will enjoy and have fun controlling what you do.
- When you imitate your child's nonverbal or verbal communication, you are helping your child learn to use his or her early communication skills to have an effect on others.

412 ***Wait with anticipation.*** When you are waiting for your child to initiate or respond to you, show with your eyes, face, and body that you are attending to your child and that you expect your child to stay and do something back with you.

Practical Suggestions

- In achieving balanced turn-taking, adults commonly have difficulty identifying which turns to wait for. Wait for your child to do *anything*.
- Some children may have very slow reaction times and can take as long as 5 seconds before doing something. If your child acts like this, silently count to 5 before initiating some other action.
- Make sure you do not wait so long that you disrupt the flow of interaction.

421 ***Act as a playful partner.*** Think of your role in your child's development to be that of a playful partner. To have an effective and satisfying relationship with your child, concentrate less on accomplishing tasks or goals and more on having fun and enjoying your child.

Practical Suggestions

- Being a playful partner may be hard because parenting is ladened with tasks that need to be accomplished. However, your child lives in a world of play and fun, not work. The more you act as a playful partner, the more opportunities you will have to join your child's activity on his or her terms rather than your own.

- All parents have their own internal models about how they should act. To some degree these models are learned from their own parents. For your child to learn in the early phases of life, you must be playful with your child, even though this may not be the way you have learned to act as a parent.
- Being a playful partner does not interfere with your child learning to respect you; rather, playful interaction will help you to establish the type of warm, mutual, and caring relationship that is necessary to be an effective parent as your child grows older.
- In some families, one parent has fun with the child and the other becomes the taskmaster. Reflect on the degree to which this occurs in your family. Who is the fun parent and who is the taskmaster? Encourage the taskmaster to think about how to become more like the fun parent.

514 ***Act in ways my child can act.*** When you interact with your child, modify what you do and the way you do it so that your behaviors mirror the kinds of activities that your child typically does.

Practical Suggestions

- Imitate some of your child's actions. Notice how your child stays with you and attends more to you when you do this.
- Play with the toys and objects that your child is playing with and in the same way as your child. Your child will attend and interact more actively when you interact with the toys and objects your child prefers.
- Review a videotape of you playing with your child. How well are you matching your actions to your child's spontaneous behavior?
- When you match your child's actions, talk with your child using words that fit your child's actions, such as *come, go, eat, mom, dog,* or *truck.* These words are more meaningful to your child and thus easier to learn than words like *two, three, red, yellow, horse,* and *barn.*

535 ***Match my child's interactive pace.*** When you interact with your child, use a pace of interaction that is similar to your child's pace.

Practical Suggestions

- Consider that your child's pace of interaction may be faster in movement and slower in thinking and interpretive processing than is yours. You and your child can miss connecting with each other when your child is on an action fast track and you are on a thinking fast track.
- Give your child silent time to initiate contact with you. Silent time can be a signal for your child to interact.

Developmental Domain: Cognition

Pivotal Behavior: Initiation

C-2 **Initiation** refers to the extent to which children begin activities on their own rather than following the direction or lead of their parents and other adults. Children who are initiators make their own choices and decisions about the nature and direction of their activities. They initiate across a variety of situations, such as having conversations with others, starting new games, changing activities with the same toys, or asking for help to solve problems.

Facts To Consider About Initiation

C-201 Child-initiated behavior is the hallmark of active learning.

Through 6 years of age, children's *cognitive learning occurs primarily through active learning*. During this period of development, parents cannot directly teach children to reason, classify, remember, understand, or solve problems. Rather, children acquire these skills through the discoveries they make on their own. These discoveries result from children continuously applying their current behaviors, which reflect what they know and how they understand, to their routine play activities, and by extending these behaviors to different contexts with different objects and people. The more children practice their behaviors, the more they gain new information and become aware of the limitations of their current ways of thinking and reasoning. Children gradually modify their thinking so that it incorporates the information and insights they discover through their play and social interaction.

Active learning occurs when children are consciously involved in an activity and trying to make sense out of their experiences. Parents can encourage children's active learning by responding to whatever activities children initiate. When children initiate an activity, it is their choice to participate in that activity. This choice reflects their interests, intentions, and abilities and is a personal investment in what they are doing. As a result, *children are more likely to be actively involved in activities they initiate.*

Parents often try to encourage their children to engage in interactions by enticing them to respond to an activity or communication that they have initiated. Parents therefore deprive their children of opportunities to learn to be initiators, because the parents, not the children, are the ones who are making the choices about what toys or objects to play with and what to do with them.

A better way to engage children in interaction is to *wait* for children to select toys and initiate an activity. Parents can use such a situation as an opportunity for social play by using Responsive Teaching strategies such as "follow my child's lead." This will give children the opportunity to learn how to be an initiator and is more likely to result in children becoming active and staying in the interaction.

C-202 The play behaviors children initiate on their own are generally reflective of their current level of thinking, understanding, and reasoning.

The way children play changes systematically as they progress from one level of development to the next. For example, at 3 to 4 months developmental age, children put most objects they encounter in their mouths. At 5 to 6 months, children play with objects by banging them together. At 8 to 9 months, they become fascinated with placing objects inside containers and cylinders. At 12 months, they begin using objects according to their intended function.

Children proceed through this sequence of play behavior at a rate that is consistent with their developmental age rather than their chronological age. Furthermore, when children start using higher level play behaviors, such as using objects functionally, they normally decrease their use of lower level play behaviors, such as mouthing or banging. If parents try to prompt their children to engage in higher level behaviors, such as encouraging them to play functionally with a toy, when their play is characterized mostly by lower level behaviors, such as placing objects in their mouth, children will revert to engaging in the lower level behavior as soon as parents stop prompting the higher level behavior.

The way children play with objects is determined primarily by their current thinking and understanding. Children who put objects in their mouths have the physical strength and dexterity to use these objects in more appropriate ways. They put objects in their mouths because they are fascinated with them—their actions suggest that they perceive objects as things to be put into their mouths and nothing else.

Because children's play reflects their current developmental level, *children who have developmental problems play like younger, normally developing children.* However, their play behaviors have the same impact on their learning as age-appropriate play behaviors have for typically developing children. Children with developmental problems initiate behaviors that are just as reflective of their current reasoning and understanding as are the age-appropriate behaviors produced by children who are developing typically. The best way for these children to move to the next stage of cognitive functioning is to apply their current behaviors to the objects and people they encounter in their routine daily activities.

C-203 All children initiate developmentally meaningful behaviors.

All children, regardless of how severe their developmental problems might be, are capable of initiating some type of behavior, which constitutes a child-initiated activity. If children engage in behaviors such as looking at an object, making a noise, or turning their head, these are behaviors they have initiated on their own, and the fact that these behaviors may not be associated with age-appropriate developmental functioning does not negate their importance for cognitive learning and development. Rather, *each of the behaviors that children with learning problems produce is developmentally meaningful.*

If children are 18 months old but functioning at the 6- to 9-month developmental level, they will produce behaviors that are similar to the behaviors produced by typically developing 6- to 9-month old children. Although these are extremely low-level behaviors for 18-month-old children, they are developmentally appropriate behaviors for children who are functioning at the 6- to 9-month level of development. Because children learn cognitive skills by applying their existing behaviors to their world, *the low-level developmental behaviors that children with developmental problems produce promote the same type of cognitive learning that occurs with younger, typically developing children.*

The main problem with the self-initiated behaviors of children with developmental problems is not so much *what* they do, but rather *how often* they do it. Many of these children do not engage in sufficiently high rates of active learning to enhance their developmental growth. Rather than giving up on the idea that their children can be active learners, parents need to consider how they can encourage their children to have higher frequency of child-initiated behaviors. *Parents can assist children with developmental problems by encouraging them to increase the frequency with which they initiate whatever behaviors interest them.*

C-204 The idea that children learn through routine, self-initiated activity contrasts with many developmental and therapeutic activities.

The concept of active learning is based upon the idea that *virtually any activity can provide opportunities for cognitive learning* so long as children are actively engaged. This concept is very different from the way that many special therapies and interventions are implemented with young children. Many intervention services—such as speech–language pathology, physical therapy, parent education, and early intervention—attempt to promote children's learning primarily through formal instructional activities in clinics, classrooms, or individualized instruction. Children are often less actively engaged in many of these formal learning activities than they are when they are involved in their normal daily routines.

Most formal intervention and therapy services reflect an adult-centered, school-based view of learning. They are based upon the highly questionable assumption that the kind of learning that occurs during informal, daily routines is not sufficient to help children acquire higher level developmental skills. However, because learning can occur in nearly any situation, so long as children are actively engaged, *formal learning experiences are no more likely to influence learning and development than are children's participation in their everyday routine activities.* However, because parents have had years of classroom instruction and have learned much in the context of formal instruction, many are willing to believe that their children's developmental needs can be addressed this way.

In reality, developmental learning occurs mostly during the course of routine interactions when children are alert and engaged in active learning, not during formal instruction. If intervention only provides formal learning activities and does not try to enrich children's routine daily experiences, these interventions will simply not have a substantial impact on children's developmental learning, no matter how much the intervention costs or how talented the professional is with children.

Parents who have children with developmental problems commonly worry about whether they are providing their children a sufficient number of intervention services to address their problems. Because of this, they often enroll their children in multiple intervention service programs carried out by highly skilled professionals: yet *children's learning is more a function of their own activity than it is of the reputation or costs of an intervention service.* Regardless how many formal interventions or therapies children receive, parents still have the greatest impact on their children's developmental growth. The reason for this is quite obvious. Only parents, not interventionists, have consistent opportunities to encourage their children to be actively involved in the routine activities where developmental learning is most likely to occur.

C-205 The types of toys that are available and the ways that adults ask children to use them can affect children's use of active learning strategies.

Parents promote active learning by (a) providing children toys and objects that they can handle and manipulate by themselves, (b) giving children the chance to initiate their own actions with these objects, and (c) encouraging children to play with objects in ways that reflect their understanding and interests.

If children are given toys they can use only with the help of an adult, then children will look to the adult for help. In fact, if children are not able to manipulate or handle toys by themselves, they cannot initiate play with them, and the toys will have little if any impact on their developmental learning. *Children are only likely to engage in active learning when they are provided toys and materials they can handle independently.*

How do we know that children are able to use a toy? The answer is quite easy. We simply need to provide a child with a toy and observe what he or she does with it. If a child immediately picks up the toy, begins to manipulate and handle it, and continues playing with it for more than a few seconds, then very likely this is a toy the child can handle independently. However, if a child attempts to pick up the toy but is unsuccessful and quickly turns away from it, this is a clear indication that it is a toy that the child cannot handle independently.

When parents wait for children to initiate an activity with a toy, they will likely observe that children do not initially play with toys the way they were designed to be played with. Rather, children play with toys by using their existing play schemas. For example, if children are at the stage of development where they are primarily interested in banging objects, when they are presented with a toy stove with cooking utensils they will likely bang the cooking utensils on the stove.

Adults tend to perceive objects as having predetermined functions that dictate what we do with them (e.g., a fork is something that we eat with; a comb is something that we use to comb our hair). Many adults perceive children's toys in the same way. A play stove is for pretend cooking, not for banging. Stacking rings are objects to be placed on a peg, not objects to be mouthed, banged against other objects, or thrown on the floor. But if parents discourage children from playing with toys the way they understand and want to, they will prevent their children from using their current knowledge and understanding as a means to play with these toys, thus interfering with their children's engaging in active learning. *Parents are more effective at fostering active learning when they encourage their children to play in ways that reflect their thinking.*

C-206 Children are more likely to respond to information, guidance, or direction related to activities they initiate.

Activities children initiate are the ones they are most interested in learning about. Parents can promote children's learning by responding to their behavior in a manner that encourages and supports them to continue the activities that they have initiated. One way parents provide this support is by giving guidance, direction, or information that complements children's activity and enables them to do what they want to do.

Children are highly attentive and responsive to information that helps them accomplish what they are interested in doing. In this regard children are no different than adults. If someone provides us information and support that makes it easier for us to accomplish what we want to do, we will likely respond positively to this information and remember and apply it to similar situations in the future. However, when parents provide information or guidance that is not directly related to what children have initiated, children must pull themselves away from an activity that interests them to respond to their parents. Because children are so self-centered, it takes great effort for them to respond to these kinds of requests. As a result, children often ignore and fail to respond to information or guidance that is not related to the activities that they have initiated.

Children are very likely to understand the significance of information that relates to activities that they have selected or acted upon. When adult guidance and information is directly related to children's self-initiated activities and interests, children simply need to incorporate their parents' information into their ongoing activities. This requires relatively little effort, especially if this information helps children accomplish what they want to do.

C-207 Children are likely to attend longer when adult interactions focus on actions or activities that the children themselves have initiated.

An important prerequisite to cognitive learning is that children be attentive both to what they are doing and to the adults who are interacting with them. In fact, in many early intervention programs, gaining children's attention is often the first step toward attempting to promote developmental learning.

A major key to gaining children's attention is to provide them information or experiences that are directly related to what interests them at the moment. Children who seem to be inattentive most of the time often become highly engaged and attentive to activities or people they find interesting. In fact, children who have been diagnosed with an attention disorder often spend long periods of time in activities that are interesting to them. Perhaps their problem has less to do with their lack of ability to pay attention and much more to do with their lack of interest in the activities and experiences they are being asked to attend to.

Parents can gain their children's attention by supporting the activities their children initiate, which are the activities of greatest interest to them. For example, a child who is generally inattentive may spend hours playing with a toy truck that he has chosen. If this child's parents were to ask him to do something related to his truck, the child would be highly attentive and responsive to them. However, if his parents try to direct his attention to activities that he did not initiate, the child's attention to his parents will be limited. Parents can help their children become more attentive by providing information and guidance that supports their children's involvement in the activities that they have initiated.

Child-initiated activity is so critical to development because it is the context in which children are most attentive. Not only are children attentive to what they are doing, but they are also attentive to the adult, particularly when the adult provides information or asks them to do things that supports their interests. If adults focus their interactions on routine activities initiated by children, they will help children develop the habit of being attentive. In time, this pattern of adult responsiveness will reduce children's distractibility or inattention.

Discussion Points

C-201 Child-initiated behavior is the hallmark of active learning.

- Cognitive learning occurs primarily through active learning.
- Active learning occurs when children are consciously involved in an activity.
- Children are more likely to be actively involved in activities that they initiate.

C-202 The play behaviors children initiate on their own generally reflect their current level of thinking, understanding, and reasoning.

- The way children play changes systematically from one level of development to the next.
- The way children play with objects is determined primarily by their current thinking and understanding.
- Children who have developmental problems play like younger, normally developing children.

C-203 All children initiate developmentally meaningful behaviors.

- Each of the behaviors that children with learning problems produce is developmentally meaningful.
- Low-level developmental behaviors produced by children with developmental problems promote the same type of cognitive learning that occurs with younger, typically developing children.
- Parents can assist children with developmental problems by encouraging them to increase the frequency with which they initiate whatever behaviors interest them.

C-204 The idea that children learn through routine, self-initiated activities contrasts with many developmental and therapeutic activities.

- Virtually any activity can provide opportunities for cognitive learning.
- Formal learning experiences are no more likely to influence children's learning and development than are children's active participation in everyday routine activities.
- Children's learning is more a function of their own activity than of the reputation or cost of intervention services.

C-205 The types of toys that are available and the ways that adults ask children to use them can affect children's use of active learning strategies.

- Children are only likely to engage in active learning when they are provided toys and materials they can handle independently.
- Parents foster active learning by encouraging children to play in ways that reflect their thinking.

C-206 Children are likely to respond to information, guidance, or direction related to activities they initiate.

- Activities children initiate are the ones they are most interested in learning about.
- Children are highly attentive and responsive to information or experiences that help them accomplish what they are interested in doing.
- Children are very likely to understand the significance of information that relates to activities they have selected and are acting upon.

C-207 Children are likely to attend longer when adult interactions focus on actions or activities that the children themselves have initiated.

- Gain children's attention by providing information or experiences that are directly related to what interests them at the moment.
- Parents can gain their children's attention by supporting the activities their children initiate.

RT Strategies That Promote Initiation

113 ***Get into my child's world.*** Make three adjustments to view the world as your child does. First, establish a mutual physical relationship with your child. Make eye contact and interact on the same physical level as your child. Second, interact by playing or communicating like your child. Mimicking behaviors such as babbling, cooing, smiling, and using a playful face lets your child know that you are willing to interact on your child's terms. Third, consciously strive to try to understand the world as your child does. Remember that most experiences do not have the same meaning to your child as they do to you.

Practical Suggestions

- Play with your child in a face-to-face position. Interact with your child on his or her physical level so that he or she does not have to look up to see you.
- Make eye contact with your child when you are playing or interacting with him or her.
- Consider that, as your child begins to experience the world, he or she must make sense of his or her experiences. Your child sees and understands the world very differently than you do.
- Consider that as your child matures, he or she will continually rediscover his or her world. The world as your child understood it at the 3-month stage of development takes on a new meaning at the 9-month stage. The changes in thinking and understanding that occur in the early years of

development lead your child to perceive and experience objects or events he or she was familiar with from a dramatically new perspective.

- Play in the small ways your child does without pressuring him or her to do anything other than stay involved in the interaction.

115 ***Expect my child to interact.*** Show by your face, hands, and body language that you are anticipating that your child will do something with you. Act in animated ways to make this even more effective.

Practical Suggestions

- Allow your child time to initiate contact with you. Silent waiting provides the opportunity for your child to initiate an activity on his or her own.
- During silent waiting, "wait with anticipation," using body gestures or facial signals for your child to interact with.
- If your child attempts to move away before engaging in interaction, gently hold or restrain him or her until he or she has completed one to two interactive turns with you.

125 ***Communicate less so my child communicates more.*** Talking too much is one of the major obstacles to having balanced interactions between adults and children. To learn how to speak, it is important for your child to hear language stimulation, but it is even more important for your child to practice the sounds and words he or she already knows. You will communicate less if you use short sentences, do not repeat what you have said, and wait for your child to say more. This may result in longer periods of silence and quiet during the interaction. However, your child will quickly learn to fill this void with his or her own vocalizations and language.

Practical Suggestions

- Consider how speaking in short sentences and saying less to your child will give your child more opportunity to do something during the interaction.
- Experiment using short, medium, and long sentences with your child. Observe how your child responds to different sentence lengths.
- Review a videotape of you interacting with your child. Count the number of times that you repeat what you say with your child.
- Keep track of the number of times you repeat yourself during 5 minutes of play with your child. Consider if you are repeating yourself more than is necessary.

134 ***Play with my child with toys.*** When you play with your child with toys, begin by playing with the toys as your child does, then gradually show him or her new ways to use them.

Practical Suggestions

- Play with the toys your child is playing with. Your child will attend and interact more with you when you play with the things that your child has chosen.
- Consider that it is important for your child to be able to interact with you without needing to do anything "right" or to engage in any particular activity with toys.
- After you have established routine patterns of back-and-forth play with toys, gradually introduce new or more appropriate ways of play with your child.

231 ***Respond to unintentional vocalizations, facial displays, and gestures as if they were meaningful conversation.*** Often children make sounds for sensory play but not for communicating intentionally. Every action your child makes can become a communication. The more you respond to your child's actions, the quicker your child will learn to use these actions to exchange meanings with you and others.

Practical Suggestions

- Get into the habit of responding to your child's sounds, even when they are just for self-play and do not have any obvious meaning or communicative intent.
- If your child makes sounds while playing but does not use sounds to communicate his or her intentions, he or she has not yet learned that sounds can get people's attention. To help your child learn to use his or her sounds as communication, respond more to your child's sounds than to his or her facial displays or touches.

311 ***Communicate without asking questions.*** Parents often try to control what their children do by asking them to do things. A simple strategy for reducing the number of times you are directing or controlling your child is to "not ask questions."

Practical Suggestions

- Rather than asking your child questions, when you interact with him or her label, comment, notice, express delight or pleasure, and provide information related to what your child is doing.
- As you stop asking questions you will begin to understand how much you are actually directing what your child does. This is a good time to consider that, even if you reduced the number of your directives by half, you would still have numerous opportunities to guide and direct your child.
- Do not repeat questions to which your child has not responded.
- Occasionally ask your child to do things, but try to make requests that are closely related to what your child is already doing.

- Children learn best when they initiate activities of their own choosing. The more you ask questions when you play or interact with your child, the less opportunity your child will have to initiate his or her own activities.

523 ***Follow my child's lead.*** Respond to your child in a manner that is compatible with or complements your child's activity and intentions. Play with toys or engage in activities in the *same manner as your child.* Do not make your child play with toys in the manner for which the manufacturer designed them unless that is the way your child chooses to play with them.

Practical Suggestions

- Whatever your child is playing with is what interests your child at the moment. Consider how much more you are motivated to engage in activities that interest you and to learn and remember information that you find interesting. Children are no different when it comes to the motivating power of their interests.
- When you follow your child's lead, you are actually responding to your child's interests. The more you respond to your child's interests, the greater the number of interests your child will have, and the stronger these interests will be.

Developmental Domain: Cognition

Pivotal Behavior: Exploration

C-3 Exploration refers to the extent to which children investigate or handle objects and events. Children who explore can be contrasted with children who only passively observe or briefly come in contact with things in their world. Children explore by using all their senses—by mouthing, throwing, handling, looking, and listening. Exploration is characterized by active involvement, experimentation, and observation.

Facts To Consider About Exploration

C-301 Exploration is the basis for discovery learning.

Many of us have been taught information or skills and then have tried to apply them to a real-life situation. We thought we understood what we were being taught, but when we attempted to apply it we were not sure how to use the information. We did not understand the complexities of the information we were taught as well as we thought we had.

However, after several attempts to use this information, we begin to discover what we had to do to make it useful and to appreciate the significance of the information or skill. Only after trying to use it in a real-life experience does newly learned information take on a personal meaning and become part of our working knowledge.

All children, whether they are developing normally or have developmental problems, learn in the same way. *They can learn by having another person teach them, or they can learn by discovering through their own active exploration.* But unless children discover information first hand, they will not have the personal knowledge needed to make sense of it. Without fully understanding the information presented to them, children often have difficulty remembering it and are unlikely to use it in their daily routines.

Discovery learning results from children exploring and manipulating objects or experiences in their environment. Parents can guide children's discovery learning by providing them with appropriate materials and keeping them engaged, but for children to learn the information that is the foundation for their thinking and understanding, it is essential that they discover it themselves.

Every time parents teach children something, they keep them from discovering it for themselves. On the other hand, whatever parents encourage children to discover by themselves will remain with them for the rest of their lives.

C-302 Knowing and understanding are multidimensional–multimodal tasks.

It is useful to imagine what it is like for young children to learn and acquire the skills, knowledge, and understanding they need to develop their thinking and reasoning. As far as we know, *in the early years of life, children experience the world with no prior knowledge or understanding about the things they experience.* This must be an extraordinarily wondrous yet confusing phenomenon. Virtually all of children's early experiences present them with a wealth of information for which they have no prior context. Perhaps because everything is so new to them, young children take in their world with all of their senses: seeing, touching, tasting, smelling, and manipulating.

Knowledge is not just facts and information from an encyclopedia; knowledge is a multimodal phenomenon. Before children learn the names and uses of objects, they know what they look like, how they feel, what they taste and smell like, what happens when certain actions are performed on them, and how they relate to other objects or experiences. *The names and functions of objects are far less critical to early cognitive learning than are the sensory and personal information children get about their world.* If children do not have a rich, personal experiential knowledge, the name or functions of objects or experiences mean little to them.

For young children, objects and experiences exist in terms of appearance, texture, taste, and capacity to be acted upon. Children cannot know or understand their world unless they have first-hand knowledge of these qualities, and the only way they can acquire this is through exploration. By looking, touching, mouthing, and manipulating, children come to understand what objects and experiences really mean. This experiential knowledge is therefore the foundation for children to learn the names of objects and experiences and to understand what their uses are.

C-303 As children's cognitions change, they rediscover new possibilities.

Children's knowledge and understanding of their world change rapidly during the early years of developmental growth. These changes are reflected by the way they play and interact with objects. For example, objects that children at 6 months of age perceived as primarily useful for banging and mouthing become objects that children use for simple functional activities at age 12 to 15 months and objects that children transform and incorporate into their pretend play at 24 months. Although we as parents tend to focus on the new behaviors children acquire during successive phases of developmental growth, perhaps *the most important component of cognitive development is the change in children's perceptions and understanding that give rise to their new skills and behaviors.*

On a regular basis *during the first few years of developmental growth, children rediscover objects, activities, and experiences that they encountered numerous times in the past.* Because of the changes in their knowledge and understanding, these "rediscoveries" can be so different from their previous perceptions and understanding that it is almost as if they had never experienced them before.

This process of rediscovery partly explains why children are so interested in exploring and manipulating objects and materials in their environment. Children can continually play with, examine, and perform actions on the same toys and activities because each day these experiences take on new meaning. Although this type of play and exploration may seem tedious and boring to parents, it can be exciting and stimulating for young children who continually discover new ways of perceiving and understanding their experiences.

Parents need to remember that exploration for young children is quite different than it is for them. Adults simply do not undergo the changes in thinking and understanding that young children do. Parents must recognize that their children are constantly discovering new qualities and features of objects and experiences that they were not aware of before. Parents can support children's efforts to explore their environment by engaging in joint reciprocal interactions with them.

C-304 Similar concepts can be learned through a variety of experiences.

In general, *any object or activity that children can explore or manipulate can provide information or experiences that help children develop higher level concepts.* However, there are two important things to consider when regarding this issue.

First, children are more likely to learn information and concepts that are directly related to their immediate interests. Sometimes parents and professionals restrict children's access to toys and activities so that they can direct children's attention to objects or attributes of objects that are related to the skills and concepts they want their children to learn. When parents do this, however, they limit children's opportunities to engage in activities that might interest them. How much children explore and learn from their experiences depends on how interested they are in the stimulation available to them. The more children have the opportunity to play with a wide range of toys, materials, and activities, the greater the likelihood they will find things that will interest them and engage them in meaningful exploration.

Second, children are continually learning from each of their daily, routine activities. Cognitive concepts are ways of organizing and classifying information that have application across a wide range of objects, experiences, and relationships. Objects or experiences children encounter in their daily activities that have qualities and features related to a cognitive concept (e.g., the "in and out" spatial relationship) provide children opportunities to learn these concepts. Toys provide only limited examples of a concept. *Children can learn the same concepts from the common objects and experiences they encounter in their daily routine.*

Children's cognitive learning is more likely to occur when they are exposed to a variety of objects and experiences. Parents should provide their children with as many different kinds of toys and experiences as possible; however, parents should also encourage their children to explore objects and materials that are part of their routine experiences. These include objects and materials children encounter in the park, the car, and stores, as well as during routines such as eating, dressing, and bathing.

C-305 Exploration is child initiated, not a guided tour.

Learning through *exploration is a high-demand, high-energy activity*—much more difficult than being taught by others. Christopher Columbus set out to explore the world to find answers to questions that no one else knew. To determine whether the world was round or flat, Columbus carried out an arduous voyage, putting his life on the line to gather this information. Through his explorations, Columbus learned firsthand that the world was round.

Contrast this with how we learn about the world today. Early on we are told that the world is round. We are shown globes and maps that depict the world as round. We learn facts about the world that we probably do not fully comprehend. The early explorers engaged in hard, demanding work to discover this information. When we are taught by others, we do not devote anywhere near the effort that explorers did to learn. By learning information from another person, we cut short the effort required for learning, but we acquire only a superficial understanding of the information.

Should children's early concepts be rooted in a superficial understanding of facts or be derived from firsthand, in-depth knowledge and understanding of their world? Many parents play with their children as if they were leading them on a guided tour. Tours select what people learn rather than encourage them to discover and experience things for themselves. Many parents do the same thing with their children. They play with their children by explaining and showing them what to do or how to handle what they are experiencing. *When parents guide children's exploration, they interfere with their children's engaging in the intensive work that exploration requires.* They encourage their children to become passive participants rather than to engage in the exploration that is needed to understand the world more personally and intimately.

There are a number of things that parents need to teach directly to their children, because children are unlikely to discover them on their own. But is it sufficient for children to learn the concepts that will be the basis for their thinking and learning for the remainder of their lives in this manner? Might not young children who have limited knowledge and understanding need to learn early concepts through firsthand, in-depth experiences? Might it be that after they acquire in-depth knowledge and understanding of basic cognitive concepts, children become more adept at comprehending information provided by others?

To promote children's cognitive growth, parents need to encourage children's exploration and discovery learning rather than provide information or solutions to children's challenges. This may be slow and tedious, but it will help children acquire a personal, in-depth knowledge of their world.

C-306 Curiosity is a critical tool for learning.

Children's exploration is fueled by their wonder about how they personally relate to their world. If we observe children when they are exploring, we will find that they are far more interested in how they personally affect objects than they are in the objects themselves. For example, babies are fascinated with rattles because they are a type of object that babies can successfully hold, manipulate, and make noise with.

Early cognitive growth is much more than the accumulation of facts and information. A major component of cognitive growth is children's discovery of the meaning and significance of objects and experiences in relationship to their own skills and abilities. *Children tend to be more curious and more likely to explore objects and experiences that they can directly affect.* As long as they can handle and manipulate toys, children are likely to explore them, but when children have difficulty handling or manipulating toys or objects, they quickly lose interest. The same phenomenon applies to children's experiences with people. Children are attentive to any adult from whom they can get a response by using behaviors such as eye gaze, smiling, or vocalizing, but if children are not successful at getting adults' attention, they quickly lose interest in interacting or relating with them.

Children's early concepts are based upon how they personally relate to objects and experiences. "Mommy" is not a specific person with a unique appearance, voice, touch, and smell. Rather, "mommy" is defined in terms of the way children relate to or experience their mother: someone who feeds them, comforts them, plays with them, and responds to their needs. In the early stages of cognitive growth, anyone who fulfills these functions may fit children's concept of mommy. Similarly, from very early ages, children have the ability to distinguish the difference between colors, but not until children discover that different colors can affect how they interact with objects or people does the concept of color have real meaning for them.

C-307 Play provides children opportunities to explore.

Many of us find it difficult to understand how play contributes to children's cognitive learning. We think of learning as something that results from goal-directed activity, not from random or haphazard activity. Because children's play seems so non–goal directed, we view play more as something to occupy and amuse children than as an activity that results in meaningful learning.

This view of children's play is probably shaped by our own personal experiences in trying to learn. Most of us learn new skills or knowledge by engaging in disciplined, goal-directed activity. If we do not apply ourselves to the task of learning, we are unlikely to acquire what we hope to learn.

There are two misperceptions associated with this reasoning. The first is that children's play is random and has little purpose. If we observe carefully, we will notice that, *when children play, they manipulate or explore objects or toys systematically.* When children are at the 6-month developmental stage, they likely explore objects by mouthing, banging, visually examining, or throwing. If children are at the 9- to 12-month developmental stage, they will explore by putting objects inside other objects, stacking objects on top of each other, examining the details of objects, and noticing the kinds of sounds or movements they can make with these objects. When children are 18 months old they will explore how objects can be combined together into complex activities, such as feeding a doll with a toy bottle or using objects to reenact activities that are frequent occurrences in their lives, such as put a doll to sleep in a toy bed. Although children's play may not fit adult notions of goal-directed activity, viewed from children's perspective, play appears to be highly systematic and creative exploration.

The second misperception is that children do not exert much effort when they play. Children enjoy what they do when they play. In fact, when play is no longer fun, children will stop playing and find something else to do. But, despite the fact that they enjoy themselves, *children work hard when they play by continually manipulating and exploring different developmental behaviors.* If we observe children playing by themselves with toys they can handle independently, we will see that they quickly find ways to play with those toys. More than likely, they will play throughout the entire observation, pausing only to make sure that someone is watching them or to shift from one activity to another.

How much more can children do? Even though they are having fun, when children play they continually use their developmental skills to explore objects and materials. By constantly exploring the properties and actions of objects and materials, children gain new information that leads them to more advanced levels of thinking and understanding.

Discussion Points

C-301 Exploration is the basis for discovery learning.

- There are two ways that children can learn: being taught by others or discovering on their own.
- To explore means to experience first hand.
- Discovery learning results from children exploring and manipulating objects or experiences in their environment.
- Every time parents teach children something, they keep them from discovering it for themselves.

C-302 Knowing and understanding are multidimensional–multimodal tasks.

- In the early years of life, children experience the world with no prior knowledge or understanding about things they experience.
- Knowledge is not just facts and information from dictionaries or encyclopedias.
- The names and functions of objects are far less critical to cognitive learning than are the sensory and personal information children get about their world.

C-303 As children's cognitions change, they rediscover new possibilities.

- Children's knowledge and understanding of the world change rapidly during the early years of developmental growth.
- The most important component of cognitive development is the change in children's perceptions and understanding that give rise to their new skills and behaviors.
- As children's perceptions of the world change, they rediscover objects and activities they experienced in the past.

C-304 Similar concepts can be learned through a variety of experiences.

- Any object or activity children can explore or manipulate can provide information and experiences that help children develop higher level concepts.
- Children's cognitive learning is more likely to occur when they are exposed to a variety of objects and experiences.
- Cognitive learning derives from children's exploration of objects and experiences in their daily routines, not just from toys or activities designed to promote specific skills and concepts.

C-305 Exploration is child initiated, not a guided tour.

- Exploration is a high-demand, high-energy activity.
- When parents guide children's exploration of their environment, they interfere with their children engaging in the intensive work that exploration requires.

C-306 Curiosity is a critical tool for learning.

- Exploration is fueled by children's wonder about how they personally relate to their world.
- Children tend to be more curious and more likely to explore objects and experiences that they can directly affect.

C-307 Play provides children opportunities to explore.

- When children play, they manipulate or explore objects or toys systematically.
- Children work hard when they play by continually manipulating and exploring different developmental behaviors.

RT Strategies That Promote Exploration

132 ***Sustain repetitive play or action sequences.*** Young children often go through lengthy periods where they play with the same toys or do the same things with objects over and over again. Children persist at repetitive play because the object or action is interesting to them. Continue playing like your child is playing, even if you get bored with what your child is doing.

Practical Suggestions

- Value your child's repetitive play. This is the type of behavior children commonly do at various stages of child development. Consider how repetitive play promotes constructive learning.
- Children typically repeat sensorimotor behaviors such as mouthing, banging, or throwing until these behaviors no longer interest them. Encourage your child to continue these behaviors so your child will lose interest in them more quickly. This will reduce the time it takes to move on to a new behavior.
- Try to get your child to perform higher level or new behaviors. After attempting this, observe how your child goes back to doing repetitive, lower level sensorimotor behaviors as soon as he or she has the opportunity to do what he or she wants.

211 ***Observe my child's behavior.*** Observe your child methodically. Notice and listen to the subtle signs and sounds your child uses in various situations.

Practical Suggestions

- Make a list of your child's typical behaviors. Then imitate your child for several days (e.g., 1 week). After this period, write down another list describing what your child does when he or she plays or communicates. Did imitating your child make you more aware of the little things he or she does? Why do you think this happened?
- If you want your child to do something or learn something in particular, you might miss all the things your child is actually doing. Observing and

understanding what your child is currently doing will make you more effective at helping your child learn what you would like him or her to do.

- Professionals can lead parents through observations of their children by describing their own observations while playing with the child or watching the child on videotape.
- Professionals can ask parents to describe videotaped observations of their children playing. Comment immediately about behaviors that parents did not describe.

321 ***Expand to show my child the next developmental step.*** Children need parents and others to show them the next step in both play and communication. Remember to "show your child the next step" in whatever he or she does. By doing this, you will expose your child to new information while keeping him or her interacting with you.

Practical Suggestions

- Make sure that your expansions are related to your child's behavior and activities in ways that show new meanings and purposes of the behavior.

325 ***Change the environment.*** Make simple changes in familiar environments to challenge your child to notice more of the world and to explore and seek solutions.

Practical Suggestions

- Move cups and utensils that are usually placed in the same drawers of a play stove or books that are placed on the same shelves to change the environment and encourage your child to do something differently.
- Consider that changes in the environment encourage flexibility and will help some children move away from ritualized behavior.

441 ***Value what my child is doing.*** View what your child is doing as important, interesting, and meaningful. Do not dismiss what your child does simply because it is not what other children do at your child's age level.

Practical Suggestions

- Make a list of the things your child has done since the last intervention session. Focus on the positive aspects of your child's behavior.
- Videotape your child in several situations: playing alone, playing with you, and playing with other children. Review the video to identify what your child is doing. Keep this video as a record of your child's accomplishments.
- Professionals should consistently comment on what children are doing during intervention sessions. Celebrate what children are doing. Discuss with parents the importance or developmental significance of their children's behavior.

511 ***Interpret my child's behavior developmentally.*** View your child's behavior as a meaningful reflection of his or her current level of cognitive, social, and language competence. Many of the behaviors that children with developmental problems produce are not typical for their chronological age; however, the things they do and the ways they behave are generally similar to the developmental behaviors of younger children.

Practical Suggestions

- Use a developmental profile such as the *Developmental Rainbow* (Mahoney & Perales, 1996) to identify the behaviors that your child is currently producing.
- Consider that the way your child communicates, plays, and reacts to social situations is a reflection of how your child understands, reasons, or solves social and nonsocial problems at his or her stage of developmental functioning. Whether children are developing typically or have developmental problems, the way they act and communicate is a reflection of how they currently think and reason.
- Professionals should continually discuss with parents that their children's behaviors are typical for younger children. Emphasize that these behaviors are developmentally important because they are the building blocks for higher developmental skills.

513 ***Request actions that match my child's developmental level.*** Limit requests for your child to do or say things to behaviors that are within your child's range of accommodation. Your child will have difficulty responding to behaviors and communications that exceed his or her range of accommodation.

Practical Suggestions

- Review a videotape of you and your child playing together. Write down the behaviors that you have asked your child to do. Look up these behaviors on the *Developmental Rainbow* (Mahoney & Perales, 1996) or other developmental profile. Notice how your child was more reactive and engaged when you asked him or her to do things that were within his or her range of accommodation. Notice how your child became passive or ignored you when you asked him or her to do things that are difficult (i.e., beyond the child's range of accommodation).
- Consider how you react when you are asked to do something that you do not know how to do.
- Increase your child's opportunities to succeed with you by asking him or her to do things within his or her developmental capabilities.

523 ***Follow my child's lead.*** Respond to your child in a manner that is compatible with or complements your child's activity and intentions. Play with toys or engage in activities in the same manner as your child. Do not make your child play with toys in the manner for which the manufacturer designed them unless that is the way your child chooses to play with them.

Practical Suggestions

- Whatever your child is playing with is what interests your child at the moment. Consider how much more motivated you are to engage in activities that interest you and to learn and remember information that you find interesting. Your child is no different when it comes to the motivating power of his or her interests.
- When you follow your child's lead you are actually responding to your child's interests. The more you respond to your child's interests, the greater the number of interests your child will have, and the stronger these interests will be.

Developmental Domain: Cognition

Pivotal Behavior: Problem Solving

C-4 Problem Solving refers to the degree to which children persist with tasks that pose some challenge or difficulty. Children who are problem solvers make several attempts to solve a problem and continue to experiment with different solutions, even though they may not be successful. They frequently assess their impact on the environment. They are creative in attempting to deal with novel and challenging situations.

Facts To Consider About Problem Solving

C-401 Problem solving: persisting in the face of challenge.

Problem solving is the pivotal behavior with which children apply the skills or behaviors they currently possess to develop solutions to challenging or unfamiliar situations. *Children exhibit problem solving when they persist with tasks that they are unable to resolve quickly.* Children have numerous opportunities to problem solve during their routine play and interactions. The ability to solve problems is needed when children encounter new toys, when others communicate to them in ways they cannot easily understand, or when they are asked to do things that are beyond their capabilities.

Problem solving is productive only when children already possess many if not all of the skills and abilities that are necessary for dealing with the situation. Children who attempt to solve problems for which they possess none or few of the required skills are ineffective. It would be like "spinning one's wheels." When children do not have the skills to address a challenging situation, it makes sense to withdraw from the situation or seek others to solve the problem for them.

Most children are quite good at identifying situations that are beyond their capabilities. Children who have learning problems, however, sometimes withdraw too easily from problems for which they possess many of the necessary skills. They need to learn to stay engaged with activities that challenge them. To help children with learning problems develop their problem-solving skills, parents must be able to accurately judge the degree to which their children have the capabilities for addressing these situations. When parents encourage children to persist at situations that are within their range of capabilities, they will help their children expand the range of uncertainty in which they are willing to apply themselves. However, when parents overestimate children's abilities and encourage them to attempt problems that are beyond their capabilities, their children are unlikely to succeed.

Children should be encouraged to engage in problem solving only occasionally. It takes considerably more effort for children to solve problems than to engage in easy activities. If parents ask children to engage in problem-solving behavior too frequently, they risk wearing them out. However, if they occasionally encourage problem-solving behavior in situations their children can manage, they will prepare their children to learn how to engage in problem solving at times and in situations that are necessary and appropriate.

C-402 Problem solving means learning what does not work as well as what does work.

To develop their problem-solving skills, *children must learn not only what strategies can be used to solve a problem but also what strategies are not effective.* As important as it is for children to learn effective ways for handling problems, it is equally important that they discover and understand why certain behaviors are not part of the solution. The information children learn from the strategies they try that *do not* work is as important as the information they learn from the strategies that *do* work.

Parents should use RT strategies to support all of children's behaviors, including unsuccessful and successful resolutions to challenging situations. In other words, *children must be given opportunities to fail, but not so much that it leads to frustration* and causes them to withdraw from the activity or have emotional outbursts. If children are on the verge of becoming distraught because of their failure to achieve success, parents should intervene and show children how to deal with the problem to reduce their frustration and keep them engaged in the activity.

Achieving a balance between encouraging children to confront challenge and preventing them from becoming overly frustrated is difficult. However, children must be allowed to attempt strategies that do not work to have the opportunity to learn what behaviors are not effective at solving problems. Becoming overly frustrated by their inability to resolve problem situations could result in children staying away or withdrawing from challenging situations.

C-403 Situations become problems if they obstruct children from doing what they want.

While playing or interacting with their children, parents sometimes obstruct them from what they are doing or are interested in doing. They may hide an object the child needs, create a physical barrier for the child to get around, or withhold something that the child can obtain only by producing a behavior that the adult demands. In doing this, parents are trying to motivate their children to engage in problem-solving behavior and thereby promote their ability to reason or think logically.

This reasonable approach to promoting problem-solving behavior only works if children are willing participants. *Problems are defined only in terms of what children want to do.* Children who understand this game, who are able to reason quickly, and who tend to persist in their interests may take delight in these types of interactions and rise to their parents' challenges—but these are not qualities exhibited by many children with developmental problems, who take more time to reason or figure things out, often do not persist in pursuing their interests, and may not have the cognitive maturity needed to understand that parental obstruction is a game. Because they have developmental problems, these challenging interactions may be very difficult for them. *The obstructions imposed by parents may stop children from pursuing their interests and may impede their activity rather than motivate them to solve the problem.*

There is nothing wrong with *occasionally* obstructing children from engaging in an activity, however. In fact, this can be useful for making interactions fun and interesting as well as for promoting children's problem-solving skills. But if obstruction becomes the main focus of parents' interactions with children, it could result in a highly directive pattern of adult–child interaction. When parents pose challenges too frequently, they risk discouraging their children from participating in the activity. *Too much obstruction can cause children to terminate their interactions after short periods of time.*

C-404 Obstructions: The bigger they are, the faster they quit.

There is no good reason for young children, or anyone else, to attempt to work on a problem that is beyond their capabilities. Reasonable people focus their efforts on tasks they are capable of doing. The saying "choose your battles" reflects this idea. At very early ages children size up situations in terms of whether they feel they have the skills needed to handle them. *Children instinctively avoid or quickly withdraw from tasks they perceive as exceeding their capabilities.*

Perhaps one of the more important differences between children with different levels of ability is the way they estimate their capacity to succeed at solving problems. Children who are extremely bright see themselves as having the ability to succeed at problem situations, even though those situations require strategies and behaviors that may be beyond what they are capable of doing. Children with average ability often choose challenges that only slightly exceed their current capabilities, whereas children with learning problems avoid challenges unless they are certain they have most, if not all, of the required skills.

If parents pose problems by creating obstructions that are difficult or require considerable effort, children with learning problems are more likely to withdraw from the situation than other children. However, *if parents pose problems that are within their children's range of capabilities, children are more likely to persist at trying to solve the problem,* even if they have developmental problems.

C-405 Collaborate in children's problem solving by following their reasoning.

A typical scenario is that while children are playing with their parents they try to do something and, after failing, look to their parents for assistance. Often, *children encounter problems because they use faulty reasoning or logic to try to overcome an obstacle.* How can parents encourage their children's use of problem-solving behavior in these situations?

There two ways parents can respond to this situation. One is to respond to the child's request and show them how to address the problem. Children are likely to react in one of two ways to this type of assistance. First, they might use the parents' assistance to get around the problem, without paying attention to how their parent solved the problem. Second, they might actually attend to what their parent did but, without imitating or repeating their solution, resume their play from the point of the parents' intervention.

A second way is to respond to the child's request by imitating the ineffective behaviors he or she has used to resolve the problem. By doing this parents collaborate in children's failure while at the same time encouraging them to try something else. Rather than using children's requests as an invitation to take over the situation, parents sustain children's involvement in the activity by imitating their behavior and encouraging them to try something different. Parents can demonstrate the correct solution after children have tried several different strategies. The assistance provided at this point will be very meaningful because children have persisted in their efforts.

Both types of parental responses can effectively sustain children's engagement in interaction. However, the first type is effective mostly at encouraging children to explore or practice and does little to promote problem solving. In contrast, the second strategy uses this opportunity to encourage children to use their problem-solving skills. *When parents collaborate with their children's faulty problem solving, they support and encourage their children to generate alternative solutions.*

C-406 Interact with children to generate solutions.

Problems are solved through trial-and-error learning. First we try using one strategy or behavior to deal with the problem, and if that fails we try something different. Problem solving requires that we alter our behavior to come up with a successful solution rather than perseverate on unsuccessful solutions. When confronted with challenge, many children will attempt to use the same strategy or behavior repeatedly, even though it does not successfully address the problem. To become effective problem solvers, these children need to learn how to generate a different solution.

How do children learn this basic rule of problem solving? At early developmental ages, most children do not understand the need to generate alternative behaviors when the behavior they are using is not successful. Parents can *encourage trial-and-error learning by taking turns with problem-solving strategies that do not work.* In other words, when children have difficulty doing something, parents can join in children's activity by (a) imitating their unsuccessful strategies, (b) modeling a series of unsuccessful strategies that they themselves generate, and (c) demonstrating a successful solution.

As parents sustain children's active engagement by taking turns with them, children gain firsthand experience by observing their parents using trial-and-error procedures to arrive at a solution to a problem that they themselves are experiencing. Because they are personally invested, repeated exposure to these kinds of episodes will be very meaningful to them. This will help children begin to see that this trial-and-error pattern of behavior is something they can do whenever they encounter problems.

C-407 Become children's partner, not the solution for their problems.

Many parents have a natural tendency to help their children when they seek assistance with a problem. In fact, it is often easier to step in and show children how to solve a problem than to encourage them to solve it on their own. Yet, children are unlikely to become problem solvers if parents do not encourage them to attempt to solve problems on their own. Children are not born problem solvers. They learn to become problem solvers by attempting to address the problems they encounter in routine play and daily living experiences.

Children are more likely to persist in problem solving when parents become partners in the problem-solving process. Parents can respond to children's requests to help them with challenges by taking turns with them, imitating children's efforts to address problems, and following children's leads by producing behaviors that support the strategies children generate to address problem situations. By becoming children's partners, parents deescalate the frustration children experience when they fail to succeed. By engaging in balanced, reciprocal interactions with their children, parents transform the dynamics of a frustrating, challenging problem into an enjoyable activity in which they share their children's desire and struggle to overcome obstacles or challenges.

The way parents interact with children shapes children's understanding of what they can do in problem situations. *When parents act as children's partners and encourage their efforts to generate alternative solutions, they teach their children to initiate solutions to problems on their own.* If parents intervene to solve children's problems whenever they request assistance, children learn that they do not need to solve challenges on their own but need to seek the assistance of others.

Discussion Points

C-401 Problem solving: persisting in the face of challenge.

- Children exhibit problem solving when they persist with tasks they are unable to resolve quickly.
- Problem solving is productive only when children already possess many if not all of the skills necessary for dealing with the situation.
- Children need to learn to stay engaged with activities that challenge them.

C-402 Problem solving means learning what does not work as well as what does work.

- Problem solving not only entails discovering what works but also finding out what does not work.
- Children must be given opportunities to fail, but not so much that it leads to frustration.

C-403 Situations become problems if they obstruct children from doing what they want.

- Problems are defined only in terms of what children themselves want to do.
- Obstructions imposed by parents may stop children from pursuing their interests and may impede their activity rather than motivate them to solve the problem.
- Too much obstruction can cause children to terminate their interactions after short periods of time.

C-404 Obstructions: The bigger they are, the faster they quit.

- Children instinctively avoid or quickly withdraw from tasks they perceive as exceeding their capabilities.
- If parents pose problems that are within their children's range of capabilities, children are more likely to persist at trying to solve the problem.

C-405 Parents collaborate in children's problem solving by following their reasoning.

- Children encounter problems when they use faulty reasoning or logic to try to overcome an obstacle.
- When parents collaborate with their children's faulty problem solving, they support and encourage their children to generate alternative solutions.

C-406 Parents should interact with children to generate solutions.

- Problems are solved through trial-and-error learning.
- Parents can encourage trial-and-error learning by taking turns with problem-solving strategies that do not work.

C-407 Parents should become children's partner, not the solution for their problems.

- Many parents have a natural tendency to help their children when they seek assistance.
- Children are more likely to persist in problem solving when parents become partners in the problem-solving process.
- When parents act as children's partner and encourage their efforts to generate alternative solutions, they teach their children to initiate solutions to problems on their own.

RT Strategies That Promote Problem Solving

312 ***Imitate my child's actions and communications.*** You can imitate any behavior that your child produces. If your child has little interest in interacting with you, you can get your child's attention by imitating behaviors that may even be inappropriate or bizarre (e.g., rocking, thumb-sucking, loud shrieking or crying, throwing objects). Imitation has two functions. First, it helps to establish an interactive relationship with your child that is based upon what your child is doing. Second, imitation gives your child an immediate opportunity to control what you do.

Practical Suggestions

- Notice how imitation encourages your child to increase the variety and scope of his or her behavior and does not reinforce undesirable behavior.
- Consider that one important outcome of imitation is that your child will enjoy and have fun controlling what you do.
- When you imitate your child's nonverbal or verbal communication, you are helping your child learn to use his or her early communication skills to have an effect on others.

321 ***Expand to show my child the next developmental step.*** A child needs parents and others to show him or her the next step both in play and communication. Remind yourself to show your child the next step in whatever your child is doing.

By doing this, you will expose your child to new information while keeping him or her interacting with you.

Practical Suggestions

- Make sure that your expansions are related to your child's behavior and activities in ways that show new meanings and purposes of the behavior.

322 ***Expand to clarify my child's intention or to develop my child's topic.*** Adults can increase the complexity of children's activity or communication in a manner that preserves the intention or purpose of what they had been doing. For example, if your child is building a tower that is three blocks high, you can expand by building a tower that is four blocks high.

Practical Suggestions

- Make sure that your expansions are never the sole focus of your interactions with your child. Rather, introduce expansions only occasionally into your child's activity.
- If your child shows no interest in following your expansion, go back to your child's original activity to keep him or her actively engaged.
- If your child is not responding to your expansions, modify your expansions so that they are within your child's range of developmental abilities and compatible with his or her interests and sensations.

323 ***Wait silently for a more mature response.*** You can encourage your child to use higher level behaviors by occasionally waiting to respond when your child produces his or her "old" immature behaviors. Many children prefer to do easy behaviors. However, if you wait before responding to your child, your child may show you that he or she knows how to do more mature behaviors. Remember that waiting can only be effective at encouraging your child to do what he or she is already able to do.

Practical Suggestions

- Wait for your child to produce behaviors that you have seen him or her do only several times before. If your child produced a more advanced behavior only a few times in the past, this may not yet be a behavior that is easy for your child to do.
- If your child does not produce the behavior you are "waiting" for within 5 seconds, simply model the behavior you would like and continue the activity without insisting that your child imitate or produce the behavior on his or her own.

324 ***Play for a purpose.*** Sometimes children have difficulty starting a purposeful action and knowing what to do next. *Occasionally* respond to your child's purposeless activity by helping him or her engage in actions that might lead toward a more purposeful goal.

Practical Suggestions

- Model a simple behavior to suggest what your child can do. Monitor your child's response to what you did very carefully. If your child follows your suggestion, continue to guide your child to more purposeful activity. If your child turns away from you or becomes less active, let him or her go back to doing what he or she wants to do.

512 ***Know the developmental skills my child seems ready to learn.*** Your child is most likely to learn from or be able to respond to developmental behaviors that extend from his or her current developmental skill level to the next highest developmental level. This is referred to as your child's range of accommodation.

Practical Suggestions

- Use the *Developmental Rainbow* (Mahoney & Perales, 1996) to identify behaviors that fall within your child's range of accommodation in the areas of fine motor, gross motor, expressive language, social interaction, and object interaction (i.e., behaviors that fall within the range of Developmental Age − 1 month to Developmental Age + 1 month).
- Identify behaviors that exceed your child's current range of accommodation. These are behaviors or skills that are more than 1 month higher than your child's current developmental level.
- Professionals should continually provide parents information about their child's developmental behaviors to help them adjust their concept of their child's range of accommodation as their child develops higher level skills and competencies.

522 ***Follow my child's focus of attention.*** What your child is paying attention to is indicated by what he or she is looking at, listening to, or touching. The sounds, objects, people, or actions that your child attends to are all reflections of his or her interests. To follow your child's focus of attention, you must become sensitive and responsive to the subtle cues that reflect your child's focus of attention. Continue to follow your child as his or her attention shifts from one thing to another.

Practical Suggestions

- Consider that young children become absorbed in their immediate experiences. Children's activity and what they attend to are dominated by their immediate interests. As children lose interest in something, they quickly shift the focus of their attention to aspects of the environment that seem more captivating.
- What your child is interested in is partly dependent on his or her current level of developmental functioning. For example, midway in the first year of development, children are captivated by the physical properties of objects such as taste, texture, shape, and sound. Later in the first year, as children's development changes, children are more interested in the function of objects—what they can do—than they are in the properties of objects.

Developmental Domain: Cognition

Pivotal Behavior: Practice

C-5 Practice refers to children repeating behaviors and activities both in the same way and by varying them. Children practice these behaviors both by themselves and with other people. Episodes of practice are prolonged in duration and occur with several objects and people.

Facts To Consider About Practice

C-501 Practice provides children with the opportunity to master and determine the uses of behaviors.

Learning developmental skills involves much more than simply acquiring a new behavior. When children first learn developmental skills or concepts, their use of new behaviors might be primitive. They might use them correctly but awkwardly or produce them with considerable effort. In addition, they might use these behaviors only in the contexts in which they were learned and thus fail to recognize their potential for a much wider range of contexts.

Children must learn to use newly acquired behaviors with a high degree of proficiency. The behavior needs to become an automatic response that children use effortlessly and intuitively. Those who are involved in sports understand that *the only way to become proficient with a skill is through practice.* Professional athletes spend extraordinary amounts of time trying not just to learn skills but to overlearn them so that they can use them in competition without thinking.

This same principle applies to children who are learning developmental skills. Simply acquiring new skills is not sufficient to make them become a part of children's spontaneous behavior. Rather, children need to practice and repeat new skills so that they can produce them without thinking. Play is the context in which children practice and repeat developmental skills. The more children are encouraged to play, the more capable they become of using newly learned developmental behaviors as automatic responses.

Practice and repetition help children learn how newly acquired behaviors and concepts can be used. Through practicing new behaviors in a variety of settings and with different toys and people, children discover how they can be used with a range of objects, people, and settings.

C-502 To acquire new developmental behaviors or ways of thinking, children must give up old behaviors and ways of thinking.

Children's development can be described as a process in which they acquire the skills and behaviors that enable them to function more efficiently and productively. In many cases, new developmental skills and concepts do not help children do things they were previously unable to do. Rather, *higher level developmental skills provide children more effective ways of doing or thinking than lower level skills.* For example, when children first learn to walk, they are already capable of getting around their environment independently by crawling, scooting, or rolling. When children take their first steps, they find that they can move faster and have fewer accidents than they could by crawling or other means of locomotion.

To use higher level skills, children must abandon their lower level skills. Children cannot crawl and walk at the same time—they must do one or the other. The more they crawl, the less they walk; likewise, the more they walk, the less they crawl. Although this may be self-evident, seldom do we consider how critical this is to the developmental process. For example, for children to acquire higher level motor skills (e.g., walking) they must give up their use of lower level motor skills (e.g., crawling). So long as children are content with using crawling as a means of moving, there is no reason for them to want to walk. Motor development not only entails learning to walk, it also involves giving up crawling.

The principle applies to many of children's developmental skills. For example, one major developmental milestone is when children transition from banging objects to putting objects inside containers. Children cannot do both of these developmental behaviors at the same time. The more they do of one, the less they do of the other. Why would children abandon developmental skills they already know in order to use higher level development skills they do not know? One possibility is that *children will abandon lower level skills when they discover that new behaviors provide a more effective way of doing or thinking* than the old behaviors.

What drives this process? What makes children want to walk when they can already get around their environment? We do not know the answer to this question, but if we consider what children typically do, we can come up with a reasonable explanation. When children play, they practice the skills and concepts they are in the process of learning. They repeat the same behaviors with toys and objects many times before they move on to practicing or repeating new concepts and skills. This practice or repetition not only helps children become skilled with newly learned developmental behaviors. *Practice helps children discover the limitations of their current behaviors.* By engaging in repetitive play, children gradually become aware of different possibilities they would like to explore. To the extent their current behaviors are ineffective at helping them explore these possibilities, children seek alternative behaviors. Their increasing awareness and interest in the world, coupled with their discovery of the limitations of their current behavior, motivates them to learn behaviors that will help them do what they want.

C-503 Repetition and practice are the most common features of children's play.

Developmentally appropriate behaviors are any behaviors that children commonly do at a particular developmental level that are considered to have some role in helping them learn and develop. For example, at the 4- to 6-month developmental age level it is developmentally appropriate for children to bang and throw objects. It is also developmentally appropriate for children from 2 to 4 years of age to pretend. Just as pretend play contributes to the learning and development of older children, banging plays a role in helping young children learn and develop. *Practice or repetition is a developmentally appropriate behavior throughout the early childhood years.* Young children continually repeat the same actions, behaviors, or routines when they play.

They may engage in the same actions with toy trucks in the morning, afternoon, and evening, and still continue to engage in the same activities on the next day and the day after that.

What makes a good athlete? Practice and repetition. Accomplished athletes spend many hours practicing skills until they master them. Athletes enjoy practicing the same behaviors, particularly when they see themselves becoming more proficient with them. Although most of us would never want to put ourselves through the practice regimen of an athlete, we do not consider this form of practice to be unnecessary or unproductive. We recognize that athletic excellence requires a level of skill proficiency that can only come from practice and repetition.

Although most typically developing children exhibit high levels of practice and repetition in their play, many children who have developmental problems do not. Moreover, because children with developmental problems need more repetition to learn or discover new information than do typically developing children, their lack of practice and repetition can make their learning problems even worse. If parents feel their children are not engaging in the amount of repetitive play that most children do, they need to *encourage their children with developmental problems to practice and repeat their existing developmental skills and behaviors as much as possible.*

The way that parents interact with their children can contribute to their children's failure to engage in sufficient amounts of practice and repetition. *Parents may get tired of doing the same thing with children long before their children get tired of them.* Out of boredom, they may try to introduce new toys or actions to encourage their children to do something different. Yet, often the behaviors they try to get their children to do are ones that their children are neither capable of nor interested in doing, and parents' attempts to vary activities can inhibit children's participation in the interaction.

To avoid this problem, parents must keep interactions with their children as interesting as possible. However, they must also be careful not to interfere with their children as they practice or repeat activities they prefer. If a child with developmental problems continually repeats the same behavior, parents need to remember that repetition is critical for their child to gain proficiency and discover the limitations of his or her current developmental behaviors. When those behaviors have outlived their usefulness, children will stop doing them. However, until this occurs, parents must patiently support their children's play.

C-504 Children with developmental problems do not practice or repeat deficient behaviors.

Some parents of children with developmental problems view much of their children's behavior as a reflection of their developmental problems. For example, if a child is diagnosed with mental retardation, some parents identify most of what their children do as "mentally retarded" behavior.

In contrast to this, Responsive Teaching views all of children's behavior, regardless of how delayed it might be, as children's strengths, not as a manifestation of their learning problems. *Children's play is developmentally appropriate even if it is not like the play behaviors children typically produce at their age levels.* Most of what children do when they play is a reflection of their current knowledge and understanding. Although these behaviors may be delayed for a child's age, they are the only tools children have to learn higher level behaviors.

Some parents are afraid that if they encourage their children to practice or repeat behaviors, they might reinforce lower level behaviors. However, when younger, typically developing children produce these same behaviors, their parents usually take great delight in them and are not concerned that they will impede their children's developmental growth. According to reinforcement theory, if parents reward their children for producing a behavior, the probability that children will produce that behavior in the future should increase. But this is not the way that play and social behavior works for young children. *Encouraging children to practice or repeat behaviors produced typically by younger children does not reinforce lower forms of behavior;* rather, when parents do this, they are reinforcing their children's efforts to practice. The specific behaviors children produce at any one time are determined mostly by their current knowledge and understanding, not by parents' reinforcement. As children's knowledge and understanding change, so too will the types of behaviors they practice and repeat

Children's knowledge and understanding is highly dependent upon their learning about the uses and limitations of their current behaviors. Because they gain this knowledge mostly by acting on their environment, *the more parents encourage children to practice lower level behaviors, the quicker children will learn higher level developmental behaviors.*

C-505 Children cannot be stopped from practicing or repeating the developmental behaviors they naturally want to do.

When children are between 5 and 12 months of age, they commonly mouth, bang, or throw toys. Parents may not take delight in what their children are doing, but they tolerate and at times encourage these behaviors because these are the things that children typically do at these stages of developmental functioning. But when children are 1½ to 2 years of age, parents will often discourage these types of behaviors, because they consider them to be socially inappropriate for this age level. Parents may try to stop their children from doing these behaviors by removing objects, restraining their children, or redirecting them to engage in some other type of behavior.

So long as their parents are around to remind them, children often refrain from doing these behaviors. However, it is interesting to observe what children do when parents are not around to discourage lower level behaviors. Almost without thinking, children go right back to doing the behaviors their parents tried to prevent. Parents' efforts to stop these behaviors have only a temporary effect. They have little impact on what children do when they play by themselves.

Stopping children from practicing lower level behaviors only prevents them from doing the things they know how to do. The best way parents can encourage their children to give up lower level behaviors is to encourage them to practice and repeat them as much as possible. *The more children practice and repeat lower level behaviors, the sooner they will discover other possibilities and seek out more advanced behaviors.* Preventing children from engaging in behaviors that they feel compelled to do, only limits children's opportunities to discover and learn higher level developmental behaviors.

C-506 Children do not spontaneously practice and rehearse behaviors that they learn through directed instruction.

Because they are so concerned about their children's developmental problems, *parents and adults often use direct instruction as a method for helping children learn higher level behaviors.* Direct instruction entails prodding children to produce higher level skills using procedures such as asking children to do something, modeling, eliciting imitation, physical prompting, or reinforcing. If adults repeat this enough times, they eventually get their children to produce these behaviors in response to their prompts or requests. In fact, these methods of direct instruction are the only way to encourage children to engage in developmental behaviors that they do not know how to do.

Yet, *soon after children learn a higher level behavior or skill through direct instruction, they typically revert to engaging in activities that reflect their current level of development.* Seldom do children follow up an episode in which they were encouraged to produce a higher level behavior by practicing or repeating that behavior on their own.

Direct instruction has been described as an important method for teaching children with learning problems because of its proven success at helping them learn and produce targeted behaviors in response to adult requests. The shortcoming of this procedure, however, has been its failure to help children remember and use these behaviors in settings other than where the instruction took place. *Children do not remember and generalize because direct instruction does not encourage children to practice and repeat the behaviors they are taught.* When children do not overlearn developmental behaviors through practice and repetition, it is unlikely that they will remember these behaviors or use them spontaneously in contexts other than where they were originally trained.

Discussion Points

C-501 Practice provides children with the opportunity to master and determine the uses of behaviors.

- Learning developmental skills involves much more than simply acquiring a new behavior.
- The only way to become proficient with a skill is through practice.
- Practice and repetition help children learn how newly acquired behaviors and concepts can be used.

C-502 To acquire new developmental behaviors or ways of thinking, children must give up old behaviors and ways of thinking.

- Higher level developmental skills provide children with more effective ways of doing or thinking than lower level skills.
- To use higher level skills, children must abandon their lower level skills.
- Children will abandon lower level skills when they discover that new behaviors provide a more effective way of doing or thinking.
- Practice helps children discover the limitations of their current behaviors.

C-503 Repetition and practice are the most common features of children's play.

- Practice or repetition is a developmentally appropriate behavior throughout the early childhood years.
- Parents should encourage children with developmental problems to practice and repeat their existing developmental skills and behaviors as much as possible.
- Parents often get tired of doing the same thing with children long before children get tired of them.

C-504 Children with developmental problems do not practice or repeat deficient behaviors.

- Children's play is developmentally appropriate even if it is not like the play behaviors children typically produce at their age levels.
- Encouraging children to practice or repeat behaviors typically produced by younger children does not reinforce lower forms of behavior.
- The more parents encourage children to produce lower level forms of behavior, the quicker they will acquire and use higher forms of developmental behavior.

C-505 Children cannot be stopped from practicing or repeating the developmental behaviors they naturally want to do.

- Stopping children from practicing lower level behaviors only prevents them from doing the things they know how to do.
- The more children practice and repeat lower level behaviors, the sooner they will discover other possibilities and seek out more advanced behaviors.

C-506 Children do not spontaneously practice and rehearse behaviors that they learn through direct instruction.

- Parents and adults often use direct instruction as a method for helping their children learn higher level behaviors.
- Soon after children learn a higher level behavior or skill through direct instruction, they typically revert to engaging in activities that reflect their current level of development.
- Children do not remember and generalize because direct instruction does not encourage children to practice and repeat the behaviors they are taught.

RT Strategies That Promote Practice

122 ***Keep my child for one or two more turns than usual.*** Gradually extend the number of turns your child stays engaged in interaction with you.

Practical Suggestions

- Engage in behaviors and activities that your child prefers to do.

- Consider that the longer your child stays engaged in an activity, the more opportunities he or she has to practice and learn developmental skills.
- Count the number of complete turns between you and your child before your child shifts his or her focus to a different activity or breaks away from you.
- Determine how the length of your child's episodes of turn-taking changes across contexts and activities.
- Gradually increase the number of turns your child stays in interaction with you. If your child typically engages in episodes of six to seven turns, encourage him or her to interact for eight turns.

132 ***Sustain repetitive play or action sequences.*** Young children often go through lengthy periods where they play with the same toys or do the same things with objects over and over again. Children persist at repetitive play because the object or action they are doing is interesting to them. Continue playing like your child is playing, even if you are getting bored with what your child is doing.

Practical Suggestions

- Value your child's repetitive play. This is the type of behavior children commonly do at various stages of child development. Consider how repetitive play promotes constructive learning.
- Children typically repeat sensorimotor behaviors such as mouthing, banging, or throwing until these behaviors are no longer of interest to them. Encourage your child to continue these behaviors so that your child will lose interest in them more quickly. This will reduce the time it takes to move on to a new behavior.
- Try to get your child to perform higher level or new behaviors. After attempting this, observe how your child goes back to doing repetitive, lower level sensorimotor behaviors as soon as he or she has the opportunity to do what he or she wants.

133 ***Join perseverative play (make it interactive).*** When your child is perseverating or playing in self-stimulatory ways, enter into your child's world and make the play interactive. After you have successfully entered your child's world, gradually show your child other ways to play.

Practical Suggestions

- If your child does the same thing with every toy (e.g., pretends that all objects are trains), join your child's play rather than try to force your child to use objects in a different way. It is more important to use anything that interests your child as an opportunity for interaction than it is for your child to break his or her compulsive behaviors. Compulsive behaviors almost always decrease over time.

- Often, children use stereotypic, repetitive behaviors (e.g., rocking, flapping their hands) to avoid interacting with others. Make your child's stereotypic behavior an opportunity to interact with you. Place yourself next to your child, imitate your child's stereotypic behavior, and notice how your child starts to pay attention to you.
- If your child engages in stereotypic behavior such as "hand flapping" while interacting with you, ignore the behavior and focus on the activity you are doing with your child.
- Never imitate or encourage self-destructive or harmful behavior. For self-destructive behaviors (e.g., head banging, biting self) make sure your child has protective clothing (e.g., gloves, long-sleeved shirts) or equipment (e.g., helmet).

241 ***Explore how RT strategies can be used to enhance my child's participation throughout daily routines.*** You can help your child learn language and cognitive skills by using RT strategies in a wide range of activities, such as caretaking, household chores, car rides, games, video watching, and teaching activities.

Practical Suggestions

- Your child will learn how to participate more effectively in everyday routines when you infuse RT strategies into your routine interactions.
- Consider how RT strategies can be applied to daily activities such as feeding, holding and comforting a child, changing clothes, brushing teeth, and so forth.
- Make a list of all the ways that you have incorporated RT strategies into your routine experiences with your child.
- Professionals can model and coach the parent to use RT strategies to carry out a typical childcare routine (e.g., feeding the child, changing diapers).

422 ***Interact for fun.*** There are many reasons that parents interact with children. They can interact to take care of their children's physical needs, comfort their children, teach their children, or just be with them. Use the strategy "interact for fun" to motivate yourself to spend at least one third of the interactions you have with your child focused on having fun.

Practical Suggestions

- Give your child opportunities to influence you in playful ways. You can promote this by making exaggerated reactions to the little things your child does.
- Become your child's favorite toy by acting like a toy your child can manipulate, control, and enjoy.
- Consider the importance of interacting with your child more during enjoyable times than during stressful ones. You are more likely to help your child learn when you join your child's enjoyable moments.

424 ***Repeat activities my child enjoys.*** Keep doing activities that your child finds fun and amusing. The more you emphasize these activities, the more you and your child will enjoy being with each other.

Practical Suggestions

- Unlike adults, children may do things many times before they get tired of the activity. When you repeat activities your child enjoys, you may tire of the activity long before your child does. However, if you continue this activity to promote your child's enjoyment, your child will learn that interacting with you is enjoyable.
- Children develop a sense of humor when parents join in their amusement. The more you support activities your child enjoys, the more your child will learn to share amusing and enjoyable things with you. Your child will make the effort to bring joy to you the more you make your child's enjoyment a focus of your interactions with him or her.

513 ***Request actions that match my child's developmental behavior.*** Limit your requests for your child to do or say things to behaviors that are within your child's range of accommodation. Your child will have difficulty responding to behaviors and communications that exceed his or her range of accommodation.

Practical Suggestions

- Review a videotape of you and your child playing together. Write down the behaviors that you have asked your child to do. Look up these behaviors on the *Developmental Rainbow* (Mahoney & Perales, 1996) or other developmental profile. Notice how your child was more reactive and engaged when you asked him or her to do things that were within his or her range of accommodation. Notice how he or she became passive or ignored you when you asked him or her to do things that are difficult (e.g., beyond his or her range of accommodation).
- Consider how you yourself respond when you are asked to do something that you do not know how to do.
- Increase your child's opportunities to be successful with you by mostly asking him or her to do things he or she has the developmental capabilities to do.

514 ***Act in ways that my child can act.*** When you interact with your child, modify what you do and the way you do it so that your behaviors mirror the kinds of activities that your child typically does.

Practical Suggestions

- Imitate some of your child's actions. Notice how your child stays with you and attends more to you when you do this.

- Play with the toys and objects that your child is playing with and in the same way as your child. Your child will attend and interact more actively when you interact with the toys and objects your child prefers.
- Review a videotape of you playing with your child. How well are you matching your actions to your child's spontaneous behavior?
- When you match your child's actions, talk with your child using words that fit your child's actions, such as *come, go, eat, mom, dog,* or *truck.* These words are more meaningful to your child and thus easier to learn than words like *two, three, red, yellow, horse,* and *barn.*

Developmental Domain: Communication

Communication refers to the ability of children to engage in conversational exchanges in which they express their feelings, needs, observations, and thoughts and respond to the requests, feelings, observations, and thoughts of others.

Pivotal Behavior: Joint Activity

CM-1 Joint Activity refers to the degree to which children engage in active, reciprocal interactions with their communication partner. Children's interactions with their partner are characterized by collaboration and exchange. Children and their partner direct their interactions toward each other and respond to each others' behaviors and cues.

Facts To Consider About Joint Activity

CM-101 Children's social interactions are their first conversations.

Children learn language as a result of engaging in more frequent and sophisticated communication with other people. *Before children learn to use words to communicate, they must first learn to engage in nonverbal social interactions.*

Conversation is the process whereby two or more people exchange sensations, emotions, observations, and thoughts. When children engage in social interaction with adults before they are able to speak, they are actually engaging in primitive conversations. *Children's earliest conversations involve exchanges of physical sensations (e.g., touch, movement, sound)* and are usually not conscious efforts to exchange information.

As children have more opportunities to engage in social interaction, they become increasingly conscious of this shared experience. Children learn to anticipate and play a more active role in these joint activities. The type of information they exchange becomes more complex, mirroring their developing awareness of their sensational world. By the time most children acquire their first words, this process has become very adultlike, to the point where children can communicate without words most of the information they will use their first words for. Before learning to say "mama," "dada," "more," "give me," "help me," and "I love you," children use sounds, babbling, gestures, and smiles to convey these concepts. Words have meaning to children only after they have learned to communicate the concepts these words represent nonverbally.

CM-102 Children with language delays are often delayed in nonverbal communication.

Children who have delayed language development often engage in infrequent nonverbal communication with their parents and others. This problem may result from a number of factors. First, they may prefer playing by themselves, even when other people are nearby. Second, they may avoid initiating contact with other people unless they are hungry, tired, uncomfortable, or have some other unmet need. Third, they may end interactions quickly, either by turning their face or bodies away when someone tries to initiate contact with them or by discontinuing social interaction after short periods of time.

Children develop their ability to communicate by interacting with others. *If children do not engage in frequent joint activities, they simply will not have sufficient opportunities to learn how to communicate.* So long as they are not interested in interacting with others or communicating nonverbally on a regular basis, they will have little interest in words or language.

Parents can help their children become more interested in and enjoy interacting with other people. They can do this by aggressively seeking opportunities to interact with their children. When parents communicate with their children, they should do and say the kinds of things their children do or say, follow their children's lead, and be animated and enthusiastic. If parents give in to their children's natural inclinations to be by themselves, their children will only occasionally engage in joint activities and will not have the amount of practice with preverbal conversation that they need to develop language and communication.

CM-103 Communication is an advanced level of social interaction: Children must be actively involved in joint activity to learn how to communicate.

Most adults have had the opportunity in high school or college to take a foreign language class. Instructors' attempts to engage students in conversations with the foreign language during class tend to be a contrived rather than a real communication experience. Typically, students learn vocabulary in these classes by memorizing the words in each week's lesson through rote repetition. Most foreign-language students are successful at learning words, phrases, and grammatical structures long enough to get a passing grade; however, few would claim to be proficient at communicating in that language, and most would be embarrassed to say even a few spontaneous phrases.

This experience illustrates the concept that language evolves from joint activity. In foreign-language classes, language instruction seldom occurs in the context of meaningful social exchanges with another person. To the contrary, students tolerate rather than participate actively in the communication experiences in these classes. They may have learned words, phrases, or grammatical structures, but in most cases did not learn how to use them to communicate. Memorizing words and becoming knowledgeable about the sounds and grammatical rules of a foreign language is not the same thing as learning to use that language to communicate.

Yet despite this experience, there is no mystery in how to learn to speak a foreign language. If we go to a foreign country and place ourselves in a situation where we have to communicate in that language, we will learn that language fairly rapidly. The need to socialize with others would force us to engage in joint interactions with them. Through this process we would begin to acquire the words and grammar we need to communicate.

Children learn how to communicate in the same way that adults learn a foreign language. If children are taught words in contexts that are not meaningful social experiences, they are unlikely to learn how to use these words to communicate. For example, we might try to teach a child a word by drawing his attention to a picture, labeling the picture, and asking the child to repeat it. The child might be successful at labeling the picture if we ask him to; however, the child is unlikely to ever use this word in routine social situations where the word would be appropriate—no different from one's success in learning a foreign language in high school or college.

Language and communication can be learned only in the context of joint activities with others. For example, when parents label an object or activity during joint activities, children are highly likely to remember the word and use it spontaneously in other situations. What makes the word memorable is that it is presented in the context of a meaningful social activity in which the word is relevant to an experience children are sharing with their parents.

CM-104 Joint activities occur when children and parents (a) interact equally and (b) have a common focus of attention.

Joint activity routines are situations in which children and their parents engage in the same physical or communicative activities. *Any interaction can help a child learn how to communicate so long as both the child and the parent are doing the same things together.* These interactions could occur during daily routines such as dressing, feeding, carrying or transporting, bathing, or putting children to sleep. They can also occur when parents and children play together. These episodes, which can last little more than a few minutes at a time, could involve games such as pat-a-cake or peek-a-boo as well as supporting and elaborating children's play with toys. The more parents and children engage in joint activities (i.e., do the same things together), the more rapidly children will learn to communicate.

Joint activity routines become predictable exchanges that create a safe context in which children can (a) practice new behaviors and (b) attempt to resolve challenges to their current way of thinking and communicating. Just as we adults learn new things best in familiar situations, so too *the familiarity of joint activity routines makes them excellent situations in which children can learn.* They allow children to participate in repetitive events that they can master. *Joint activities are effective so long as they are inventive, playful, and interesting to both children and adults.* Parents can enhance common routines such as pat-a-cake, row your boat, or games such as stacking, hiding, exchanging, and other events by adding new sounds, words, or movements.

CM-105 Joint activities do not always need to involve toys; parents can be children's most effective toy.

To build social relationships and learn to communicate, children need to learn how to interact with people for the pleasure of being with them and not just to satisfy their needs. The ways that parents interact with children shape children's ideas about how to relate to other people. *When parents routinely engage in one-to-one interactions with their children that focus on having fun with shared experiences and ideas, parents teach their children to enjoy being with people.* These encounters motivate children to seek opportunities to interact with other children and adults, which is essential for learning language and communication.

If children engage in too much solitary play, they are unlikely to notice how their parents do things and how they communicate. *By becoming their children's most valued toy, parents can help children learn to relate with other people on a personal basis.* To become an effective toy, parents can take on the characteristics of toys, such as being mobile and fun, providing surprises and challenges, being responsive to the way their children experience physical sensations, being more interesting than other distractions, and being available and manipulable by the child.

CM-106 Joint activity is a persistent lifestyle—not just occasional participation in games or activities.

To promote children's communication, it is helpful for parents to plan specific times during the day to engage in joint activities with their children. These planned episodes should not be longer than 5 to 10 minutes at a time. When parents engage in these scheduled joint activities, they need to make sure that they are reciprocal interactions that are focused on objects, activities, and topics that are of interest to their children.

In addition to these planned activities, *it is also important that joint activities become an integral, spontaneous part of children's daily routines.* For children who naturally seek out opportunities to socialize with others this should not be a problem. Each time these children initiate social contact, parents simply need to use RT strategies to sustain their children's involvement in the interaction.

If children have a tendency to seek out their parents and others only to get their needs met, these children will not obtain the opportunities for socialization they need to learn to communicate, unless their parents make conscious efforts to interact with them.

Some children with communication problems habitually ignore people. Parents must be careful not to accept this pattern of behavior by rationalizing that their children are happier playing by themselves. Parents should insert themselves into their children's activities so that they routinely have a social partner during their daily activities. *When parents are assertive in interacting with their children, children will eventually prefer to interact more with people than with objects.* Children will make rapid progress in learning how to communicate more effectively as this occurs.

Other children may stay in close proximity to people throughout the day, yet seldom socialize or communicate with them. Ironically, although these children are in constant proximity with others, they live a life of social isolation. Parents need to fight their children's tendency to be withdrawn and isolated. Whenever they are with them, they must make conscious efforts to engage their children in balanced, reciprocal interactions.

CM-107 The longer children remain engaged in joint activities, the more sophisticated their communication will become.

One of the most important things parents can do to help their children become communicators is to increase the amount of time they remain in interactions with them. Too often young children have brief, dead-end interactions with adults in which one partner complies with the requests or meets the needs of the other but do not sustain the interaction. A common example of this would be a parent asking her child, "Do you want to do this?" and the child responding with a brief word or behavior and then returning to his activity without communicating further.

By keeping children a little longer in interactions, parents provide their children increased opportunities for learning language. This is a far more effective way of helping children learn to communicate than trying to teach them words or phrases. Children will gain the practice they need to become effective communicators when their parents simply increase the amount they do with them. *Length of interaction is a more important goal for early language development than the numbers of words children learn.* Children will naturally increase their vocabulary and begin to use more language after they increase the length of their interactions.

CM-108 Children must learn to give in order to get.

To establish a rich routine of joint activities, *parents normally need to respond unconditionally to their child.* However, children also need to learn how to play an active, reciprocal role in interactions. *Children cannot only be the recipient of their parents' attention; they must also initiate actions and other interactive bids in return.*

In most cases, children develop this active role as a natural consequence of adults becoming increasingly responsive to them. However, children who are not interested in social interaction often tolerate being with and receiving attention from adults without giving anything back. There is nothing enjoyable about giving unconditional attention to children who barely notice the person who is trying to communicate with them. Furthermore, children will not become effective communicators until they learn to respond reciprocally to adults.

Most children who have problems engaging in social interaction eventually learn to become responsive to others when their parents are persistent and patient at being highly responsive to them. Yet, there are some children who will enjoy the attention and responsiveness of their parents but not respond reciprocally unless their parents pressure them to do this. One way parents can do this is by waiting for short periods of time (e.g., up to 10 seconds) after they have produced a turn for their children to give some indication of social recognition. *When parents inject this type of pressure into highly responsive joint activity routines, children will gradually learn to respond in order to get their parents' attention.* Parents need to be careful to balance the demands they place on their children, so that their pressure for their children to respond does not discourage them from remaining in the interaction.

Discussion Points

CM-101 Children's social interactions are their first conversations.

- Before children learn to use words to communicate, they must first learn to engage in nonverbal social interactions.
- Children's earliest conversations involve exchanges of physical sensations (e.g., touch, movement, sound).
- Children learn to communicate nonverbally by engaging in social interaction.

CM-102 Children with language delays are often delayed in nonverbal communication.

- Children who have language delays often have a low frequency of nonverbal communication.

- If children do not engage in frequent joint activities, they simply will not have sufficient opportunities to learn how to communicate.

CM-103 Communication is an advanced level of social interaction: Children must be actively involved in joint activity to learn how to communicate.

- Children learn how to communicate in the same way adults learn a foreign language.
- Language and communication can be learned only in the context of joint activities with others.

CM-104 Joint activities occur when children and parents (a) interact equally and (b) have a common focus of attention.

- Any interaction can help a child learn how to communicate so long as both the child and the parent are doing the same things together.
- The familiarity of joint activity routines makes them excellent situations in which children can learn.
- Joint activities are effective so long as they are inventive, playful, and interesting to both children and adults.

CM-105 Joint activities do not always need to involve toys; parents can be children's most effective toy.

- One-to-one interactions with children that focus on having fun with shared experiences and ideas help children learn to enjoy being with people.
- By becoming their children's most valued toy, parents help children learn to relate with other people.

CM-106 Joint activity is a persistent lifestyle—not just occasional participation in games or activities.

- Joint activities need to become an integral, spontaneous part of children's daily routines.
- When parents are assertive in interacting with their children, children will eventually prefer to interact more with people than with objects.

CM-107 The longer children remain engaged in joint activities, the more sophisticated their communication will become.

- Parents can help their children become communicators by increasing the amount of time they remain in interactions with them.
- Length of interaction is a more important goal for early language development than the numbers of words children learn.

CM-108 Children must learn to give in order to get.

- Joint activity normally begins with the adult responding unconditionally to the child.
- Children cannot only be the recipient of their parents' attention; they must also initiate actions and other interactive bids in return.

- When children are habitually unresponsive, adults should apply gentle pressure for children to respond to them.

RT Strategies That Promote Joint Activity

111 ***Be physically available and interactive.*** Be accessible or within your child's touch. Touch your child frequently to make the engagement more real for him or her.

Practical Suggestions

- Consider that being with your child and physically interacting with your child can be very different things. You are not physically available simply because you are with your child.
- Spend time together with your child by attending visually to what he or she is doing.
- Make sure that a substantial part of your time with your child involves physically interacting with him or her. Keep a chart or log of how much this actually occurs.

115 ***Expect my child to interact.*** Show by your face, hands, and body language that you are anticipating your child will do something with you. Act in animated ways to make this even more effective.

Practical Suggestions

- Allow your child time to initiate contact with you. Silent waiting provides the opportunity for your child to initiate an activity on his or her own.
- During silent waiting, wait with anticipation by using body, gestures, or facial signals for your child to interact.
- If your child attempts to move away before engaging in interaction, gently hold or restrain him or her until the child has completed one to two interactive turns with you.

123 ***Play back and forth with sounds.*** Your child may produce vocalizations or sounds that do not have obvious purpose or meaning. Interact with your child by simply imitating or responding promptly with animation to these vocalizations. If your child continues to vocalize with you, vary your vocalizations in response to him or her to transform this interaction into playful back-and-forth sound play.

Practical Suggestions

- Get into the habit of responding to your child's sounds, even when they are part of your child's self-play. The more you respond to your child's sounds, the more your child will communicate with sounds.

- Consider that when you get into a give-and-take rhythm of exchanging sounds with your child, you are teaching your child the social conventions about how to talk with others.
- Nursery rhymes and songs provide an excellent resource for back-and-forth sound play. Sing a few short phrases of a song, and wait for your child to make a sound or other action before singing the next few phrases.
- Limit your child's sounds or speech when it interrupts or prevents you from engaging in back-and-forth interaction. From the earliest phases of development, teach your child that communication is not a one-way street but requires giving you time to talk as well.

124 ***Get from my child as much as I give.*** For children to learn, they need to give in order to get. Expect your child to play an active role in interaction. Your child's developmental well-being is dependent on his or her being an active rather than a passive participant in interactions.

Practical Suggestions

- Use simple exchange games to practice showing your child how to give and not always to be on the taking end.
- Build a turn-taking habit. Help your child learn the social rule of give and take by making turn-taking a habit in play and communication.
- Get into a give-and-take rhythm of talking with your child so that your child will learn that interrupting is not appropriate.
- Share the terminations. Be sure that neither you nor your child is the one who always ends social contacts. At least half of the time you should determine when the interaction ends.

125 ***Communicate less so my child communicates more.*** Talking too much is one of the major obstacles to adults having balanced interactions with children. To learn how to speak, it is important for your child to hear language stimulation, but it is even more important for your child to practice the sounds and words he or she already knows. You will communicate less if you use short sentences, do not repeat what you have said, and wait for your child to say more. This may result in longer periods of silence or quiet during the interaction. However, your child will quickly learn to fill this void with his or her own vocalizations and language.

Practical Suggestions

- Consider how speaking in short sentences and saying less to your child will give your child more opportunity to do something during the interaction.
- Experiment using short, medium, and long sentences with your child. Observe how your child responds to different sentence lengths.
- Review a videotape of you interacting with your child. Count the number of times that you repeat what you say with your child.

- Keep track of the number of times you repeat yourself during 5 minutes of play with your child. Consider whether you are repeating yourself more than is necessary.

131 ***Play face-to-face games without toys.*** Use simple games with your child such as songs, nursery rhymes, hand games, and games with other parts of the body that require simple sequences in which your child can play an active role.

Practical Suggestions

- Consider the kinds of games that you have seen your own parents or other parents play with young children.
- Find books that describe simple games that parents can do with young children.
- Professionals can show parents how to modify games to make them balanced, interactive routines. It is especially important to simplify games that are difficult for children who are developmentally young.

414 ***Be more interesting than my child's distractions.*** Children learn more from their parents than from toys. Consequently, you need to become animated so that you are more attention-getting than the toys and other inanimate objects in your child's world that do little to help your child learn to socialize and communicate.

Practical Suggestions

- Use animation to regain your child's attention. If your child is not attentive to you, act in entertaining ways to gain his or her attention.
- Act like your child's favorite TV and video characters. Watch your child's TV and video programs, and act out the events that get your child's attention.
- Share in your child's excitement. When your child becomes interested and excited with his or her favorite toy, enter your child's world by using this toy to play with him or her.

422 ***Interact for fun.*** There are many reasons that parents interact with children. They can interact to take care of their children's physical needs, comfort their children, teach their children, or just be with them. Use this strategy to motivate yourself to spend at least one third of the interactions you have with your child focused on having fun.

Practical Suggestions

- Give your child opportunities to influence you in playful ways. You can promote this by making exaggerated reactions to the little things your child does.

- Become your child's favorite toy by acting like a toy your child can manipulate, control, and enjoy.
- Consider the importance of interacting with your child more during enjoyable times than during stressful ones. You are more likely to help your child learn when you join your child's enjoyable moments.

Developmental Domain: Communication

Pivotal Behavior: Joint Attention

CM-2 Joint Attention refers to the degree to which children have frequent bouts of eye contact and other sharing behaviors, such as vocalizations with their communication partner. Children show their partner what they want or are interested in by using vocalizations, gestures, looking, or words. They also follow the gestures, facial displays, eye gaze, or other communications their partners use to direct their attention.

Facts To Consider About Joint Attention

CM-201 Children learn the meaning of language by using context and nonverbal cues to decipher the relationship of words and phrases to the feelings, observations, objects, or actions they refer to.

If we were to go to a foreign country, how would we determine the meaning of the language of that country? Those who have had this experience can readily acknowledge that it is a difficult task, yet this is exactly what children must do to learn language. One of the first things to do is to determine the individual words. Listening to a foreign language is like listening to a constant flow of sound. At first it seems impossible to determine where one word ends and the other begins. However, if speakers communicate slowly, use only one or a few words at a time, and pause to mark their messages, it becomes easier to decipher the words they are speaking.

How well we determine meaning is dependent upon the effectiveness with which speakers use (a) cues such as facial features or eye gaze to display affect, (b) pointing and gesturing to direct attention, or (c) words that refer directly to what we are involved with. This can occur only if speakers are willing to adjust to our limited ability to perceive language and use context cues to determine the meaning of language.

Like adults who are learning a foreign language, *children learn the meaning of words from the context of their interactions with others*—by using the same kinds of context cues that adults use to learn a foreign language. In other words, *children depend on parents' gestures, eye gaze, smiles, voice intonation, and repetition of phrases to learn words.* They also rely on their *parents speaking slowly and distinctly and using words that label the feelings, actions, or objects with which their children are involved.*

CM-202 Children make eye contact with parents when parents persist at making eye contact with them.

There are three ways that mutual eye contact helps children learn how to communicate. First, *eye contact is one of the most basic ways of establishing a social relationship.* Only if there is mutual eye contact are adults and infants engaging in a social relationship.

Second, mutual *eye contact is one of the most direct ways of sharing physiological and emotional states.* Through eye contact, children and adults can communicate whether they are alert or fatigued; whether they feel happy, affectionate, or sad; or whether they are interested or disinterested.

Third, *parents and children use mutual eye contact to monitor each other's attention.* After repeated episodes of mutual eye gaze, children eventually learn to follow their parents as they shift their attention to various objects or features in the environment. Children will interpret the meaning of their parents' language in relationship to what they are attending to.

Similarly, by monitoring what their children are looking at, parents can determine whether their children are attending to them or to other objects or events. This enables parents to communicate using words that coincide with what their children are attending to, making it easier for children to understand the meaning of their parents' language.

It is relatively easy to establish eye contact with most young children. Children are usually interested in looking at the faces of familiar people, but if parents communicate without face-to-face contact, children's opportunities for eye contact are limited.

A potentially serious problem is when children are more interested in things than they are in people. Some children may be uninterested and even fearful, uncomfortable, or overstimulated by eye contact with another person, causing them to avoid eye contact and terminate interaction. Parents can establish eye contact with these children by getting into a face-to-face position with them. Because this position might be intrusive and unpleasant, parents need to make eye contact as soothing and entertaining as possible. When children terminate or avoid eye contact, parents should reposition themselves and try to reestablish eye contact.

CM-203 Children attend to their parents when parents are attentive to their children.

An important prerequisite for children who are learning new skills is that they pay attention to the adults with whom they are interacting. A common problem associated with children who have developmental problems, however, is that they have a very short attention span. In some instances, this problem may not be a problem at all. That is, children who are developmentally young typically attend to people and activities for very short periods of time. As children attain higher levels of developmental functioning, they naturally increase the amount of time they attend. Insofar as children's attention is influenced by their level of developmental functioning, it is no surprise that when children have delayed development, they often display attentional skills similar to younger, typically developing children. However, as these children mature, they should increase the amount of time they sustain their attention.

Children's attentiveness is also related to their behavioral style, or temperament, which is influenced by their biological or genetic makeup. For example, children who have a predisposition to be very active will naturally spend less time attending to activities in which their physical activity is restricted. In contrast, children who are temperamentally "easy" will attend for longer periods of time, because they are physiologically built that way.

If children have difficulties attending that are not typical for their developmental age, parents need to make extra efforts to gain their attention. One way to help children become attentive, even if they are very active, is to be highly responsive to their interests and activities. *When parents are attentive to activities or behaviors that children are interested in, almost instantly children become attentive and cooperative with them.* When parents are responsive, they are more likely to ask their children to pay attention to information that is related to their current interests or activities. *After children successfully attend to their parents during activities that are interesting, they will better attend to their parents in less interesting situations.*

CM-204 Children learn to follow their parents' focus of attention when parents use multiple cues to direct their attention.

Children cannot determine what a word means simply by hearing someone say it. Rather, *to determine what words mean, children rely on adults to direct or guide their attention to the feelings, objects, or events to which the words refer.* Until children become skilled at being able to follow adults' focus of attention, they are highly dependent on adults using concrete strategies such as physically helping them to touch or see the object, action, or attribute to which the word refers. Children are not born with the ability to follow adults' focus of attention. Their ability to detect and understand what adults are referring or attending to is a developmental skill children learn gradually during the first 2 years of life.

One way *parents help children learn to follow their attention is by exaggerating their use of nonverbal cues* when they communicate with them. These nonverbal cues include showing, touching, pointing, or using exaggerated facial features that depict the meaning of a word. They also include repeated instructions for their children to attend to certain aspects of the environment until they have made certain that children are aware of what they are referring to (e.g., "See the pretty doll? Shayla, look at that! Look at that doll over there!"). In addition, parents can accompany these directions with exaggerated intonation, accentuated facial features (such as a surprise face), and clearly pointing to the object.

Although almost all parents naturally use nonverbal communication with their children, it is important to emphasize this with children who are having difficulty learning language. As children grow older, this type of communication may seem to be too babylike; but no matter how old children are, if they are having difficulty acquiring language, nonverbal cues are essential to helping them determine what their parents are talking about. Children simply cannot learn language efficiently if they have difficulty determining to what their parents' communication refers.

CM-205 Children learn to direct their parents' attention by controlling their parents' behavior.

To learn to communicate, children must be able to direct others' attention to what they want, either to share contact or to get information. Directing parents' attention involves two different acts: (a) requesting parents to notice something (e.g., "Look at that!") and (b) asking for information or assistance (e.g., "What's that?"). These elements of joint attention are referred to as "directing the adults' focus of attention."

During the first 12 months of life, children direct parents' attention more by accident than on purpose. When a child looks toward an object and the parent responds by picking it up, it is likely that the child is not aware of his or her ability to influence what the parent did. At about 9 to 12 months of age, many children begin using concrete behaviors to direct adults' attention. For example, they might lead their parents by the hand to what they want their parents to notice. This type of physical directing is effective because it helps parents know exactly what the child wants. However, compared with the way parents direct the attention of others, it is highly inefficient. Parents use gestures, vocalizations, or actual words to indicate what they want others to attend to. Because children's primitive ways of directing attention requires so much physical effort, during their second year of life children seek more efficient ways of directing attention by using nonverbal gestures, signals, and, eventually, words.

What causes children to modify how they direct parents' attention? One important factor is the development of their ability to use signs and symbols. Children cannot use gestures to direct others' attention until they understand that gestures can be used to represent something other than what they are (e.g., reaching using outstretched fingers is not only an act of reaching but represents the idea "I want that"). But it takes time for children to realize that the same behaviors they used to obtain an object, such as extending their hand, can also be used as a symbol to communicate "I want that." Children must become aware that their behavior is not only a personal attempt to get something but is also a social behavior that can affect the people with whom they are interacting.

A second factor in how children modify the way they direct their parents' attention is that they become aware of their ability to control the behaviors of others. Children learn to use language to direct the behavior of others only if they first understand that they have the ability to control others. Children's feelings of control derive from their becoming aware that their parents and others respond to their behavior. When parents respond to their children, they are allowing their children to exert control over them. *The more often children experience controlling what their parents do with them, the more quickly they become aware of their ability to direct their parents' attention.*

Unless children learn to direct parents' focus of attention, their opportunities to use parents as a resource for words, names, or other information about objects, activities, or experiences will be restricted. Children will make dramatic improvements in the rate they learn new language only after they develop this critical skill.

C-206 It takes time for children to learn to develop joint attention.

Children normally develop their joint attentional skills during the first 24 months of life. *Children who have learning or developmental problems take much longer to learn to engage in joint attention than do typically developing children.* For example, if a child is developing at a rate of 2 months for every 3 months of chronological age, that child has a 33% delay in her development. This child will take about one third longer to develop joint attention than a typically developing child and will thus likely be about 36 months old before she fully attains joint attention.

What are the implications of this? First, for parents to help their children communicate, particularly through the first 3 years of life, *it is important to make mutual eye contact with them.* This is a powerful form of attention that makes it easier for children to figure out what their parents are referring to. It also makes it easier for parents to follow their children's attention and helps parents use language that is directly related to their children's experiences.

Second, *parents need to be as clear as possible about what they are communicating.* They can never provide too many context and nonverbal cues with their children. The easier parents make it for their children to understand what they are talking about, the sooner their children will acquire and use words. If children have to work hard to understand what their parents are saying, conversations will be less meaningful, making it more difficult for them to learn language.

Third, *parents need to engage in interactions that are highly responsive to their children's behavior and intentions.* Prompt and frequent responses to children's behavior helps children become aware of how their behavior can be used to direct the attention and behavior of others.

Discussion Points

CM-201 Children learn the meaning of language by using context and nonverbal cues to decipher the relationship of words and phrases to the feelings, observations, objects, or actions they refer to.

- Children learn the meanings of words from the context of their interactions with others.
- Children depend on parents' gestures, eye gaze, smiles, voice intonation, and repetition of phrases to learn words.
- Parents should speak slowly and distinctly and label the feelings, actions, or objects with which their children are involved.

CM-202 Children make eye contact with parents when parents persist in making eye contact with them.

- Eye contact is one of the most basic ways of establishing a social relationship.
- Eye contact is one of the most direct ways of sharing physiological and emotional states.
- Parents and children use mutual eye contact to monitor each other's attention.

CM-203 Children attend to their parents when parents are attentive to their children.

- To learn new developmental skills, children must pay attention to the adults with whom they are interacting.
- When parents are attentive to activities or behaviors that children are interested in, almost instantly children become attentive and cooperative with them.
- After children successfully attend to their parents during activities that are interesting, they will better attend to their parents in less interesting situations.

CM-204 Children learn to follow their parents' focus of attention when parents use multiple cues to direct their attention.

- To determine what words mean, children rely on adults to direct or guide their attention to the feelings, objects, or events to which the words refer.
- Parents help children learn to follow their attention by exaggerating their use of nonverbal cues.

CM-205 Children learn to direct their parents' attention by controlling their parents' behavior.

- To learn to communicate, children must be able to direct others' attention to what they want, either to share contact or to get information.
- The more often children experience controlling what their parents do, the more quickly they become aware of their ability to direct their attention.

CM-206 It takes time for children to learn to develop joint attention.

- Children who have learning or developmental problems take much longer to learn to engage in joint attention than do typically developing children.
- To promote children's joint attention, parents must make mutual eye contact, provide context and nonverbal cues, and be highly responsive to children's behaviors and nonverbal communications.

RT Strategies That Promote Joint Attention

113 ***Get into my child's world.*** Make three adjustments to view the world as your child does. First, establish a mutual physical relationship with your child. Make eye contact and interact on the same physical level as your child. Second, interact by playing or communicating like your child. Mimicking behaviors such as babbling, cooing, smiling, and making a playful face let your child know that you are willing to interact on your child's terms. Third, consciously strive to try to understand the world as your child does. Remember that most experiences do not have the same meaning to your child as they do to you.

Practical Suggestions

- Play with your child in a face-to-face position. Interact with your child on his or her physical level so that he or she does not have to look up to see you.
- Make eye contact with your child when you are playing or interacting with him or her.
- Consider that as your child begins to experience the world, he or she must make sense of his or her experiences. Your child sees and understands the world very differently than you do.

- Consider that as your child matures, he or she will continually rediscover his or her world. The world as your child understood it at the 3-month stage of development takes on a new meaning at the 9-month stage. The changes in thinking and understanding that occur in the early years of development lead your child to perceive and experience objects or events he or she was familiar with from a dramatically new perspective.
- Play in the small ways your child does without pressuring him or her to do anything other than stay involved in the interaction.

211 ***Observe my child's behavior.*** Observe your child methodically. Notice and listen to the subtle signs and sounds your child uses in various situations.

Practical Suggestions

- Make a list of your child's typical behaviors. Then imitate your child for several days (e.g., 1 week). After this period, write down another list describing what your child does when he or she plays or communicates. Did imitating your child make you more aware of the little things he or she does? Why do you think this happened?
- If you are concerned that your child do something or learn something in particular, it will become more difficult for you to see all the things your child is actually doing. Observing and understanding what your child is currently doing will make you more effective at helping your child learn what you would like him or her to do.
- Professionals can lead parents through observations of their children by describing their own observations while either playing with the child or watching the child on videotape.
- Professionals can ask parents to describe videotaped observations of their children playing and comment immediately about behaviors that parents did not describe.

222 ***Respond immediately to little behaviors.*** Little behaviors are behaviors such as burps, change of visual regard, kicking legs, waving hands, facial displays, and so forth.

Practical Suggestions

- Even if your child is not directing his or her "little behaviors" to you, and even though these behaviors have no apparent purpose or meaning, by responding immediately you can transform these behaviors into meaningful social interactions.
- Immediate responding to your child's solitary play and self-speech will help your child become more aware of you and more apt to engage in social exchanges.
- Review videotaped observations to see how quickly you respond to your child's behavior.

312 ***Imitate my child's actions and communications.*** You can imitate any behavior that your child produces. If your child has little interest in interacting with you, you can get your child's attention by imitating behaviors that may even be inappropriate or bizarre (e.g., rocking, thumb-sucking, loud shrieking or crying, throwing objects). Imitation has two functions. First, it helps to establish an interactive relationship with your child that is based upon what your child is doing. Second, imitation gives your child an immediate opportunity to control what you do.

Practical Suggestions

- Notice how imitation encourages your child to increase the variety and scope of his or her behavior and does not reinforce undesirable behavior.
- Consider that one important outcome of imitation is that your child will enjoy and have fun controlling what you do.
- When you imitate your child's nonverbal or verbal communication, you are helping your child learn to use his or her early communication skills to have an effect on others.

411 ***Be animated.*** Children are more likely to stay interacting with adults who are childlike and exciting. Help your child interact and pay attention to you by making conscious efforts to be animated.

Practical Suggestions

- Notice how it is easier to get your child to interact and keep him or her in interaction when you use expressive faces and make games out of your child's sounds and actions.
- Exaggerate your movements when you are playing with your child. Your child will attend more closely to your movements when you move in interesting, unpredictable ways.
- Even if your child has serious developmental problems, your child is more likely to learn when you interact with him or her more as a play partner than a teacher. Help your child learn by playing in your child's world of actions.
- How animated parents are with their children is often a function of their personality and how they feel at the moment. However, even people who naturally tend to be animated with children, often need to make a conscious effort to do so.

415 ***Accompany my communications with intonation, pointing, and nonverbal gestures.*** Make sure to communicate with your child using inflection, intonation, and nonverbal gestures and cues.

Practical Suggestions

- Observe how your child is more attentive when you communicate with inflected versus monotonic voice and when you accompany your communications with nonverbal gestures.

- Review a videotape of you communicating with your child. Then rate how well you think you are using intonation and nonverbal communication with your child. How can you make your communications with your child livelier?

424 ***Repeat activities my child enjoys.*** Keep doing activities that your child finds fun and amusing. The more you emphasize these activities, the more you and your child will enjoy being with each other.

Practical Suggestions

- Unlike adults, children may do things many times before they get tired of the activity. When you repeat activities your child enjoys, you may tire of the activity long before your child does. However, if you continue this activity to promote your child's enjoyment, your child will learn that interacting with you is an enjoyable activity.
- Children develop a sense of humor by parents joining in their amusement. The more you support activities your child enjoys, the more your child will learn to share amusing and enjoyable things with you. Your child will make the effort to bring joy to you the more you make your child's enjoyment a focus of your interactions with him or her.

522 ***Follow my child's focus of attention.*** What your child is paying attention to is indicated by what he or she is looking at, listening to, or touching. The sounds, objects, people, or actions that your child attends to are all reflections of his or her interests. You must become sensitive and responsive to the subtle cues that reflect your child's focus of attention. Continue to follow your child as his or her attention shifts from one thing to another.

Practical Suggestions

- Consider that young children become absorbed in their immediate experiences. Children's activities and what they attend to are dominated by their immediate interests. As children lose interest in something, they quickly shift the focus of their attention to aspects of the environment that seem more captivating.
- What your child is interested in is partly dependent on his or her current level of developmental functioning. For example, midway in the first year of development, children are captivated by the physical properties of objects such as taste, texture, shape, and sound. Later in the first year, as children's development changes, children are more interested in the function of objects—what they can do—than they are in the properties of objects.
- The more you follow your child's focus of attention, the greater insight you will develop about how your child perceives and understands the world.

Developmental Domain: Communication

Pivotal Behavior: Vocalization

CM-3 Vocalization refers to the degree to which children practice or repeat sounds including grunting, vocalizations, singing, or words. Children vocalize frequently when they are alone and when they are with others. Vocalization refers only to the frequency of sound production, without regard to its complexity or meaning.

Facts To Consider About Vocalization

CM-301 Children learn to produce sounds by practicing their vocalizations.

Deaf children typically produce sounds during the first 4 to 5 months of life. These sounds are indistinguishable from sounds produced by children with normal hearing, yet at approximately 5 months of age their vocalizations decrease dramatically, to the point that many deaf children produce no vocalizations at all.

Like deaf children, hearing children also undergo transformations in the quality of their vocalizations at the 5-month age of development. In contrast, at about 5 months the sounds of children without hearing impairment begin to take on some of the characteristics of the language to which they are exposed. As children approach the one-word stage of language development, their vocalizations have most of the features of spoken language, such that many of their vocalizations may be mistaken for real words.

The fact that children with hearing impairment are able to produce sounds shortly after birth indicates that *initially children's sound production is an automatic, biological response.* However, the dramatic decline in vocal production by deaf children at 5 months of age—as well as the development of sounds produced by children who hear, which continues through 5 years of age—indicates that *children's long-term vocal development depends on receiving vocal feedback to their sounds, which encourages them to practice and produce more complex vocalizations.*

Parents can have a significant impact on the rate that children practice vocalizations by making sure that they respond to each of the vocalizations their children produce. Even children who do not vocalize much will increase the rate they practice vocalizing if their parents become highly responsive to the few vocalizations that they do make.

CM-302 Children must make sounds before they will speak.

For children to attain the vocal proficiency needed to produce their first words, they must spend considerable time during their first 2 years of life practicing sounds, both by themselves and with others. *If children are not proficient at vocalizing, they will not produce words, even if they have the cognitive and social skills needed for learning language.* This means that parents and others need to make special efforts to engage quiet children in vocal exchanges. Unless these children become habitual vocalizers when they interact with others, they will find it difficult to attempt pronouncing words. This will interfere with the development of their verbal communication

COMMUNICATION

skills. Parents must not let their children communicate only by using gestures or other nonvocal communication. *They must make every effort to offset their children's tendencies to be quiet by being highly responsive to the slightest vocalizations their children make.* They must make sure that they vocalize continually when they interact with their children and use sounds or words that match their children's.

Parents should avoid using language their children are not yet using. Rather, they should produce the kinds of nonverbal sounds their children are already producing by imitating children's noises, playing back-and-forth sound games, or taking turns singing songs.

CM-303 Quiet babies make quiet adults, who make quieter children.

How children behave when they interact with their parents can have a dramatic effect on the way their parents interact with them. *If children are quiet when they interact with their parents, their quietness may cause their parents also to become quiet.* If children's natural tendencies to be quiet cause their parents to vocalize less with them, these children in turn will receive less verbal feedback than they would if they were more vocal. This *decreased verbal feedback can reinforce and strengthen quiet children's inclination not to vocalize or talk.* This makes it even more difficult for these children to attain the vocal fluency they need to be able to speak.

As a result, parents need to be careful about how they interact with their quiet babies. They must guard against being seduced into silence by their children's quietness. They must make special efforts to constantly use simple vocalizations with their children, and they must become highly responsive to the few subtle vocalizations their children produce. These types of interactive exchanges will encourage their children to vocalize more and will combat their tendencies to be quiet. It will help their children develop the vocal skills they need to be able to produce words.

CM-304 Children may be quiet when they have motor impairments that impede their ability to make sounds.

Children are often able to produce various speech sounds in some words but not in others. Combining sounds requires intricate movements that can be very different in different sound contexts. For example, a *b* is not just a *b*. Different muscle combinations are needed to make a *b* for *boat, baby, brother, beanbag, bye-bye,* and *baa baa, black sheep.*

The complex combinations of muscle movements needed for producing sounds are relatively easy for most children. However, for children who have developmental problems, such tasks may be difficult and frustrating. *Many children with language delays tend to be quiet and do not vocalize much because they have motor difficulties that interfere with their oral–motor development.* This may be a particular problem for children with general motor problems, such as children with Down syndrome and cerebral palsy, as well as for children with apraxia (dyspraxia) and other speech problems.

Quiet children must be encouraged to develop their vocal abilities to prevent them from developing the habit of communicating without sounds. Parents can encourage their children to practice sounds by engaging in interactions that involve playful, reciprocal exchanges of sounds. Even if children have oral–motor problems, over time this type of practice will improve children's oral–motor coordination. Ultimately, this will help children develop the skills they need to produce complex sounds, words, and word combinations. The more children are encouraged to babble, use jargon, or play with sounds, the quicker they will develop the oral–motor proficiency needed to become effective vocalizers.

CM-305 Vocalization (vocal play) leads to more conventional sound production.

Reciprocal play with sounds allows adults to show children more mature ways of vocalizing. While interacting with children, parents can model conventional sounds immediately after children attempt to produce sounds or words. By responding to children's immature sounds with conventional sounds that match children's communicative attempts, parents have a greater likelihood of encouraging children to practice. The more this exchange of sounds is matched to children's current efforts to produce sounds, the more children will become aware of how they sound and thus will be open to change.

A very helpful game for children learning to speak is sound imitation. In this type of exchange, parents first imitate the child, then vary their imitations to more closely approximate conventional sounds and words. These exchanges encourage children to play back and forth with sounds. They enable parents to demonstrate how to produce more mature speech sounds.

Many parents are anxious to transform their children's sounds into words. However, they will be more successful at helping children learn to talk by simply playing back and forth with sounds. It is easier for children to sustain their involvement in sound exchanges when parents focus more on helping them practice sounds that more closely resemble adults' sound patterns than on saying real words.

CM-306 Children develop oral–motor skills most effectively in social communicative contexts—not in rote, repetitive drills.

Many professionals recommend that children engage in oral–motor exercises to prepare for speech. These exercises are rote, repetitive drills designed to help children learn the vocal-motor skills required for speech. However, because speech sounds are reflexive and have different muscular requirements when they combine with other sounds, a more efficient procedure for helping children develop the muscles for speech is by practicing speech sounds in communicative episodes that occur throughout the day.

Tongue, lip, and other oral–motor exercises may be recommended to strengthen children's oral–motor system. Although these exercises have some benefit, they fall far short of the kind of direct exercise children get from practicing sounds with their parents. *Children are more likely to practice their speech sounds with communication partners who make interactions enjoyable and provide models of how to produce the next sound or word.*

Speech is a social event, not just a motor action. Consequently, making sounds for speech is much more than a physical training issue—it is also a social issue. To learn appropriate speech sounds, children not only need to learn to physically produce sounds, they also need to experience how others make sounds so that they can use this feedback to modify their primitive sounds into more conventional sounds.

To learn to speak clearly, children need to attend to their conversational partners and engage in frequent interactions in which they can fine tune their sounds to those they get back from others. Oral–motor training that is conducted as a rote exercise as opposed to a social event does little to help children learn to use oral–motor skills in the rapid-fire interactions that take place during routine conversations.

Discussion Points

CM-301 Children learn to produce sounds by practicing their vocalizations.

- Initially children's sound production is an automatic, biological response.
- Children's long-term vocal development depends on receiving vocal feedback to their sounds, which encourages them to practice and produce more complex vocalizations.

CM-302 Children must make sounds before they will speak.

- If children are not proficient at vocalizing, they will not produce words, even if they have the cognitive and social prerequisites for learning language.
- Parents must make every effort to offset their children's tendencies to be quiet by being highly responsive to the slightest vocalizations their children make.

CM-303 Quiet babies make quiet adults, who make quieter children.

- If children are quiet when they interact with their parents, their quietness may cause their parents also to become quiet.
- Decreased verbal feedback from parents can reinforce and strengthen quiet children's inclination not to vocalize or talk.

CM-304 Children may be quiet when they have motor impairments that impede their ability to make sounds.

- Many children with language delays tend to be quiet and do not vocalize much because they have motor difficulties that interfere with their oral–motor development.
- Quiet children must be encouraged to develop their vocal abilities to prevent them from developing the habit of communicating without sounds.

CM-305 Vocalization (vocal play) leads to more conventional sound production.

- Reciprocal play with sounds allows adults to show children more mature ways of vocalizing.
- Children sustain their involvement in sound exchanges when parents focus more on helping them practice sounds that more closely resemble adults' sound patterns than on actually saying real words.

CM-306 Children develop oral–motor skills most effectively in social communicative contexts—not in rote, repetitive drills.

- Children are more likely to practice their speech sounds with communication partners who make interactions enjoyable and provide models of how to produce the next sound or word.
- To learn to speak clearly, children need to attend to their conversational partners and engage in frequent interactions in which they can fine tune their sounds to those they get back from others.

RT Strategies That Promote Vocalization

123 ***Play back and forth with sounds.*** Your child may produce vocalizations or sounds that do not have an obvious purpose or meaning. Interact with your child by simply imitating or responding promptly with animation to these vocalizations. If your child continues to vocalize with you, vary your vocalizations in response to him or her to transform this interaction into playful back-and-forth sound play.

Practical Suggestions

- Get into the habit of responding to your child's sounds, even when they are part of your child's self-play. The more you respond to your child's sounds, the more your child will communicate with sounds.
- Consider that when you get into a give-and-take rhythm of exchanging sounds with your child, you are teaching your child the social conventions about how to talk with others.
- Nursery rhymes and songs provide an excellent resource for back-and-forth sound play. Sing a few short phrases of a song, and wait for your child to make a sound or other action before singing the next few phrases.
- Limit your child's sounds or speech when it interrupts or prevents you from engaging in back-and-forth interaction. From the earliest phases of development, teach your child that communication is not a one-way street but requires giving you time to talk as well.

125 ***Communicate less so my child communicates more.*** Talking too much is one of the major obstacles to adults' having balanced interactions with children. To learn how to speak, it is important for your child to hear language stimulation, but it is even more important for your child to practice the sounds and words he or she already knows. You will communicate less if you use short sentences, do not repeat yourself, and wait for your child to say more. This may result in longer periods of silence or quiet during the interaction. However, your child will quickly learn to fill this void with his or her own vocalizations and language.

Practical Suggestions

- Consider how speaking in short sentences and saying less to your child will give your child more opportunity to do something during the interaction.

- Experiment using short, medium, and long sentences with your child. Observe how your child responds to different sentence lengths.
- Review a videotape of you interacting with your child. Count the number of times that you repeat what you say with your child.
- Keep track of the number of times you repeat yourself during 5 minutes of play with your child. Consider if you are repeating yourself more than is necessary.

222 ***Respond immediately to little behaviors.*** Little behaviors are behaviors such as burps, change of visual regard, kicking legs, waving hands, facial displays, and others.

Practical Suggestions

- Even if your child is not directing his or her "little behaviors" to you, and even though these behaviors have no apparent purpose or meaning, by responding immediately you can transform these behaviors into meaningful social interactions.
- Responding immediately to your child's solitary play and self-speech will help your child become more aware of you and more apt to engage in social exchanges.
- Review videotaped observations to see how quickly you respond to your child's behavior.

312 ***Imitate my child's actions and communications.*** You can imitate any behavior that your child produces. If your child has little interest in interacting with you, you can get your child's attention by imitating behaviors that may be inappropriate or bizarre (e.g., rocking, thumb-sucking, loud shrieking or crying, throwing objects). Imitation has two functions. First, it helps to establish an interactive relationship with your child that is based upon what your child is doing. Second, imitation gives your child an immediate opportunity to control what you do.

Practical Suggestions

- Notice how imitation encourages your child to increase the variety and scope of his or her behavior and does not reinforce undesirable behavior.
- Consider that one important outcome of imitation is that your child will enjoy and have fun controlling what you do.
- When you imitate your child's nonverbal or verbal communication, you are helping your child learn to use his or her early communication skills to have an effect on others.

515 ***Communicate the way my child communicates.*** Communicate in ways that your child is currently able to do (e.g., respond to your child's movements with movement and gestures, respond to sounds with sounds, and respond to one- or two-word utterances with one- or two-word utterances).

Practical Suggestions

- Notice that when you communicate more like your child, your child communicates more with you. Interact with your child for 2 to 3 minutes using the types of words, inflections, or gestures your child uses. Then interact with your child for another 2 to 3 minutes communicating with the type of language you would use with an adult. Keep track of the amount of time your child is actively involved in interaction in these two situations. Consider why these differences occur and what implications they have for helping your child learn to speak.
- Talk baby talk. Childcare books used to advise parents not to talk "baby talk" to their children because it was believed that children needed exposure to adult models of language to learn how to communicate in a mature way. More recently, however, child development research has reported that children are more likely to attend to and participate in conversations when their parents use baby talk.

Developmental Domain: Communication

Pivotal Behavior: Intentional Communication

CM-4 Intentional Communication refers to the degree to which children attempt to make their intentions known to their communication partner. Children are intentional communicators when they are effective at using nonverbal communication, words, or both to make their needs, feelings, and observations known to others. They use the words and language they know to communicate their intentions.

Facts To Consider About Intentional Communication

CM-401 Intentional communication occurs when children get others to understand their feelings, needs, and observations.

Learning to communicate intentionally evolves gradually as children become aware of their ability to convey their feelings, needs, and observations to others. This is a complex process. It begins with children using instinctive behaviors such as crying, looking, or reaching. As children recognize how these behaviors elicit predictable reactions from others, they begin to discover their capacity to convey their needs, feelings, and observations. They become aware that they can use these behaviors to fulfill their desire for nurturance, comfort, and social contact. Children develop intentional communication by first learning to use nonvocal signals (e.g., smiling, reaching), then learning to use vocalizations, and finally learning to use words to communicate their feelings, observations, and needs.

The development of intentional communication is influenced by several factors, including children's (a) increasing awareness of their selves and the world about them, (b) mastery of their ability to produce vocalizations and gestures, (c) ability to remember and use symbols to represent events, and (d) desire to become more effective at making their intentions known to others.

Language development is propelled by children's increasing awareness and understanding of their ability to communicate their intentions. *If children have no interest in making their intentions known to others, they have no reason to learn to use words or to try to understand the meaning of words.*

Long before children acquire their first words, they develop sophisticated methods of letting others know how they feel, what they want, and what they are interested in looking at or doing. Unless children develop these skills, they will have little interest in using words to communicate during their routine interactions with others, even if they are capable of learning words through rote memorization. However, as children become more proficient at communicating their feelings, needs, and observations with nonverbal signals, *their increasing desire to convey their intentions motivates them to notice and learn the words and communication devices that parents and others use to communicate with them.* This process enables children to acquire and begin using an astonishing amount of language in relatively short periods of time.

Consequently, the key to helping children learn words to communicate is to make sure they have frequent opportunities to communicate nonverbally with others. Through this process children not only learn the meaning of words, they also develop an appreciation of how words can be used to communicate the feelings, needs, and observations they desire to share with others.

CM-402 The first step toward becoming an intentional communicator is understanding that gestures and vocalizations can be used to express feelings and needs.

Children's communications are fostered by parents and adults who treat children's behavior as if it had meaning. For example, if a child moves her hand unintentionally, parents can transform this movement into a communicative greeting and respond to it by saying "hello!" *Any sound or movement can become a communicative behavior if it regularly has an effect on a partner.* At first, communication is a connection between persons rather than an exchange of intended meanings. Infants begin to communicate as their parents respond to the primitive unintentional behaviors they produce.

Parents cannot wait for children to produce intentional communication before they respond communicatively to children's nonverbal signals. Rather, they need to respond to the multitude of subtle, unintentional behaviors children produce, so that children learn to recognize that anything they do can have a communicative effect. Children need to become aware that their behavior can get someone's attention, send information, or communicate their intention. Children send messages all the time, even when they are not intending to do so. If parents ignore their children's little sounds and movements, they can inadvertently discourage their children from using them as a means for social communication.

The only way children learn that their gestures and vocalizations can be used to express feelings and needs (i.e., become a tool for intentional communication) is by noticing the effect they have on others. *The less often parents respond to children's unintentional signals, the longer it takes children to recognize the power of these signals to convey their intentions.*

CM-403 Children become intentional communicators to the degree that their early nonverbal behaviors have effects on others.

The desire to share feelings and ideas is a basic drive of all children, regardless of their developmental level or language problems. Although this drive is stronger in some than in others, all children are motivated to learn language to enhance their effectiveness at communicating. Consequently, language does not evolve simply because of biological growth or increased oral–motor control. Rather, *children learn language because of their strong motivation to develop more effective methods of communicating with others.*

There are two ways that children can learn about the effectiveness of their communications at expressing their intentions. One is when parents and adults inform children directly about the inadequacy of their communication *by not responding* to their communication or *by correcting* them and telling them that they are using inappropriate words to communicate. For example, in preschool classrooms, teachers sometimes refuse to serve juice to children at snacktime if they use inappropriate forms of communicating for juice, such as looking, reaching, or vocalizing.

Children receive juice only when they make an effort to say the more appropriate form, "I want juice."

Another way *children can learn about the ineffectiveness of their communication is by discovering without pressure from adults that their communication has not been effective at conveying their intentions.* In this situation, adults let children know that their communications are inadequate by misinterpreting their intentions. As children recognize that they are not conveying the intentions they are trying to communicate, they will attempt to clarify their communication by varying their signals or behaviors. Children discover the inadequacy of their communication by the way adults respond to them. When adults' responses mismatch their intention, children will eventually recognize that they need to learn and use more effective ways of expressing their intentions.

There is increasing research evidence that the method in which children discover the limitations of their communication on their own is more effective at helping them learn to communicate than the method in which adults let children know more directly by ignoring incorrect communication forms or pressuring children to communicate in certain ways. If adults ignore or discourage children's incorrectly produced communications, they make it difficult for children to engage in communication at all, thus lessening their desire to communicate. However, when children discover the limitations of their communication from the mismatch of adult responses to their intentions, they still feel encouraged to communicate, because adults are reinforcing their attempts to communicate by responding to them, even though their responses are not matched to the child's intentions.

Correcting children's communication by refusing to respond to lower levels of communication is a case of "throwing out the baby with the bath water." In attempting to encourage children to produce correct forms of communication, adults are also discouraging children from communicating at all.

C-404 Children's early communications do not have to be understood, only responded to.

Parents do not need to understand every communication their children make. In fact, most of children's early communications are often unintentional and are not easily interpretable. If parents focus on children being clear too early, children will find communication difficult and unrewarding. The most important consideration for children learning to communicate is that they communicate frequently, easily, and without judgment. Parents need to make sure that their children become confident and fluid communicators. Children should not have to worry about mistakes or be self-conscious about their communication. They will learn more mature ways of communicating after they feel that they can communicate nonverbally without stress and enjoy communicating.

Learning to communicate is a physically, socially, and cognitively difficult task for young children. As a result, any interruptions, corrections, or other negative responses by parents can discourage children from attempting to communicate. This is even more important for children with language problems. Learning to communicate is more difficult for these children than it is for typically developing children. Parents must communicate with these children in ways that are easy and about meanings that are relevant to them. *Imposing certain ways of communicating may only discourage children from practicing the interactive behaviors they need to master to become habitual communicators.*

Parents whose children have language problems are naturally anxious for their children to do things "right." Nonetheless, *it is more important that children become communicators with whatever means available, however unclear, than that they communicate clearly.* Only after children are highly motivated to communicate will they be receptive to language corrections that, earlier, would have discouraged them from communicating.

CM-405 Children's first words describe their actions, experiences, and nonverbal communications.

Many parents try to teach children who are beginning to talk words that have limited use in daily communication. As a result, many children with language problems know words for colors, animals, time, and other concepts that are typically taught in school but do not know words for objects, actions, and relationships that are part of their daily interests and experiences. *Words are useful only if they relate to children's immediate experiences.* The people or actions that directly affect children, and the objects and events that children genuinely care about, are the best candidates for their first words. These words are more likely to become a part of children's natural vocabulary than concepts like numbers, letters, and colors because they reflect children's normal thoughts and intentions.

Research on early language development has shown that *children's first words are about actions, objects, and agents (doers) that they experience.* Parents can help their children communicate more quickly if they teach them words for their current experiences and nonverbal communications. Children's actions become their thoughts, and their thoughts become their words. Because we have direct access only to children's actions, their actions are the best place to begin giving them words.

CM-406 Children learn words and language rapidly as they discover how these help them communicate more effectively.

A recent study compared two methods of teaching language to young children. The first was "elicited imitation," in which the therapist asked the child to repeat words that were related to objects, pictures, or actions that the therapist showed the child. The second was "conversational recast," in which the therapist rephrased what the child said during play using more advanced language forms that retained the child's intention without asking or demanding that the child imitate the therapist.

Both methods were successful, in different ways. Elicited imitation was more effective at getting children to repeat words that the therapist modeled. Conversational recast, although slower at getting children to repeat the therapist's words, was much better at helping them learn words they could say spontaneously.

This study raises the question of why conversational recast is more effective at promoting spontaneous language when elicited imitation seems so effective at helping children repeat and learn new words. We believe the difference between these two methods is related to how they relate to children's intentions. When children are taught words using elicited imitation, the words they learn often have little to do with children's immediate interests; rather, they are related more to the materials the therapist presents to the child. Because of this, *teaching language by imitation may get children to perform but does little to help them learn to communicate spontaneously.*

On the other hand, *recasting children's language into conversational form shows children how to use language socially.* To the extent that children understand the relationship between the new words the therapist is modeling by using conversational recast and the intentions children are trying to communicate, they are likely to be motivated to use these words in the future when similar opportunities arise. Conversational recast provides children words that help them communicate their intentions. In contrast, elicited imitation provides children words or phrases that often have no relevance to their immediate intentions.

Discussion Points

CM-401 Intentional communication occurs when children get others to understand their feelings, needs, and observations.

- Learning to communicate intentionally evolves gradually as children become aware of their ability to convey their feelings, needs, and observations to others.
- If children have no interest in making their intentions known to others, they have no reason to learn to use words or to try to understand the meaning of words.
- Children learn words and grammatical structures rapidly when they become aware of how they make it easier to communicate their intentions.

CM-402 The first step toward becoming an intentional communicator is understanding that gestures and vocalizations can be used to express feelings and needs.

- *Any sound or movement can become a communicative behavior if it regularly has an effect on a partner.*
- Parents cannot wait for children to produce intentional communication before they respond communicatively to children's nonverbal signals.
- The less often parents respond to children's unintentional signals, the longer it takes children to recognize the power of these signals to convey their intentions.

CM-403 Children become intentional communicators to the degree that their early nonverbal behaviors have effects on others.

- Children learn language because of their strong motivation to develop more effective methods of communicating with others.
- Children can learn about the ineffectiveness of their communication by discovering without pressure from adults that their communication has not been effective at conveying their intentions.

CM-404 Children's early communications do not have to be understood, only responded to.

- Parents do not need to understand every communication their children make.
- Imposing certain ways of communicating may only discourage children from practicing the interactive behaviors they need to master to become habitual communicators.
- It is more important that children become communicators with whatever means available, however unclear, than that they communicate clearly.

CM-405 Children's first words describe their actions, experiences, and nonverbal communications.

- Words are useful only if they relate to children's immediate experiences.
- Children's first words are about actions, objects, and agents (doers) that they experience.

CM-406 Children learn words and language rapidly as they discover how these help them communicate more effectively.

- Teaching language by imitation may get children to perform but does little to help them communicate spontaneously.
- Recasting children's language into conversational form shows children how to use language socially.

RT Strategies That Promote Intentional Communication

221 ***Respond quickly to my child's signals, cries, or nonverbal requests.*** Before children talk, they cry or use nonverbal cues to make their needs known. By responding promptly to your child's nonverbal signals or cries, you help your child learn how to use these behaviors and to increase the rate that he or she begins to use more sophisticated behaviors to communicate.

Practical Suggestions

- Review the child development research findings by Ainsworth and Bell (1974), which indicated that parents who responded quickly to their children's cries during the first year of life had children who were better communicators in their second year of life.
- Consider that prompt responses to your child's cries and other nonverbal signals will not reinforce lower forms of behavior; rather, it will teach your child how to use these behaviors more effectively in social interactions.
- Respond promptly to your child's nonverbal signals and cries, and observe how your child becomes more attentive and responsive to you when you do this.

222 ***Respond immediately to little behaviors.*** Little behaviors are behaviors such as burps, change of visual regard, kicking legs, waving hands, facial displays, and others.

Practical Suggestions

- Even if your child is not directing his or her "little behaviors" to you, and even though these behaviors have no apparent purpose or meaning, by responding immediately you can transform these behaviors into meaningful social interactions.
- Immediate responding to your child's solitary play and self-speech will help your child become more aware of you and more apt to engage in social exchanges.
- Review videotaped observations to see how quickly you respond to your child's behavior.

231 ***Respond to unintentional vocalizations, facial displays, and gestures as if they were meaningful conversation.*** Often, children make sounds for sensory play but not for communicating intentionally. Every action your child makes can become a communication. The more you respond to your child's actions, the quicker your child will learn to use these actions to exchange meanings with you and others.

Practical Suggestions

- Get into the habit of responding to your child's sounds, even when they are just for self-play and do not have any obvious meaning or communicative intent.
- If your child makes sounds while playing but does not use sounds to communicate his or her intentions, he or she has not yet learned that sounds can get people's attention. To help your child learn to use his or her sounds as communication, respond more to your child's sounds than to his or her facial displays or touches.

232 ***Accept incorrect word choice, pronunciations, or word approximations by responding to my child's intention.***

Practical Suggestions

- Consider that, as children begin to learn language, they are more concerned with communicating ideas, observations, or needs than they are with using language correctly. Be careful not to discourage your child from communicating by trying to get him or her to say the right words in the right way.
- After you have established the habit of responding to your child's play or communicative intention, occasionally model more appropriate words or pronunciations, without making your child imitate you.

233 ***Translate my child's actions, feelings, and intentions into words.*** Children learn language best when adults respond with words that fit what they are experiencing at the moment. When you use words that match your child's actions, feelings, and intentions, such as *come, go, eat, mom, dog,* and *truck,* your words will have more relevance to what your child is experiencing than words like *two, three, red, yellow, horse,* and *barn.*

Practical Suggestions

- Become your child's living dictionary. Children's first words come from their routine actions, experiences, and sensations. You can help your child learn words more rapidly by modeling one- or two-word phrases that are directly related to what your child is currently doing, seeing, touching, hearing, or feeling.
- Become sensitive to what your child is sensing and experiencing. Give your child a word for these feelings and sensations.
- In choosing what to say to your child, consider asking yourself how your child will communicate with a particular word.

312 ***Imitate my child's actions and communications.*** You can imitate any behavior that your child produces. If your child has little interest in interacting with you, get his or her attention by imitating behaviors that may be inappropriate or bizarre (e.g., rocking, thumb-sucking, loud shrieking or crying, throwing objects). Imitation has two functions. First, it helps to establish an interactive relationship with your child that is based upon what your child is doing. Second, imitation gives your child an immediate opportunity to control what you do.

Practical Suggestions

- Notice how imitation encourages your child to increase the variety and scope of his or her behavior and does not reinforce undesirable behavior.
- Consider that one important outcome of imitation is that your child will enjoy and have fun controlling what you do.
- When you imitate your child's nonverbal or verbal communication, you are helping your child learn to use his or her early communication skills to have an effect on others.

415 ***Accompany my communications with intonation, pointing, and nonverbal gestures.*** Make sure to communicate with your child using inflection, intonation, and nonverbal gestures and cues.

Practical Suggestions

- Observe how your child is more attentive when you communicate with inflected versus monotonic voice, and when you accompany your communications with nonverbal gestures.

- Review a videotape of you communicating with your child, then rate how well you think you are using intonation and nonverbal communication. How can you make your communications with your child livelier?

521 ***Read my child's behavior as an indicator of interest.*** While interacting with your child to read your child's behavior, first observe carefully the subtle as well as obvious behaviors your child is doing, and second, use context cues to interpret your child's interests.

Practical Suggestions

- Your child's interests are likely to be very different than yours. Objects or activities that seem unexciting to you can be interesting to your child—particularly because many of them are novel experiences for your child.
- Consider that your child's interests can change from moment to moment. What interests your child on one day may not interest him or her on the next.
- Not all of your child's interests may be strong. Even if your child is not actively engaged in what he or she is doing, it is still an indicator of his or her interest.
- Use the following questions to interpret your child's behavior:
  "What does that behavior reflect about my child's interests?"
  "What is my child trying to communicate by doing that?"
- Professionals can describe the cues they see as indicators of a child's interests while interacting with them.
- Professionals should ask parents to describe what their children are interested in doing and help parents think of their children's behaviors as indicators of interest.

Developmental Domain: Communication

Pivotal Behavior: Conversation

CM-5 Conversation refers to the degree to which children engage in conversations on a variety of topics with multiple people. Children use both nonverbal communication and verbal language. They lead and follow conversations in a give-and-take style and are able to sustain and follow changes in conversational topics. They communicate for many purposes, including companionship, persuasion, information exchange, feelings, and needs.

Facts To Consider About Conversation

CM-501 Children who have language but rarely use it in conversations need frequent interactions to learn to converse.

Frequently *children who have language problems know and understand a lot of language, yet they seldom use it to express themselves in conversations.* These children have learned language more for storage and performance than for communicating in conversations. Unless they have good conversation skills, children will not progress far in language learning. *As children learn to have conversations, they will naturally learn more language,* but they will not learn to have conversations just by learning more words.

How can we help children develop their conversational skills? Parents have used three different approaches to address this issue: the automatic approach, the directive approach, and the responsive approach. In the automatic approach, parents wait for their children to learn conversations on their own. They expect that once their children know words, they have all they need for conversation. This can be a serious mistake, especially for children who have language problems. Conversation requires much more than words. Conversation requires that children engage in frequent interactions with people. Children need their parents to join them in their activities and keep them increasingly longer in conversational exchanges.

In the directive approach, parents converse with children primarily by talking to them. Often they ask their children a lot of questions and seldom respond to their children's interests but rather focus more on their own topics and interests. They act more like a teacher than their children's conversational partner. Although they are trying to help, parents actually pressure their children to do things they neither can do nor are interested in doing. These directive conversations do not last long. They often result in children becoming passive conversational partners and talking mainly to respond to their parents' questions or requests.

In the responsive approach, parents encourage children to stay in conversations by talking about whatever interests them. They respect what children know and they make conversation easier by focusing on children's current interests and language. Parents join in their children's nonverbal activities and communicate by sharing actions, gestures, facial displays, vocalizations, and, occasionally, words. They do not pressure children to use their language to communicate; rather, they try to keep their children actively engaged in social interaction with whatever means their children want to use. *Children learn the skills and rules for more mature forms of conversation through engaging in responsive, child-centered conversations.* They begin to learn new words and incorporate them into their conversations as they become more proficient nonverbal conversationalists.

CM-502 Children converse longer and more frequently when adults respond to their intentions rather than correct their speech or language.

Children learn the meaning and grammar of language by having repeated conversations with more mature speakers. As a result, parents can help their children learn language by making conversation a way of life for them. One way to do this is to *engage in playful interactions with children that focus on supporting and encouraging their interests, abilities, and motivations.* To do this, parents must avoid pressuring children to use adult forms of communication. They must accept whatever behaviors children use at first and must try to determine children's meanings and intentions rather than pressure them to communicate in adult ways.

Many believe that in order to learn, children need to be shown "correct" adult forms of communication. Not many years ago, in fact, experts recommended that parents refrain from speaking baby talk to their children, for fear that this would only encourage children to produce primitive forms of communication. But research has shown that children are more attentive and responsive to baby talk than they are to adult forms of communication.

If parents stress that their children use only correct, adult-like forms of speaking, they make it difficult for their children to remain actively engaged in conversation with them. Unless parents adapt a style of communication that is similar, or matched, to the way their children communicate, they will restrict children's opportunities to communicate and gain exposure to appropriate communication models.

Correcting children's language can also decrease the duration and frequency of conversations needed for learning. If parents refuse to accept children's immature communications, in effect they are telling children, "I will not have conversations with you until you can do something you cannot do." *Parents do not reinforce lower level behavior by responding to primitive forms of communication;* rather, they reduce the demands their children must meet to have active conversations with them. This reinforces children's efforts to communicate and increases their opportunities to learn more advanced communication behaviors.

CM-503 Children are more likely to have conversations in situations that are enjoyable, interesting, and related to what they know.

Young children are more likely to engage in conversations when they are relaxed and enjoying themselves, and are interested in and knowledgeable about the topic. As a result, it is essential that parents engage in conversations with their children that meet three criteria: (a) they are fun and playful, (b) they are based on children's interests, and (c) they are matched to children's developmental knowledge and language abilities.

First, conversations should be fun and playful. Children remain engaged in conversations much longer when they are enjoying themselves than when they are in situations in which there is little smiling or laughter. It is important that children experience conversations as sources of success, not of stress and failure.

Second, *parents' conversations need to be focused on children's interests* (i.e., what they are involved with) at the moment. Children will have little interest in conversations that remove them from their current interests. Parents will be more successful in engaging in conversations that are focused on children's current activities.

Third, parents need to *communicate about objects, actions, or characteristics that children are familiar with and that are within their range of developmental capabilities.* For example, if parents insist on communicating about the colors of objects when children are primarily interested in placing objects in and out of containers and are not at a developmental level at which they are normally expected to know their colors, children will likely disengage or avoid conversing with their parents.

CM-504 Communicating for needs is not sufficient to build a habit of conversation.

Many children with language problems communicate mainly to get their needs met and seldom communicate to socialize and share experiences with others. Unfortunately, these *children do not have enough needs to obtain the amount of interactive experience that they must have to become social communicators.* Many of these children are "easy babies." They make few demands for their parents' attention, and they seem content and capable of occupying themselves when they are left alone. However, because they do not object when left alone, these children deprive themselves of the opportunities for interaction that are needed to become effective conversationalists.

When children cry, whine, or otherwise demand their parents' attention, they are initiating social exchanges that play an important role in helping them develop their conversational skills. As parents respond to these demands, they engage in conversations with their children as they go about satisfying their needs. Although children certainly need to learn limits and boundaries and cannot be demanding their parents' attention all the time, it is important to understand that children's demands play an important role in helping them obtain the types of interactions they need to develop their conversation and language skills.

In fact, parents should be concerned if their young children do not bother them because *bothering is the basis for the conversations children need to develop language.* If children have language problems, their parents must make sure that they have frequent opportunities to interact with people. It is *not* okay for children to be alone or to play by themselves merely because they seem content: Children cannot learn to have conversations when they are playing by themselves.

CM-505 Every interaction is an opportunity to practice and learn how to have conversations.

Children will have difficulty developing communicative relationships if their parents try to promote language by teaching them words. For children who are primarily nonverbal, successful communicating means getting others' attention, sending messages, and expressing feelings. Until children experience success by communicating with the behaviors they can do, they cannot learn to become conversational partners using more advanced words or language.

It is an effort for most parents to respond to children's nonverbal behaviors as potential communications. Many parents think of children's communicative behavior primarily in terms of words, even when their children do not use words regularly. But it is important to understand children's communication more in terms of frequency and length of conversations than in terms of number of words or the length of sentences. *Children's conversational skills develop more by engaging in frequent, sustained reciprocal interactions with adults than by repeating new words or phrases* that they do not yet know. Parents can help to expand the length of children's conversational exchanges by routinely keeping children interacting one or two more turns than they normally would. As children practice interacting, they gradually learn that their role is to remain engaged in interaction rather than to dart in and out of contact with their parents. *Sustained conversational exchanges enhance children's natural opportunities for learning the words and grammatical structures that parents desire for them.* By teaching words and phrases in isolated learning activities, parents interfere with children's engaging in the spontaneous conversations that naturally promote children's acquisition of language.

CM-506 Children will become conversational when others speak to them in ways they can speak rather than in ways they can only understand.

Two tasks involved in learning language include learning to understand it and learning to use it to speak with others. These are separate, although obviously related skills. The common theory of language stimulation suggests that children's language learning is dependent upon their exposure to language stimulation. This presumes that, soon after children understand a word, they will begin to use the word in their expressive language. Language stimulation theory assumes that children's language development will be enhanced when they are exposed to language that exceeds their current expressive language skills but is within the range of their receptive language abilities. The recommendation "bathe your child with language" assumes that the more language children hear, the more they will learn.

Several studies of language development in the 1970s and 1980s that examined language stimulation theory assumed that children should learn language best when their parents spoke in ways that exceeded their expressive language abilities but was within their range of comprehension. The researchers were unable to find evidence to support this notion, however. Rather, *parents who were most effective at promoting their children's expressive language used language that was similar to that of their children.* These parents encouraged their children to use the language they already possessed and to learn words and phrases that were closely related to the words and phrases they were already using. Not only did these parents speak using words, intonation, and phrases that resembled their children's, they also responded to their children's communication as if it was meaningful and mature, with little pressure for more adult forms of communication.

Parents are more effective at *helping their children engage in conversations when they communicate with language that their children are able to use rather than communicate with the more complex language their childen understand but cannot say.* This does not mean that young children should never hear adult language, which is certainly critical for future learning, but children will become conversational more quickly when parents communicate by using language their children can use.

CM-507 Children practice language by talking to themselves; joining children's self-talk is a good way to help them learn.

When young children play by themselves, they often explore and practice new skills, including language. It is perfectly normal and developmentally useful for children to talk by themselves, even when they are with others. When children talk to themselves, they are free to do so without being constrained by the wishes of others. *Children can create and respond to their own ideas as well as practice their new language.* Many children show their most mature language when playing alone. It is very informative to observe children as they play alone to see how they communicate and what they are interested in.

Parents can be very successful at having conversations with children by occasionally joining in their children's self-talk, being cautious not to disrupt their children's enjoyment. These conversations will be effective so long as they are responsive to children's purposes. If parents change children's purpose, they may inhibit them and discourage further conversation. However, *parents' conversations that support the purpose of children's self-talk can sustain children's active participation and enhance their language and conversational development.*

CM-508 Asking children to imitate and then testing them with questions can interfere with their becoming conversational.

Parents commonly do two things when they are concerned about their children's language development. First, they ask questions that test their children's knowledge (i.e., test questions). Second, they encourage their children to repeat words or phrases (i.e., elicited imitation). Although both strategies make parents feel they are teaching their children language, they often do just the opposite: These strategies often result in children discontinuing conversations with their parents.

Why are elicited imitation and test questions such conversation killers? Children are motivated to have conversations by their interests and intentions. When parents test children by asking them to answer questions about the toys and materials they are playing with (e.g., "What color is this?") or by asking them to repeat a word, even if the parents' requests are related to children's activities, very often they have nothing to do with what children are interested in doing or communicating about. For example, colors may be an obvious characteristic of the object that a child is playing with. Nonetheless, the child may not be focused on the color of the object but rather be more interested in what he can do with the object. When parents begin asking test questions, they may inadvertently divert their child's focus from his or her own interests to those of the parents.

For example, if a child points to an object for the purpose of directing her parent to give the object to her so that she can complete an activity that interests her, and the parent interrupts this activity by asking the child to repeat the name of the object (e.g., "Truck, Janice, say truck"), the parent has disrupted the flow of the child's activity or conversation by focusing on a behavior that is important to him but not to his child.

Instead of questions and elicited imitation, *parents will be more successful promoting children's conversations by using strategies such as labeling, commenting, or exclaiming in ways that complement the child's activity.* These types of communications do not require children to abandon activities that interest them in order to respond to the interests of their parents. They provide children language models that are supportive of their activities without demanding that children produce a response that will interfere with their interests or intentions. They sustain children's engagement in play and conversation while at the same time exposing children to words and phrases that reflect high-level communication skills.

Discussion Points

CM-501 Children who have language but rarely use it in conversations need frequent interactions to learn to converse.

- Many children who have language problems know and understand a lot of language, yet they seldom use it to express themselves in conversations.
- As children learn to have conversations, they will naturally learn more language.
- Children learn the skills and rules for more mature forms of conversation through engaging in responsive, child-centered conversations.

CM-502 Children converse longer and more frequently when adults respond to their intentions rather than correct their speech or language.

- Parents should engage in playful interactions with children that focus on supporting and encouraging their interests, abilities, and motivations.
- Correcting children's language can decrease the duration and frequency of the conversations they need for learning.
- Parents do not reinforce lower level behavior by responding to primitive forms of communication.

CM-503 Children are more likely to have conversations in situations that are enjoyable, interesting, and related to what they know.

- Young children are more likely to engage in conversations when they are relaxed and enjoying themselves.
- Parents' conversations need to be focused on children's interests.
- Parents should communicate about objects, actions, or characteristics that children are familiar with and that are within their range of developmental capabilities.

CM-504 Communicating for needs is not sufficient to build a habit of conversation.

- Children do not have enough needs to obtain the amount of interactive experience that they need to become social communicators.

- Bothering is the basis for the conversations children need to develop language.

CM-505 Every interaction is an opportunity to practice and learn how to have conversations.

- Children's conversational skills develop more by engaging in frequent, sustained reciprocal interactions with adults than by repeating new words or phrases.
- Sustained conversational exchanges enhance children's natural opportunities for learning the words and grammatical structures that parents desire for them.

CM-506 Children will become conversational when others speak to them in ways they can speak rather than in ways they can only understand.

- Parents who are most effective at promoting their children's expressive language use language that is similar to that of their children.
- Parents can help children engage in conversations by communicating with language that children are able to use rather than by communicating with the more complex language they understand but cannot say.

CM-507 Children practice language by talking to themselves; joining children's self-talk is a good way to help them learn.

- Children talk to themselves to practice their sounds and ideas.
- Parents' conversations that support the purpose of children's self-talk can sustain children's active participation and enhance their language and conversational development.

CM-508 Asking children to imitate and then testing them with questions can interfere with their becoming conversational.

- Elicited imitation and test questions are conversational killers.
- Parents are more successful promoting children's conversations by using strategies such as labeling, commenting, or exclaiming in ways that complement the child's activity.

RT Strategies That Promote Conversation

135 ***Make a habit of communicating during joint activity routines.*** Playing with sounds, gestures, and words will help your child learn how to build social relationships. It teaches your child that a major way of being with people is to play with communication for its companionship value.

Practical Suggestions

- Observe how your child communicates not only with words but also with gestures and sounds. Consider how you can communicate with your child as effectively with nonverbal signals as with words or phrases before your child has words or is at the early-language stage.

- Many parents communicate with children by asking questions (i.e., "Do you want to ...?"). Often this results in a dead-end communication. The child might answer or respond to the parent but not continue the conversation. Communicate with your child by labeling, commenting, expressing delight about what your child is doing, or describing your feelings or the feelings of your child. Observe how this results in longer communicative exchanges than does asking questions.

231 ***Respond to unintentional vocalizations, facial displays, and gestures as if they were meaningful conversations.*** Often, children make sounds for sensory play but not for communicating intentionally. Every action your child makes can become a communication. The more you respond to your child's actions, the quicker your child will learn to use these actions to exchange meanings with you and others.

Practical Suggestions

- Get into the habit of responding to your child's sounds, even when they are just for self-play and do not have any obvious meaning or communicative intent.
- If your child makes sounds while playing, but does not use sounds to communicate his or her intentions, he or she has not yet learned that sounds can get people's attention. To help your child learn to use his or her sounds as communication, respond more to your child's sounds than to his or her facial displays or touches.

311 ***Communicate without asking questions.*** Parents often try to control what their children do by asking them to do things. A simple strategy for reducing the number of times you are directing or controlling your child is to "not ask questions."

Practical Suggestions

- Rather than asking your child questions during an interaction, label, comment, notice, express delight or pleasure, and provide information related to what your child is doing.
- As you try to stop asking questions, you will begin to understand how much you are actually directing what your child does. This is a good time to consider that, even if you reduced the number of your directives by one half, you would still have numerous opportunities to guide and direct your child.
- Do not repeat questions to which your child has not responded.
- Occasionally ask your child to do things, but try to make requests that are closely related to what your child is already doing.
- Children learn best when they initiate activities of their own choosing. The more you ask questions when you play or interact with your child, the less opportunity your child will have to initiate his or her own activities.

321 ***Expand to show my child the next developmental step.*** Children need parents and others to introduce the next step in both play and communication. Remember, if you "show your child the next step" in whatever your child is doing, you will expose your child to new information while keeping him or her interacting with you.

Practical Suggestions

- Make sure that your expansions are related to your child's behavior and activities in ways that show new meanings and purposes of the behavior.

322 ***Expand to clarify my child's intention or to develop my child's topic.*** Adults can increase the complexity of children's activity or communication in a manner that preserves the intention or purpose of what they had been doing. For example, if your child is building a tower that is three blocks high, you can expand by building a tower that is four blocks high.

Practical Suggestions

- Make sure that your expansions are never the sole focus of your interactions with your child; introduce expansions only occasionally into your child's activity.
- If your child shows no interest in following your expansion, go back to your child's original activity to keep him or her actively engaged.
- If your child is not responding to your expansions, modify them so that they are within your child's range of developmental abilities and compatible with his or her interests and sensations.

323 ***Wait silently for a more mature response.*** You can encourage your child to use higher level behaviors by occasionally waiting to respond when your child produces his or her "old," immature behaviors. Many children prefer easy behaviors, but if you wait to respond, your child may show you that he or she knows how to do more mature behaviors. Remember that waiting can only be effective at encouraging your child to do what he or she is already able to do.

Practical Suggestions

- Wait for your child to produce more mature behaviors only if you have seen him or her do them several times before. If your child produced a more advanced behavior only a few times in the past, it may not yet be a behavior that is easy for your child.
- If your child does not produce the behavior you are waiting for within 5 seconds, simply model the behavior you would like and continue the activity without insisting that your child imitate or produce the behavior on his or her own.

413 ***Respond to my child in playful ways.*** Occasionally do silly and playful things with your child. Your child is more likely to be attentive and engaged with you when you interact in childlike, playful ways.

Practical Suggestions

- One way to engage your child is to touch him or her in affectionate and playful ways.
- If your child plays with toys in rote, repetitive ways, with little attention or interest, try doing unusual and inventive things with these objects.
- Some adults are uncomfortable playing in silly, childlike ways. Consider that being funny or silly is a small price to pay to encourage your child to interact with you.

515 ***Communicate the way my child communicates.*** Communicate in ways that your child is currently able to do. Respond to your child's movements with movements, respond to his or her sounds with sounds, and respond to his or her one- or two-word utterances with one- or two-word utterances.

Practical Suggestions

- Notice how when you communicate like your child, your child communicates more with you. Interact with your child for 2 to 3 minutes using the types of words, inflections, or gestures your child uses; then interact with your child for another 2 to 3 minutes, communicating with the type of language you would use with an adult. Keep track of the amount of time your child is actively involved in interaction in these two situations. Consider why these differences occur and what implications they have for helping your child learn how to speak.
- Talk baby talk. For several years, childcare books have advised parents not to talk baby talk to their children. It was believed that children needed to be exposed to adult models of language in order to learn to communicate in a mature way. More recently, child development research has reported that children are more likely to attend to and participate in conversations when their parents use baby talk.

523 ***Follow my child's lead.*** Respond to your child in a manner that is compatible with, or complements, your child's activity and intentions. Play with toys or engage in activities in the same manner as your child. Do not make your child play with toys in the manner that the manufacturer designed them unless that is the way your child chooses to play with them.

Practical Suggestions

- Whatever your child is playing with is what interests your child at the moment. Consider how you are much more motivated to engage in activities that interest you and to learn and remember information that you find interesting. Your child is no different than you are when it comes to the motivating power of interest.
- When you follow your child's lead, you are actually responding to your child's interests. The more you respond to your child's interests, the greater the number of interests your child will have and the stronger these interests will be.

Developmental Domain: Social–Emotional Functioning

Social–Emotional Functioning refers to children's feelings of security and ability to adjust to the demands of family life and routine social interactions.

Pivotal Behavior: Trust

SE-1 Trust refers to the degree to which children have a trusting and warm relationship with their primary caregiver. Children seek out, or touch base, with their caregiver for comfort or security. They take pleasure in the presence of the caregiver, frequently sharing information or objects and/or giving him or her eye contact, smiles, or hugs.

Facts To Consider About Trust

SE-101 Attachment refers to children's trust and dependency on their mothers, fathers, and other primary caregivers.

Attachment refers to how children relate to their parents and other caregivers during the early years of life. *The developmental significance of attachment derives from the ways that children trust and depend upon adults.* Attachment is not only a reflection of the manner that parents (caregivers) interact with children. It is also the product of the inborn characteristics of children themselves. If children are naturally interested in people and have an "easy" temperament or behavioral style, they will likely develop strong attachments to their primary caregivers. However, *if children are not naturally interested in people, are more interested in objects than in people, and have a "difficult" temperament, they may have problems establishing strong attachment relationships,* even though their primary caregivers engage in highly responsive and nurturing interactions with them.

It is important to distinguish between parents' love for their children and children's attachment to their parents. Almost all parents and children have a deep love for each other, regardless of how attached they are. Attachment has little to do with parents' love for their children or vice versa. Rather, children's attachment to their parents is the product of their temperament or behavioral style, their interest in interacting and inclination to interact with their parents, as well as the manner in which parents or caregivers interact with them.

SE-102 Children's attachment is manifested by their seeking out and trusting their parents and other primary caregivers.

Attachment refers to the emotional interdependency that develops between children and their parents during the first year of life. Through this relationship, children fulfill parents' needs to love and nurture while parents in turn provide children the support they need to develop their social and emotional competencies. This relationship does not form immediately or even shortly after birth but evolves over a much longer time. It is the product of children's cognitive awareness and social experiences. The foundations for this relationship are established during the first 24 months of life. However, *emotional attachment is a dynamic, lifelong relationship which evolves continuously throughout life.*

This emotional dependency begins to take shape when children develop preferences to be with their mother, father, or other familiar adults. Children manifest this by observing and attending to adults and, what is more important, by becoming excited and taking pleasure in their company. They show this preference through nonverbal signals of pleasure and excitement including eye gaze, smiling, body posture, and gestures.

The primary skill or ability that children acquire through their attachment relationships is the ability to trust and care for another person. Children exhibit strong attachments to their parents and other adults as they develop an awareness of their own vulnerability and begin to *trust* that the nurturance, guidance, and information that these parents or adults provide will not harm them but will protect them and serve their best interests. Children's fearfulness of strangers, which begins to emerge at approximately 8 months developmental age, reflects their growing awareness of differences between adults they know whom they can trust as opposed to adults whom they are not certain they can trust. Prior to this, children have little understanding about their vulnerability to other people and circumstances. Children become wary of strangers as they begin to grasp the extent of their vulnerabilities, and recognize the uncertainty of whether strangers are trustworthy. As children begin to trust in their parents and other familiar adults, they also become wary of others. Children do not know that other people can be trusted to safeguard and protect them the way their parents do.

SE-103 Children's attachment relationships with their parents or primary caregivers predict their social–emotional functioning later in life.

There is a strong relationship between *how attached children are to their parents during the first 2 years of life and how well they get along with their peers, relate to other caregivers and adults, and adjust to preschool or childcare later in early childhood.* The social–emotional skills that children acquire through their attachment relationships with their parents provide the foundation for their ability to form social relationships and cope with stress and anxiety later in their lives. Children's early attachment experiences form a personal lens through which they view and interpret the social–emotional experiences they have throughout the early childhood years. Children's abilities to establish social relationships and cope with challenges in childcare, preschool, and other early childhood settings are directly affected by the expectations and competencies they develop through their safe and nurturing relationships with their parents and other caregivers.

Children who establish positive attachment relationships with their primary caregivers are more likely to view interactions with others as positive experiences. The caring and trusting *relationships they form with their parents and other caregivers help them develop the skills and mind-set for caring for other children, trusting other nurturing adults who care for them, and complying with the social demands and expectations encountered in different contexts.*

However, if children have difficulty forming strong attachment relationships with their primary caregivers, their hesitancy to trust and care for their parents and other caregivers interferes with their ability to form positive social relationships in later childhood. The anxiety and wariness children experience with their parents carry over to their relationships with others. When children have had negative attachment experiences, they often lack confidence that new situations and new people will provide them a safe harbor to seek nurturance, guidance, or support. Children's inability to form strong trusting relationships with the people who play the most important roles in their lives, their parents and primary caregivers, interferes with their ability to establish caring and trusting relationships with the other children and adults they encounter outside their family later in their lives.

SE-104 Disrupted attachment relationships affect children's social–emotional behavior.

Attachment disruptions are deteriorations or breakdowns in the attachment relationships between children and their primary caregivers. Attachment disruption can range from acute or mild to chronic or severe.

Acute and mild attachment disruptions involve situations in which parents establish a positive attachment relationship with their children during the early months of life and then experience episodes such as hospitalization, depression, or marital or relationship difficulties that interfere with their ability to interact with their children. However, as parents recover from these episodes, they resume having frequent, nurturing, and responsive interactions with their children, thus reestablishing a positive attachment relationship.

Chronic and severe disruptions occur when children have multiple placements during their first few years of their lives before obtaining a permanent home. In this situation, children experience a series of episodes in which their evolving attachment relationships with their caregivers are abruptly discontinued when they are placed in another setting.

Many children experience mild disruptions in their relationships with their primary caregivers during the early years of life. Children may react to these disruptions by exhibiting behavior problems such as crying, irritability, aggressiveness, and sleeping or eating problems. *Generally, social–emotional problems that children develop as a result of mild attachment disruptions can be corrected as the attachment relationship is repaired.* Mild attachment disruptions are relatively normal occurrences for young children. Although they are distressing, most children are sufficiently resilient to reestablish normal social–emotional behavior soon after their parents recover.

Severe disruptions can have a much more serious impact on children's social–emotional functioning. Only a small number of children experience severe disruptions in their attachment relationships. These children may develop significant social–emotional problems that persist over long periods of time (e.g., aggression, withdrawal, dysregulation, uncooperativeness). These problems do not result because these children are spiteful, manipulative, malicious, or inappropriately attention seeking. Rather they are manifestations of these children's persisting feelings of wariness and anxiety, as well as their fearfulness at caring for and trusting their new caregivers.

Severe disruptions in children's attachment relationships will have persisting negative influences on their social–emotional functioning, which may be manifested up through adolescence. At times, parents need to use developmentally appropriate discipline to address children's negative and inappropriate behaviors. But these children are not likely to become happier, less aggressive, and more cooperative unless their caregivers bathe them with nurturing and responsive interactions. Children will learn to care for and trust their new caregivers only after they feel confident that their relationship with them is permanent and will not be terminated, as were their previous attachment relationships. When they feel this confidence, children will begin to display fewer social–emotional problems. However, this process requires persistence and patience on the part of caregivers. More often than not it takes years, not days or weeks, to occur.

SE-105 Fathers and other primary caregivers play a critical role in the formation of children's ability to trust.

Children's attachments to their mother are clearly the first attachments they establish and are the relationships most likely to predict later social–emotional functioning. However, children form similar attachments to their fathers and other caregivers (e.g., grandparents, relatives, significant others) as they do to their mothers.

Children's attachment to their other caregivers is promoted by the same responsive and nurturing interactions that contribute to their attachment to their mothers. Furthermore, *the pattern of children's attachment to fathers and other caregivers follows the same pattern as attachment to their mothers.* Near the end of their first year of life, children develop strong preferences to be with these adults, they prefer being close to these adults rather than with others, and they become fearful or anxious when these adults leave them.

One of the most significant features of children's attachment relationships with other adults, as with their mothers, is the caring and trust that they develop. *Insofar as children's relationships with their fathers and other caregivers provide additional opportunities to learn to trust another human being, these experiences contribute to their ability to deal with later social relationships.*

Having more than one attachment figure gives children additional access to a comforting and nurturing adult during times of distress. It also provides a safety net that helps children become less vulnerable to the minor attachment disruptions that occur with one caregiver or the other. Multiple attachment figures increase children's opportunities for social–emotional support and enhance children's potential to develop the skills they need to become more socially independent and to cope with interpersonal and emotional challenges.

Multiple attachment figures become an even more critical source of support for children with conditions such as autism who have difficulty forming attachments because of their biological conditions. These children need frequent opportunities for social interaction with adults to learn to enjoy and become more interested in interacting with others. One caregiver may not have the energy or time that is necessary for engaging these children in the amount of responsive interaction they need to develop these social–emotional skills.

SE-106 Children's attachment relationships with adults depend upon how much adults engage in warm and responsive interactions with them.

Parents need to spend time with their children for children to develop positive attachments with them. But time is not the only important factor. If parents are full-time caregivers but only occasionally engage in one-to-one interactions, they may fail to provide their children the amount of interactive experience necessary to become attached to them. This commonly happens when parents attend to their children's needs (e.g., dressing, feeding, toileting, safety) but seldom play or socialize with them (e.g., if parents spend much of their day on the telephone, watching TV, and doing household chores but only occasionally interacting with their children, or if they let their children play with other children but seldom become involved in their play themselves).

Parents can even spend considerable amounts of time engaging in one-to-one interaction, yet still be ineffective at promoting their children's attachment. This could happen if parents structure their interactions around fixed schedules and are not responsive to their children's needs, or if parents' interactions consist mostly of disciplining their children or teaching them developmental behaviors.

Two ingredients make parents' time with their children an attachment enhancing experience. One is the degree to which parents engage in one-to-one interactions with their children. When parents are with their children, they make frequent efforts to "touch base," at least for short periods of time. *The other is how responsive parents are with their children.* Parents focus on supporting, encouraging, and enriching what their children are doing. They keep their interactions fun and enjoyable, and respond to their children's needs for warmth, affection, and acceptance.

Responsive interactions promote children's attachment because of the impact they have on children's feelings. When parents are responsive and nurturing, their children are more likely to enjoy themselves and feel that they are accepted and valued. This encourages children to become more actively involved in the interaction and to remain engaged for longer periods of time. Children are also more apt to seek out and prefer being with their parents frequently throughout the day. By engaging in responsive interactions, parents set in motion an interactive pattern that increases the amount of enjoyable and emotionally rewarding time children have with them, which is the fuel that fosters their attachment relationship.

SE-107 Children who are attached to highly responsive adults learn to function independently in later childhood.

Some parents are reluctant to become highly responsive and nurturing for fear that this will prevent their children from becoming independent. It is understandable that parents want their children to learn to be independent, since this is a skill that will be important to children's success as they grow older. However, while responsiveness fosters children's attachment to adults, it also helps children learn the skills they need to become independent.

Responsive interactions promote three skills that play an important role in helping children assert their autonomy with their parents: (a) initiating social interaction, (b) making choices, and (c) developing feelings of self-esteem. Generally, *children who assert their autonomy during interactions with their parents develop the ability to function independently in early childhood settings when parents are not present.*

First, when parents interact responsively, they wait for their children to *initiate* an activity before they respond. Rather than trying to engage children by asking questions or by placing toys or objects in their view, they observe their children and wait for them to do something before responding. By waiting, responsive parents provide children more opportunities to initiate and thus teach their children that their role is to be "an initiator of action." This style of interaction helps children gain confidence in their ability to initiate, which makes them more apt to use this skill in their interactions with others.

Second, responsive parents encourage children to make *choices*. By frequently responding to and supporting children's choices, responsive parents enhance their children's opportunities to learn to make choices. As parents encourage and support children in the choices they make, children gain greater confidence that (a) they are capable of making choices, (b) their role is to make choices, and (c) the choices they make are good.

Third, responsive parents promote children's self-esteem by continually communicating that they are capable or competent. They do this by (a) responding to the actions that children initiate, (b) respecting the choices children make, and (c) asking children to do things at which they can succeed. Children's feelings of self-esteem are greatly influenced by how their parents and others view their behavior. If parents consistently respond to children in a way that communicates that they value their behavior, children develop self-perceptions of being competent or capable, regardless how competent children actually are.

SE-108 Children's attachment behaviors progress through predictable developmental stages.

Some of the behaviors associated with children's attachment are developmentally normal behaviors even though parents may find them embarrassing or irritating. *Up to 8 months of developmental age, children display their attachment to their parents and other caregivers by becoming excited and reacting positively in their presence.* Children prefer to be with their parents or other adults with whom they are attached, but they are generally not afraid of being held by most other adults prior to this time. In other words, until 8 months of developmental age, children display intense positive reactions to the adults they are attached to without displaying fearfulness of the adults to whom they are not attached.

Sometime between 8 and 12 months of developmental age, this pattern changes rather dramatically. Children begin to make strong distinctions between the adults to whom they are attached and those to whom they are not. *Children's preference to be with those to whom they are attached becomes more intense.* They become distressed when "strangers" come near them and attempt to pick them up or hold them. At this developmental age level, children who had little difficulty adapting when parents left them with babysitters and other caregivers, become agitated and distressed when their parents try to leave them with these same caregivers.

Children's intense reactions to separation from their parents normally persist throughout the early childhood years. But it is most intense between 12 and 18 months of developmental age, and gradually diminishes through the next 3 to 4 years. By the time most children reach the primary school age level, they rarely become anxious when they are with strangers or separated from their parents. Thus, as annoying and irritating as children's separation anxiety may be, this is a normal developmental reaction that is based upon children's legitimate fears about unfamiliar adults.

There are two things to consider about the stages of children's attachment behaviors. First, it is normal for children to have fear of strangers and separation anxiety beginning around 8 months of developmental age. These behaviors are indicators of normal social–emotional development. Children who do not go through this phase of development or who seldom show strong preference to be with their primary caregivers might not be forming normal attachment relationships.

Second, these *phases of attachment formation are related to children's developmental age.* Fear of strangers and separation anxiety are behaviors that evolve partly because of children's developing awareness of social situations. As a result, children who have developmental problems proceed through the phases of attachment development in a manner that is consistent with their developmental age, not chronological age. For example, if a child has a 50% delay in his rate of development, he will begin to go through the phases of attachment formation when he is twice as old as the typically developing child (e.g., 16–24 months). In addition, these stages of attachment may persist as much as two times longer for children with developmental problems than for typically developing children.

As a result, parents of children with developmental problems need to treat late onset of attachment behaviors in the same way they treat these behaviors in younger typically developing children. Even though children with developmental problems are older when they go through this process, their behaviors reflect the same anxieties and fears that typically developing children feel. Children's delayed attachment behaviors are normal developmental processes and are not socially inappropriate behaviors that need to be suppressed.

SE-109 Parents promote children's independence by comforting them at times of separation distress.

Fear of strangers and separation anxiety are often hard for adults to understand, but nonetheless are legitimate fears for children. From an adult's perspective there is no rational basis for children becoming fearful when they are held by a friendly adult or when they are left at childcare or with a babysitter. Parents have full confidence that the stranger will not harm their child, and that childcare providers or babysitters will attend to the needs of their child. Parents may find these fears to be even more difficult to understand because their children were not anxious or fearful in similar situations at earlier stages of development.

However, when children are experiencing these fears they do not know that they will be secure and protected with strangers or childcare providers. The way that children understand social situations as well as their personal experiences at the present time gives them little basis for believing that they will be secure or well cared for. *Children's distress with strangers or separation from their parents is genuine fearfulness and should not be treated as manipulative behavior.*

Simply demanding that children give up their fears does not reduce their fearfulness. Until children themselves figure out that they have nothing to be afraid of, they have legitimate reasons for being anxious and afraid. Although parents cannot "wish" these fears away, they can help their children cope with them by empathizing with them and treating their fears as legitimate and meaningful. Parents can do this by providing their children comfort and support when they are anxious and distressed, by reassuring their children that everything will be all right, and by staying with their children until their anxiety and distress subside. *Children will overcome stranger and separation anxiety when parents treat their fears as legitimate by comforting and supporting them.*

Several parents try to control how their children react to separation by insisting that they behave. In response to this pressure, some children may be able to suppress their negative reactions and regain their composure. Yet these children may continue to experience anxiety and wariness even though they do not express these emotions. Only when children learn to cope with their feelings do they become comfortable with people who are not familiar. *Suppressing children's emotional reactions in stressful situations will not help children develop the coping skills they need* to feel comfortable, which is critical for promoting their social–emotional well-being in the long term.

SE-110 Attachment is prerequisite to effective discipline.

Almost all children behave in ways that are harmful or inappropriate from time to time. *These situations require that parents discipline their children not only to stop these behaviors but also to teach children not to do them in the future.*

Often, gentle discipline techniques, such as talking to children about what they did and why it is wrong, empathizing with children's anger or anxieties, or sternly warning them, may be effective in addressing the problem. However, in many situations gentle discipline is simply insufficient.

For example, if children run into the street, it is absolutely essential that parents get them immediately and discipline them in a manner that will prevent them from attempting the same behavior in the future. This behavior creates a life-threatening situation, and although parents must assume responsibility for their children getting into this situation in the first place, children themselves must instinctively know that "running into the street" is never appropriate.

Similarly, there are certain aggressive behaviors children do that are more a reflection of their level of development than of their actual malice towards others. For example, a child might hit her mother as a reaction to her anger. Even if the mother was not physically harmed by the child, the mother should take immediate disciplinary action to let the child know that this behavior will not be tolerated. Restraining the child by the hand accompanied by a sharp verbal rebuke should stop the child from engaging in the behavior and let the child know it is unacceptable. Children need to learn that there are certain boundaries they may never cross, regardless how angry they might be.

There are two factors that make discipline effective with young children. The first is that *parents discipline their children infrequently.* Parents should always discipline their children for behaviors that are harmful to their children or to others or that are absolutely incompatible with important social norms. However, if parents are constantly disciplining their children, they need to consider whether the behaviors they are disciplining are reasonable, particularly in relationship to their children's level of development. Disciplining children for engaging in developmentally typical behaviors is seldom effective at reducing these behaviors in the future (e.g., disciplining a child who is functioning at the 6-month developmental level for placing objects in his mouth or disciplining an 18-month-old child at dinner time for attempting to leave the table after 5 minutes). Parents also need to consider whether there might be ways of modifying the environment, schedule, or routines to accommodate the behaviors parents view as undesirable (e.g., providing safe climbing toys in the house to provide the child an alternative to climbing on tables or counter tops, which may be dangerous).

The second factor is that parents have a strong trusting relationship with their children. *The effectiveness of discipline is not so much dependent upon what parents do to stop children from engaging in inappropriate behavior as it is on the relationship they have with their children.* Young children understand their misbehavior more as transgressions against the people for whom they care than as something that is harmful or inappropriate. The primary motivation for young children to behave is their desire to please the adults whom they trust.

If children do not have a trusting and caring relationship with the adults who are disciplining them, they are less likely to view their inappropriate behavior as a transgression against them. As a result, if adults find that they are often ineffective at disciplining children, they need to consider whether they have established the kind of relationship with their children that will command their respect.

The effectiveness of adults' discipline will improve dramatically after they establish a history of engaging in frequent responsive and nurturing interactions with their children. By enriching their relationship with their children, adults will gain greater control over their children's inappropriate behavior.

Discussion Points

SE-101 *Attachment* refers to children's trust and dependency on their mothers, fathers, and other primary caregivers.

- The developmental significance of attachment derives from the ways that children trust and depend upon adults.
- If children are not naturally interested in people, are more interested in objects than in people, and have a "difficult" temperament, they may have problems establishing strong attachment relationships.

SE-102 Children's attachment is manifested by their seeking out and trusting their parents and other primary caregivers.

- Emotional attachment is a dynamic, lifelong relationship which evolves continuously throughout life.
- The primary skill or ability that children acquire through their attachment relationships is the ability to trust and care for another person.

SE-103 Children's attachment relationships with their parents or primary caregivers predict their social–emotional functioning later in life.

- How attached children are to their parents during the first 2 years of life correspond with how well they get along with their peers, relate to other caregivers and adults; and adjust to preschool or childcare later in early childhood.
- Children's attachment relationships with their parents help them develop the skills and mind-set for caring for other children, trusting other nurturing adults, and complying with the social demands encountered in different contexts.

SE-104 Disrupted attachment relationships affect children's social–emotional behavior.

- Attachment disruptions are deteriorations or breakdowns in the attachment relationships between children and their primary caregivers.
- Social–emotional problems that children develop because of mild attachment disruptions can be corrected as the attachment relationship is repaired.
- Severe disruptions in children's attachment relationships will have persisting negative influences on children's social–emotional functioning, which may be manifested up through adolescence.

SE-105 Fathers and other primary caregivers play a critical role in the formation of children's ability to trust.

- Children's attachments to their mother are clearly the first attachments they establish.
- The pattern of children's attachment to fathers and other caregivers follows the same pattern of attachment with their mothers.
- Children's relationships with their fathers and other caregivers provide additional opportunities to learn to trust others and contribute to their ability to deal with later social relationships.

SE-106 Children's attachment relationships with adults depend upon how much adults engage in warm and responsive interactions with them.

- How responsive parents are with children is predictive of the quality of the children's attachment to them.
- Responsive interactions promote children's attachment because of the impact they have on children enjoying themselves and feeling that they are accepted and valued.

SE-107 Children who are attached to highly responsive adults learn to function independently in later childhood.

- Responsive interactions promote three skills that play an important role in helping children assert their autonomy with their parents: (a) initiating social interaction, (b) making choices, and (c) developing feelings of self-esteem.

- Children who assert their autonomy during interactions with their parents develop the ability to function independently in early childhood settings when parents are not present.

SE-108 Children's attachment behaviors progress through predictable developmental stages.

- Up to 8 months of developmental age, children display their attachment to their parents by becoming excited and reacting positively in their presence.
- Between 8 and 12 months of developmental age, children begin to develop strong preferences to be with those to whom they are attached.
- Phases of attachment formation are related to children's developmental age, not chronological age.

SE-109 Parents promote children's independence by comforting them at times of separation distress.

- Children's distress with strangers or separation from their parents is genuine fearfulness and should not be interpreted as manipulative behavior.
- Children overcome stranger and separation anxiety when parents treat their fears as legitimate by comforting and supporting them.
- Suppressing children's emotional reactions in stressful situations will not help children develop the coping skills they need.

SE-110 Attachment is prerequisite to effective discipline.

- Discipline is necessary for addressing children's aggressive, harmful, and inappropriate behavior.
- Parents should discipline their children infrequently.
- The effectiveness of discipline is not so much dependent upon what parents do to stop children from engaging in inappropriate behavior as it is on the relationship they have with their children.

RT Strategies That Promote Trust

111 ***Be physically available and interactive.*** Be accessible or within your child's reach. Touch your child frequently to make the engagement more real for him or her.

Practical Suggestions

- Consider that "being with" and "physically interacting" with your child can be very different. Simply because you are with your child does not mean you are physically available.
- Spend time with your child attending visually to what he or she is doing.
- Make sure that a substantial part of the time you spend with your child involves physical interaction. Keep a chart or log of how much this actually occurs.

112 ***Play frequently together.*** Play is an ideal way to interact with your child. Engage in several brief episodes of play with your child throughout the day. Play as often as possible, particularly when your child is alert and ready to engage in playful interaction.

Practical Suggestions

- Consider how often you play with your child and what kinds of things you do together.
- Find out what kinds of toys your child is most likely to play with at his or her current developmental age level (libraries and Web sites are great resources for this).
- Professionals can model various types of play with the child.
- Professionals can invite parents to join them as they play with the child and gradually encourage the parent to take over playing with the child.
- Professionals can share with parents the kinds of games they like to play with children.

212 ***Take my child's perspective.*** Empathize with your child's life experiences by considering what your child's interests, fears, sensitivities, sources of anger, and rewards might be. Consider what it feels like to be in your child's shoes in terms of the expectations that are placed on him or her, the stimulation he or she receives, and the enjoyment and frustration in his or her life.

Practical Suggestions

- You might never know exactly what it feels like to be your child, but you can more closely understand your child's life experiences by carefully observing the kinds of events that affect or do not affect your child.
- Rely on your own feelings and intuitions about what your child knows, cares about, and is capable of doing. Do not expect that professional tests and evaluations will tell you more about your child than you already know.
- Do not focus on the things your child does incorrectly; rather, think of reasons that might explain why your child does things that you consider to be incorrect (e.g., does not understand, does not yet have the skills or ability to do something, does not feel good).
- Consider that, like yourself, your child generally has good reasons for doing whatever he or she does. This applies to behaviors that you enjoy and approve of as well as behaviors that irritate or concern you.

221 ***Respond quickly to my child's signals, cries, or nonverbal requests.*** Before children talk, they cry or use nonverbal cues to make their needs known. Respond promptly to your child's nonverbal signals or cries to help your child learn how to use these behaviors and to increase the rate that he or she begins to use more sophisticated behaviors to communicate.

Practical Suggestions

- Review the child development research findings by Ainsworth and Bell (1974), which indicated that parents who responded quickly to their children's cries during the first year of life had children who were better communicators in their second year of life.
- Consider that prompt responding to your child's cries and other nonverbal signals will not reinforce lower forms of behavior, but rather it will teach your child how to use these behaviors more effectively in social interaction.
- Respond promptly to your child's nonverbal signals and cries. Observe how your child becomes more attentive and responsive to you when you do this.

223 ***Discipline promptly and comfort.*** When your child misbehaves, discipline him or her immediately to stop these behaviors. The discipline you use should be stern enough to get your child's attention, yet appropriate to your child's physical and developmental level (e.g., a stern "No!" to restrain your child from doing something). Timing is important for effective discipline; therefore, you should discipline your child while he or she is misbehaving or immediately afterward. Comfort your child a few minutes after you discipline him or her. The positive affection children receive from parents will help them understand that they were disciplined because of what they did and that their parents still love them as always.

Practical Suggestions

- Discipline is one way that parents respond to children's behavior. Think of discipline as a natural and immediate consequence of your child's undesirable or harmful behavior.
- Regardless what strategy you use to discipline your child (e.g., sharp rebuke, restraining), discipline should be sufficiently forceful to get your child's attention and to let him or her know that he or she has done something wrong. Discipline should *never* physically harm or injure your child.
- If you are disciplining your child more than you think you should, explore the possibility that you may not be interacting enough with your child. You will become more effective at disciplining your child the more time you spend engaging in highly responsive interactions with him or her.

421 ***Act as a playful partner.*** Think of your role in your child's development as that of a playful partner. To have an effective and satisfying relationship with your child, concentrate less on accomplishing tasks or goals and more on having fun and enjoying your child.

Practical Suggestions

- Consider that being a playful partner may be hard, because parenting is ladened with tasks that need to be accomplished. However, your child lives in a world of play and fun, not work. The more you act as a playful partner, the more opportunities you will have to join your child's activity on his or her terms rather than your own.
- All parents have their own internal models about how they should act. To some degree, these models are learned from their own parents. For your child to learn in the early phases of life, you must be playful with your child, even though this may not be the way that you have learned to act as a parent.
- Consider that being a playful partner does not interfere with your child learning to respect you, but rather playful interaction will help you to establish the type of warm, mutual, and caring relationship that is necessary to be an effective parent as your child grows older.
- In some families, one parent becomes the person that has fun with the child, and the other becomes the taskmaster. Reflect on the degree to which this occurs in your family. Who is the fun parent and who is the taskmaster? Encourage the taskmaster to think about how to become more like the fun parent.

431 ***Be physical but gentle.*** Frequently touch, hold, caress, kiss, hug, and rock your child. When you interact with your child, engage in physical play (e.g., tickling, swinging the child in the air). Make sure to be gentle and avoid causing discomfort to your child.

Practical Suggestions

- Read your child's nonverbal cues (e.g., facial displays, eye gaze, posture) to make sure that your physical activity does not exceed your child's tolerance for this type of stimulation.
- Consider how your child's first experience of love and affection occurs primarily through touch and other nonverbal cues.
- Write a list of the cues your child uses when he or she does not want to be physical in interactions.
- If your child avoids touch and is hypersensitive, touch your child only a few seconds at a time, but continue to use gentle touching as often as possible. Like adults, children have different sensitivities to touch and physical activity that reflect their biological predispositions. Your child's aversion to touch does not reflect his or her attitude about you. Over time, frequent, brief, gentle touching will help your child become more comfortable with touch.
- Infant massage is a technique many parents use with young children. Try to find books or information on infant massage, and consider incorporat-

ing it into your daily routines with your child, particularly if you and your child find this experience rewarding.

432 ***Respond affectionately to my child's cries and needs for attention.*** Respond promptly and affectionately (e.g., touch, soothing voice) to your child when he or she cries, whines, or seeks your attention. Treat your child's cries and efforts to gain your attention as an important and legitimate need that your child has to be loved and comforted.

Practical Suggestions

- Consider that your child's feelings of security will evolve from confidence that you will comfort and hold him or her when he or she needs it. Responding to your child's need for attention will not spoil your child, but rather it will help your child become more secure about your love and affection and will help your child learn to cope more effectively with his or her feelings and anxieties.
- Changes in children's development affect the extent to which parents can defer providing warmth and affection in response to children's cries or other expressions of their need for attention. In the first 2 years, parents should respond as promptly as possible to attend to their children's needs. In later years, as children feel more secure about their parents' love and have better coping skills, parents can delay their response for increasingly longer periods of time. When parents delay responding, they need to let their children know that they will address their needs as soon as they can.
- Avoid ignoring your child's needs for attention. It is normal for your child to want attention from you. Your child will develop his or her social–emotional competencies partly through the attention you provide.

Developmental Domain: Social–Emotional Functioning

Pivotal Behavior: Empathy

SE-2 Empathy refers to the degree to which children are sensitive to others' feelings and emotions and are capable of altering their own emotional state, according to the emotions of others. Children care about how others feel and are often affected by the emotions of others. They use their caregivers' reactions to gauge the safety and friendliness of situations and to regulate how to react.

Facts To Consider About Empathy

SE-201 Effective social relationships occur when children become capable of sharing emotional states with others.

Empathy is the process through which children gain awareness of the emotional states of others and take on the perspective of the people with whom they interact. Empathy is more than feeling. It refers to the *ability to match one's feelings to someone else's emotional state,* such as sharing in another person's joy, sadness, excitement, or fearfulness. Effective social relationships, whether they involve children or adults, are fundamentally empathic by nature. Relationships are most durable and satisfying when each partner appreciates how the other feels and is able to act in ways that respect those feelings or even mirror those feelings for a while.

Empathy is the process of sharing internal emotional states. Although this seems like an instinctive, intuitive process for most adults, it is a process children gradually develop during their first year of life and is a core behavior that contributes to children's social–emotional development. *Children who fail to develop the ability to empathize can develop a number of serious social–emotional problems:* They may have little interest or concern regarding the emotional state of others, they may fail to regulate their interactions to accommodate others' emotional states, and they may fail to develop typical emotional reactions and tend to be either overreactive or nonexpressive.

SE-202 Children learn how to react emotionally from their parents or caregivers.

By 2 months of developmental age, most children exhibit behavior which suggests they have three emotional states: interest, contentment, and distress. By 7 months, children's emotional repertoire differentiates into seven emotions: joy, contentment, anger, disgust, surprise, interest, and sadness. By preschool, children are able to accurately label emotions from viewing pictures and to match emotions to their appropriate context. Up through age 6 they continue to develop their ability to understand more complex emotions.

Children have innate abilities that drive this process, but their emotional development is also influenced by learning. *Children learn both how to react emotionally and how to regulate their emotions in the context of their interactions with their parents.*

There are at least two ways that parents contribute to this learning. The first is by social referencing. That is, children look to their parents for emotional guidance. How parents respond to a situation provides children information that guides their own emotional responses. If parents respond positively (i.e., interest, joy), children will often react with similar affect and engage in approach behavior (i.e., looking at, approaching, or touching a novel toy or person while displaying positive affect). If parents respond negatively, children are likely to display avoidant behavior (i.e., looking away, distancing from a novel toy or person, displaying negative affect). Infants interpret their parents' emotions *primarily* through facial expressions, but the vocalizations that accompany parents' facial expressions and physical touching convey affective information to children as well.

The second way parents influence their children's emotional development is by responding to them in a manner that matches their expressed affect (e.g., affective matching). For example, if children are fearful, parents can respond by holding them and physically reassuring their security. If children are happy, parents can respond by sharing in their joy by smiling or laughing with them.

Parental responses that are sensitively matched to children's affect provide children the support they need to regulate their own reactions. This is especially critical for helping children regulate negative affect and moods. However, if parents mismatch their children's expressed affect (e.g., respond to their children's anger with laughter) or ignore children's affect, their responses could interfere with their children developing the normal range of emotional expressions. In addition, if parents respond inconsistently to their children's negative affect, this could make it more difficult for children to regulate or gain control over their emotional responses.

SE-203 Eyes, facial displays, and body gestures are windows to children's feelings and emotions.

How do we know how young children feel or what their emotional reactions are to various people, visual displays, voices, or sounds? In fact, we never know for certain what young children are feeling. But most *children provide multiple cues to their affective state through their use of eye gaze, facial displays, and body gestures.* In general, it is not very difficult to determine what children are feeling, because they provide so many nonverbal cues to express themselves. But if parents are not attentive and sensitive to the fact that children have complex and real emotional states, they risk overlooking or ignoring their children's feelings and affective state.

How accurate parents are at detecting and interpreting their children's affective state can improve with experience. *The more frequently parents engage in one-to-one, reciprocal interaction with their children, the more accurate they will become at detecting and interpreting their children's affective state.* By engaging in face-to-face reciprocal interaction with children, parents have greater opportunities to notice the ways their children use their eyes, facial displays, and body movements to express their affect. Because affective matching requires that parents respond to children in a way that complements or supports their affective state, parents need to be as effective as possible at determining how children use their eyes, facial displays, and body movements to display their affective states such as contentment, joy, anger, disgust, or fear. They also need to learn to anticipate situations that are likely to evoke different emotional reactions from their children.

Parents who are uncertain about the ways their children express affect or the types of situations that elicit these different responses need to increase the frequency of their one-to-one interactions with them. Young children cannot tell us how they feel, but they do communicate their feelings through their nonverbal interactions. Parents can develop greater confidence in their ability to understand their children's affective responses by engaging in frequent reciprocal interactions with them.

SE-204 Intersubjectivity: setting the stage for children's emotional reactions.

One transition children undergo near the end of their first year is the "discovery of intersubjectivity." At this stage of development, children begin to understand that they can share their own feelings, and that they are capable of detecting the feelings of others. As children learn to detect the affective states of others, they use this information to regulate their emotions and behavior. For example, if their parents react to a novel object, such as an insect, with fear, their children, who have no preconceived notions, may react in the same way to insects. On the other hand, if their parents react to insects with pleasure, children may also react with pleasure.

Children learn to react emotionally (e.g., affective responding) by imitating their parents' affective responses. Through spontaneous imitation, children participate directly in common experiences (actions, communications, rituals) with their parents and others. This relationship between intersubjectivity and children's imitation is evident from two facts. First, children discover intersubjectivity at about the same time they increase their rate of spontaneous imitation. Second, children with conditions such as autism, who have difficulty learning intersubjectivity, engage in low levels of spontaneous imitation. Their imitations are often echolalic and bear little relationship to the way they were originally used by the adult. For these children, imitations are depersonalized behaviors that are stripped of the meaning they originally had, rather than shared experiences.

Children can only acquire intersubjectivity through repeated and sustained reciprocal interaction with one or more adults. As children gain familiarity with people in one-to-one interactions, they begin to notice how their own affective signals are related to their behavior (e.g., smile when they encounter familiar people). Children's awareness of common responses ultimately helps them understand that they share with adults not only behaviors (e.g., smiling) but also the feelings underlying these behaviors (e.g., joy).

If children have problems with intersubjectivity, it is critical that their parents interact frequently with them. *If children have a tendency to avoid engaging in reciprocal interaction, parents need to make even greater efforts to find or create opportunities to interact with them.*

SE-205 The more sensitive adults are to children's affective cues, the more reactive children become to adults' emotions.

Children are underreactive if they display behaviors such as looking through or past people, acting like others are not there, resisting looking at others in the eye, being in their own world, rarely smiling or laughing, responding stoically to new and exciting events, not reacting to their own name, or not becoming upset when toys are removed from them. There are at least two reasons for these behaviors. First, children may be temperamentally slow to react and fearful of social interaction. Second, children may have biologically based disorders such as autism, which limit their ability to react to social stimulation.

Although parents may find underreactive children easier to manage than overreactive children, in the long term, underreactivity may have more serious implications for their social–emotional development. Underreactive children tend to become socially isolated, withdrawn, and depressed. This condition makes it difficult for children to form friendships. In addition, because these children give so little affective feedback, it is unrewarding for parents, other adults, and peers to interact with them for extended periods of time. Thus children's tendency to be underreactive discourages others from engaging them in the fun and interesting social interactions they will need to acquire basic social–emotional competencies. As a result, *underreactivity can have a downward spiral effect on children's social–emotional development.*

Parents can fight their children's underreactivity. Just because children have biological or genetic predispositions to underreactivity does not prevent them from becoming more reactive. *If parents make a special effort to become highly responsive to the subtle, affective cues their children display, gradually their children will become more emotionally reactive.* We cannot force children to become more reactive. Asking them to respond, or prodding them physically or expressively, may only overwhelm them and discourage rather than enhance their reactivity. But the more attuned parents become to children's affective expressions, and the more they respond to even the most subtle of these behaviors, the more frequently these children will produce affective behaviors and begin to respond to the affective cues of the people with whom they are interacting.

SE-206 Depressed mothers have depressed babies; animated mothers have animated babies.

Field (Field, Hossain, & Malphurs, 1999; Hart, Field, del Valle, & Pelaez-Nogueras, 1998) observed very young children while they interacted with their friends who had been diagnosed as clinically depressed. Results from these studies were very alarming. *When babies interacted with their mothers, they tended to display the same types of depressed affect and low animation as their mothers.* In addition, when these children interacted with nondepressed adults, they continued to display the depressive features they displayed with their mothers. In other words, children seemed to acquire the affective and emotional characteristics of their depressed mothers. This study suggested that mothers' influence on their children's affect carried over to children's interactions with other adults. Thus *parental depression is not only a problem for parents; it also has implications for children's emotional state.*

Mothers of young children commonly have recurrent episodes of depression. These are caused by a variety of factors including hormonal changes after birth, mothers' concerns about their physical appearance, the work and sleep deprivation associated with caring for an infant, and the social isolation that comes from caring for their children at home.

The good news is that these episodes of depression do not constitute the types of clinical depression studied by Field. Furthermore, most parents recover from these feelings of depression after short periods of time. Because most babies are not depressed, it appears that young babies are usually able to cope with common episodes of maternal depression. However, if a mother's depression is severe or long-lasting, it is important to recognize the impact it can have on the emotional state of their young children.

In general, parents need to make sure that their children have opportunities for positive, affective, and animated interactions. If they are experiencing episodes of depression, parents can ask someone to assist them with childcare during these episodes to make sure their children have the opportunity to interact with someone who is not depressed. *Parents also need to make an extra effort to interact with their children with vitality and animation.* They should also consult with their physician to determine whether their depression can be treated with medication. This is particularly important if mothers' depression lasts longer than a few weeks.

Discussion Points

SE-201 Effective social relationships occur when children become capable of sharing emotional states with others.

- Empathy is the process through which children gain awareness of the emotional states of others and begin to take on the perspective of the people with whom they interact.
- Empathy is the ability to match one's feelings to someone else's emotional state.
- Children who fail to develop the ability to empathize can develop a number of serious social–emotional problems.

SE-202 Children learn how to react emotionally from their parents or caregivers.

- By 2 months of developmental age, children are thought to have three discrete emotional states: interest, contentment, and distress.
- Children learn both how to react emotionally and how to regulate their emotions in the context of their interactions with their parents.
- Parental responses that are sensitively matched to children's affect provide children the support they need to regulate their own reactions.

SE-203 Eyes, facial displays, and body gestures are windows to children's feelings and emotions.

- Children provide multiple cues to their affective state through their use of eye gaze, facial displays, and body gestures.
- The more frequently parents engage in one-to-one, reciprocal interaction with their children, the more accurate they will become at detecting and interpreting their children's affective state.

SE-204 Intersubjectivity: setting the stage for children's emotional reactions.

- Children learn to react emotionally (e.g., affective responding) by imitating their parents' affective responses.
- Children can only acquire intersubjectivity through repeated and sustained reciprocal interaction with one or more adults.
- If children avoid engaging in reciprocal interaction, parents need to make great efforts to find or create opportunities to interact with them.

SE-205 The more sensitive parents are to children's affective cues, the more reactive children become to their parents' emotions.

- Children are underreactive if they display behaviors such as looking through or past people, acting like others are not there, resisting looking at others in the eye, being in their own world, rarely smiling or laughing, responding stoically to new and exciting events, not reacting to their own name, or not becoming upset when toys are removed from them.
- Underreactivity can have a downward spiral effect on children's social–emotional development.
- If parents become highly responsive to the subtle, affective cues their children display, gradually their children will become more emotionally reactive.

SE-206 Depressed mothers have depressed babies; animated mothers have animated babies.

- When babies interact with depressed mothers, they display the same types of depressed affect and low animation as their mothers.
- Parental depression is not only a problem for parents; it also has implications for children's emotional state.
- Parents need to make an extra effort to interact with their children with vitality and animation.

RT Strategies That Promote Empathy

113 ***Get into my child's world.*** Make three adjustments to view the world as your child does. First, establish a mutual physical relationship with your child. Make eye contact and interact on the same physical level as your child. Second, interact by playing or communicating like your child. Mimicking behaviors such as babbling, cooing, smiling, and making a playful face let your child know that you are willing to interact on your child's terms. Third, consciously strive to try to understand the world as your child does. Remember that most experiences do not have the same meaning to your child as they do to you.

Practical Suggestions

- Play with your child in a face-to-face position. Interact with your child on his or her physical level so that your child does not have to look up to see you.

- Make eye contact when you are playing or interacting with your child.
- Consider that as your child begins to experience the world, he or she must make sense of his or her experiences. Your child sees and understands the world very differently than you do.
- Consider that as your child matures, he or she will continually rediscover his or her world. The world as your child understood it at the 3-month stage of development takes on a new meaning at the 9-month stage. The changes in thinking and understanding that occur in the early years of development lead your child to perceive and experience objects or events he or she was familiar with from a dramatically new perspective.
- Play in the small ways that your child plays without pressuring him or her to do anything other than stay involved in the interaction.

131 ***Play face-to-face games without toys.*** Use simple games with your child such as songs, nursery rhymes, hand games, and games with other parts of the body that require simple sequences in which your child can play an active role.

Practical Suggestions

- Consider the kinds of games that you have seen your own parents or other parents play with young children.
- Find books that describe simple games that parents can do with young children.
- Professionals can show parents how to modify games to make them balanced interactive routines. It is especially important to simplify games that are difficult for children who are developmentally young.

213 ***Be sensitive to my child's state.*** State refers to children's biological or physiological status. When your child becomes inactive, fussy, dull-eyed, sullen (nonsmiley), or when he or she yawns, turns away, arches his or her back, or lays down on the floor, your child may be telling you that he or she is tired, hungry, uncomfortable, or distressed. When your child smiles, vocalizes, makes eye contact, and is bright-eyed and responsive, his or her behavior suggests that he or she is alert, happy, content, and ready to engage in interaction. Your child's state can change suddenly while he or she is engaging in interaction and can shift quickly from one phase to another. Learn how to detect your child's cues. Your child's nonverbal behaviors are windows to his or her biological and physiological status.

Practical Suggestions

- Write down what your child does to indicate his or her different states.
- When you interact with your child, label his or her state as he or she produces various nonverbal behaviors.
- Professionals can help parents learn to read their children's nonverbal behaviors by becoming children's voice to describe their feelings/states

when they are playing with their parents (e.g., as the child turns away, say "I am getting tired, Mommy").

222 ***Respond immediately to little behaviors.*** Little behaviors are behaviors such as burps, change of visual regard, kicking legs, waving hands, facial displays, and others.

Practical Suggestions

- Even if your child is not directing his or her "little behaviors" to you, and even though these behaviors have no apparent purpose or meaning, by responding immediately you can transform these behaviors into meaningful social interaction.
- Immediate responding to your child's solitary play and self-speech will help your child become more aware of you and more apt to engage in social exchanges.
- Review videotaped observations to see how quickly you respond to your child's behavior.

233 ***Translate my child's actions, feelings, and intentions into words.*** Children learn language best when adults respond with words that fit what they are experiencing at the moment. When you use words that match your child's actions, feelings, and intentions such as *come, go, eat, mom, dog,* and *truck,* your words will have more relevance to what your child is experiencing than words like *two, three, red, yellow, horse,* and *barn.*

Practical Suggestions

- Become your child's living dictionary. Children's first words come from their routine actions, experiences, and sensations. You can help your child learn words more rapidly by modeling one- or two-word phrases that are directly related to what your child is currently doing, seeing, touching, hearing, or feeling.
- Become sensitive to what your child is sensing and experiencing. Give your child a word for these feelings and sensations.
- When choosing what to say to your child, consider how your child will communicate with a particular word.

433 ***Comfort my child when he or she is fussy, irritable, or angry.*** Physically comfort and soothe your child when he or she becomes fussy or angry, unless your child is so agitated that he or she cannot tolerate contact with you. If your child becomes too agitated for social contact, provide comfort after he or she regains composure. During the early years of life, your child needs your comfort and affection to learn to cope more effectively with his or her feelings.

Practical Suggestions

- How do you feel when your child becomes fussy and irritable? Your child's negative states and moods are not meant to agitate you, but rather, they occur because your child has good reasons to be irritable or angry.
- If you get angry when your child become fussy and irritable, try to empathize or identify with your child's feelings.
- Professionals can demonstrate how children can be comforted by holding them, speaking soothingly to them, and gently rocking them.

442 ***Treat my child's fears as meaningful and legitimate.*** Early in their lives, children develop fears of people, places, lights, sounds, and so forth, which may not seem fearful to adults. Understand that your child's fears stem from his or her limited understanding of different people and events. Provide comfort and support to help your child cope with fears.

Practical Suggestions

- As your child develops, his or her understanding of people, places, and sensations constantly changes. For example, fear of strangers typically begins at about 8 to 12 months of developmental age when children begin to perceive their parents as unique sources of support and protection. At this time, children become fearful of strangers they previously did not fear because they lack confidence that these strangers will protect them from harm.

Developmental Domain: Social–Emotional Functioning

Pivotal Behavior: Cooperation

SE-3 Cooperation refers to the degree to which children comply with adults' requests or suggestions and collaborate in working together with them. Children consistently make efforts to do what adults ask, or respond quickly to adults' suggestions.

Facts To Consider About Cooperation

SE-301 Children learn to be cooperative when they are successful at complying with requests made by their parents or others.

Cooperation is a habit that children develop by successfully and repeatedly engaging in cooperative activities with adults. The nonverbal, reciprocal interactions that take place between children and their parents soon after they are born are the first context in which children learn primitive forms of cooperation (i.e., work together). In these reciprocal interactions, not only are parents responding to their children's nonverbal cues and behaviors, but children are also responding to the voice, touch, and nonverbal gestures of their parents. *When early interactions are characterized by partners engaging in give-and-take activities with each other, young children are learning to cooperate (i.e., work together) with their parents.*

As children attain higher levels of development, their cooperation will gradually take on a different form. At first, children will be able to cooperate (i.e., respond appropriately to parents' guidance or requests) mainly when parents ask them to do things that are directly related to their current activity. If parents request children to do things they can easily do, children will have numerous successes at cooperating with them.

The more successful children are at responding to their parents' requests, the more opportunities they have to develop the habit of cooperation. As cooperation becomes an established pivotal behavior, children will gradually extend this habit to attempting to cooperate with requests that require greater effort. That is, as children attain higher levels of developmental functioning, they become more capable of cooperating with adult requests that require them to do things that are not directly related to their immediate interests or activities. Parents must remind themselves of the importance of strengthening children's habit of cooperation by focusing mostly on seeking children's cooperation with activities and behaviors that are well within their range of capabilities.

SE-302 Failure to cooperate: one of the major forms of misbehavior.

Parents are likely to view children as presenting behavior problems if (a) they seldom comply with what parents ask them to do or (b) they seldom cooperate in daily routines such as eating or dressing. *If children do not cooperate or comply with their parents, parents may view them as stubborn, belligerent, or even hostile.* On the other hand, if children routinely cooperate and respond appropriately to what their parents ask them to do, parents are likely to view their children as socially competent.

Cooperation is partly dependent upon children voluntarily doing what is asked of them. To the extent that cooperation is voluntary, children who are not cooperative may in fact be choosing not to do what their parents ask. However, there are two other factors that also contribute to how cooperative children are, neither of which are under children's control: children's stage of developmental growth and the nature of the demands their parents place on them.

Sometime during the end of the second year of developmental growth, children go through a stage of development in which they become focused on learning how to function independently of their parents. As part of the process of learning to be independent, children often refuse to do things their parents ask, or run away from their parents to do whatever interests them. Almost all children go through this stage of development. Many behaviors children do during this phase can be described as misbehavior. However, another way to view them is as normal developmental behaviors that are not the result of children willfully defying their parents.

Children are not likely to cooperate if their parents ask them to do things that exceed their current capabilities or are unreasonable at their level of development. If parents routinely ask children to do things that are difficult, interpreting their lack of cooperation as obstinance or defiance would be blaming children for failing to do what they are unable to do. The more often parents ask or expect their children to do things that are difficult, the more their children will fail to cooperate. Unfortunately, *parents who routinely expect their children to do things that they cannot do often perceive their children as having behavior problems,* even though their "misbehavior" is caused by the types of requests or expectations parents are asking their children to do.

SE-303 Children will comply successfully with their parents' requests when parents ask them to do things that are within their current range of ability.

Children's ability to comply with what adults ask them to do is directly related to how capable they are at doing what is asked. If the behavior being requested is one that children can clearly do, children's capacity to respond appropriately will not be limited by their lack of ability. However, requests will be more difficult to respond to if they require responses that children either are in the process of learning or are not yet capable of doing.

There are two ways parents can determine how difficult requests might be for children. *The first is to observe what children do.* If children frequently carry out the behavior that they are being asked to do, then this behavior should be well within children's capabilities and is a behavior they can clearly do. If children only occasionally carry out the behavior being requested, this is likely an emerging developmental skill, which, although within the child's range of abilities, may still be difficult to do on demand. If children have never done what is being asked of them, these behaviors are likely beyond the child's current level of development. Such requests may be reasonable insofar as they are the kinds of behaviors children typically do at the child's age. However, unless children routinely engage in these behaviors, their ability to do them when requested will be extremely limited.

The second way of judging the difficulty of requests is to *use developmental tests or profiles (e.g.,* Developmental Rainbow) *to determine whether the behavior is one that most children typically do at their current developmental level.* This requires a fairly accurate understanding of the child's current developmental age. If the child is functioning at the 12-month developmental age level, a developmental profile could be used to identify behaviors that are below the child's current range of functioning versus behaviors that are at the child's current level of functioning (e.g., behaviors listed at the child's developmental age to as much as 2 months previous to the child's developmental age) versus behaviors that are above the child's developmental functioning (e.g., behaviors that are more than 1 month above the child's developmental age). Children should be able to respond easily to requests to do things that are below their developmental age. They may have difficulty responding to requests that are at their developmental age, but they will not be able to respond successfully to requests that are above their current level of developmental functioning.

SE-304 Children are more likely to comply with their parents' requests when parents ask them to do things related to the children's immediate interests.

Many of us have had the experience of being engaged in an activity in which we were highly involved or interested, when we were asked to do something that would take us away from the activity. For example, we might have been watching a favorite television show when our child asked us to play with him. What we are being asked to do was clearly not beyond our capabilities. Nonetheless, we likely had little if any motivation to respond to our child's request, because it would take us away from an activity that interested us. It takes selflessness and maturity for adults to sacrifice doing something that interests them to comply with requests that divert them from their interests.

Children may have difficulty cooperating with their parents for this same reason. *If parents ask children to do something that pulls them away from an activity in which they are interested, they will have difficulty cooperating with what they are being asked to do.* In this situation children fail to cooperate not because they are being asked to do something that is too difficult, but because they are being asked to do something that pulls them away from what they are interested in at the moment.

If children are having difficulty cooperating with what their parents are asking them to do, it is important for parents to consider how often their requests are related to their children's interests. If children's failure to cooperate occurs primarily when they are asked to do things that are not directly related to what interests them, parents need to consider two things:

- First, helping children develop the pivotal behavior of *cooperation* is more important than getting them to comply with a request that may not be critical at the moment.
- Second, there are likely alternative ways to encourage children to do what we want them to do, by focusing our requests on children's current interests.

If breakdowns in cooperation occur primarily when parents ask children to do things that are not critical at the moment, *parents might try to direct their efforts more toward gaining children's cooperation in activities that interest them.* However, if what parents are asking children to do is truly necessary, then they need to consider how their requests can be incorporated into children's interests.

SE-305 Children will comply more often with their parents' requests when parents reduce the number of requests they ask of their children.

Some time ago, we conducted a study in which we examined how much young children complied with mothers who were highly directive versus mothers who were not very directive. The children in this study all had developmental problems and were 2½ years old. Results indicated that mothers who were highly directive requested their children to do things 2½ times more often than did mothers who were less directive. Yet the number of times children in these two groups responded to their mothers was nearly identical. Furthermore, the rate that children with developmental problems responded to their mothers' requests was nearly identical to the rate that a group of typically developing children responded to their mothers, even though their mothers made 42% fewer requests. In other words, as mothers increased the number of times they asked their children to do something, children did not increase their rate of responding to their mothers.

Results from this study have a number of interesting implications. First, they suggest that *there is a limit to how much children can respond to their parents' requests*. In this study, children responded to their mothers about eight to nine times per minute. Perhaps children's rate of responding did not increase as their mothers' requests increased, because there is only so much that children are capable of responding. Second, children appeared uncooperative (i.e., responded to a lower proportion of their mothers' requests) the greater the number of requests their mothers made. If parents reduce the number of times they ask their children to do something, children will appear more cooperative, even if they do not increase their number of responses, simply because they will be responding to a greater proportion of their parents' requests.

One key to gaining children's cooperation is for parents to limit the number of requests they make of children. If children tend to be uncooperative and parents are making many requests, then reducing (not eliminating) the number of requests will have the immediate effect of increasing the rate that their children cooperate with them.

SE-306 Children are more likely to comply with parents' requests when parents engage in frequent, reciprocal interactions with them.

When there is a concern about how to help children become more cooperative, Responsive Teaching emphasizes that cooperation is a two-way phenomenon. *Cooperation requires that parents and children respond to the requests or desires of each other* and is not just a matter of getting children to do what parents want. Children first learn how to cooperate with their parents in the context of routine, daily interactions. Children are more apt to be cooperative when their parents are highly responsive to their activities, emotions, and needs. In these reciprocal exchanges children have the opportunity both to observe and imitate the cooperative behaviors of their parents. *Interacting reciprocally with their parents helps children learn the habit of cooperation.*

Because young children have such a self-centered view of life, they are only likely to notice their parents cooperating with them when parents respond and provide assistance in activities that are of interest to them (e.g., social exchanges, play activities, or conversations in which children are highly engaged).

SE-307 Parents can gain children's cooperation by giving them frequent opportunities to make choices.

Children are more likely to cooperate when they have choices about what to do or how to cooperate with their parents. There are two reasons for this. First, when children are asked to cooperate in a situation where they have choices about what to do, they are exercising control over their own behavior. *Being able to make their own choices is one of the most basic motivators of children's early learning and development.* Second, when children are encouraged to make choices, this allows them to become involved in an activity that interests them, as opposed to being coerced to do something that is of no interest. Children's resistance to cooperate will decrease when cooperating enables them to do what they prefer.

In some ways, giving children choices may seem to be in direct opposition to getting children to become more cooperative. If cooperation means getting children to do what their parents want them to do, does providing children choices dilute this purpose? If there are no reasonable alternatives parents can offer their children, then the answer to this question is yes. Children simply need to comply with parental requests when the only alternative is to do what they are asked.

However, in many situations it is possible to present children alternatives for cooperating. Parents' goal should not just be to get children to do what they would like them to do. More important is to help their children develop the habit of cooperation. By offering alternatives, parents make it easier for their children to cooperate, and as a result promote the likelihood of their children cooperating in the future. *When parents are flexible in requesting children to do things, children are more apt to form the habit of cooperation.* By being less rigid and demanding, parents can gain greater control over their children, because their children become more willing to cooperate with them.

SE-308 Transitions are often difficult for children to cooperate with.

During a transition, parents typically have difficulty gaining their children's cooperation. *Transitions* refer to changes in children's activity such as going from one play activity to another, going from play to eating or play to bed, moving from one location to another, having a new person enter into the child's world, or otherwise removing a child from an activity he or she enjoys. Many children react to transitions by crying, whining, tantruming, physically resisting, or sulking. The question to consider is why do transitions cause children to act out? Why is this one situation where children seem to have so much difficulty cooperating with adults?

Not all children have difficulties with transitions. Children who have "easy" temperaments (i.e., children who are generally happy and who are seldom fazed by change or novel situations) often deal with transitions with much fewer problems than children who have "difficult" or "slow to warm up" temperaments. In other words, some children are born with a behavioral style that makes it easy for them to accommodate to demands for them to shift from one activity to another. *The children who have the greatest difficulty with transitions are children with a difficult temperament who react intensely to almost any novel situation or change of routine.* These children seem to be biologically wired to react strongly to almost any stressor that is placed on them. They display the same intensity in their involvement in almost any activity they undertake. Nothing is easy for these children. Transitions are just another situation to which these children have difficulty adjusting.

There are two other reasons transitions are difficult for young children. First, *children experience transitions as a process of being pulled away from their current activities without understanding what will happen in the future.* At very young ages children do not yet understand that there are legitimate reasons for shifting from one activity or situation to another, that they will be able to resume the activity they are being pulled away from at a later time, and that the new situation that they are transitioning to may be even more rewarding than the one with which they are currently involved. In other words, developmentally young children only understand their actions in the "here and now." Their concept of the future is extremely limited. If children enjoy what they are doing, and they have little understanding of what will happen as they transition from their current activity, it is not surprising that they react negatively as they are coaxed through this process.

Second, *young children are fundamentally egocentric: they have difficulty leaving activities that interest them.* When they are actively engaged in an activity that is interesting and fun, they do not have the ability to take the perspective of their parent who needs to move them from their current activity to a new situation. Children become totally immersed in their world. The more intensely they are engaged in their own activities, the more violently they react when their parents attempt to remove them from these activities. Their reaction is caused by their inability to detach from their own personal interests, to comply with the needs and perspectives of someone other than themselves. Most children are unable to take the perspective of others until they reach at least the 3-year level of developmental functioning.

It is important for parents to realize that children's negative reactions to transitions are not a sign of disrespect or hostility toward them. Rather, they are the result of children's lack of ability to control their emotions and to understand the need for the transition. As children gain greater control of their emotions, develop an understanding of the future, and learn to take the perspective of others, it will become easier for them to cooperate with transitions.

SE-309 Parents can reduce the stress of children's transitions.

How parents interact with their children can profoundly influence the way that children cope with transitions. Three strategies are particularly useful at helping children become more cooperative during transitions.

First, *anticipate how your child is likely to react during a transition.* For the most part, how children react to transitions is fairly predictable. For example, if parents allow children to play before going to bed, and their children routinely become intensely involved in their play before bedtime, they will invariably react negatively as their parents try to transition them from playing to going to bed. If parents can anticipate how their children will react to these situations, they can prepare themselves for their children's reactions, and, perhaps more importantly, try to implement strategies that might distract their children from reacting negatively.

For example, parents might insert themselves as partners in their children's play. They can continue to interact playfully with their child while taking the child to his or her room and putting on pajamas. Rather than abruptly shifting their child from play to changing clothes, this allows their child to continue playing, but shifts the focus of play (e.g., blocks vs. pajamas) without preventing the child from playing. The parent co-opts the child from reacting negatively to the transition by becoming a play partner who initially supports the child's activities and eventually bridges the child to the desired activity.

Second, *divert your child's interests.* One of the major reasons transitions are so difficult is that they pull children away from activities in which they are involved and interested. Parents can reduce children's stress by providing them a high-interest object or activity to divert them from their activity. This high-interest object can be used to shift the child's interests from the initial activity and sustain the child's cooperation through the transition. For example, if a child has a favorite doll, give her the doll before requesting that she leave an activity in which she is actively involved. Allowing the child to hold on to the doll as she transitions to the new activity or situation will help shift her interest from the original activity to the doll. This helps her become involved with a high-interest activity while going through a stressful transition.

Third, *comfort your child through transitions.* For some children, certain transitions will be stressful, regardless what parents do. Parents can help children deal with their distress by comforting and nurturing them. This requires that they maintain the perspective that there are legitimate reasons why transitions are stressful for their children. Treating children's distress by comforting them provides children the support and nurturance they need to cope with the stress of the transition.

Discussion Points

SE-301 Children learn to be cooperative when they are successful at complying with requests made by their parents or others.

- Cooperation is a habit that children develop by successfully and repeatedly engaging in cooperative activities with adults.
- When early interactions are characterized by partners engaging in give-and-take activities with each other, young children are learning to cooperate (i.e., work together) with their parents.
- The more successful children are at responding to their parents' requests, the more opportunities they have to develop the habit of cooperation.

SE-302 Failure to cooperate: one of the major forms of misbehavior.

- If children do not cooperate or comply with their parents, parents may view them as stubborn, belligerent, or even hostile.

- Children are not likely to cooperate if their parents ask them to do things that exceed their current capabilities or are unreasonable at their level of development.
- Parents who routinely expect their children to do things that they cannot do, often perceive their children as behavior problems.

SE-303 Children will comply with their parents' requests when parents ask them to do things that are within their current range of ability.

- Children's ability to comply with what adults ask them to do is directly related to how capable they are at doing what is asked.
- Children are able to do behaviors that they have been observed to do.
- Children are able to do behaviors that are at or below their current level of developmental functioning.

SE-304 Children are more likely to comply with their parents' requests when parents ask them to do things related to the children's immediate interests.

- If parents ask children to do something that pulls them away from an activity in which they are interested, they will have difficulty cooperating with what they are being asked to do.
- Parents should direct their efforts toward gaining children's cooperation in activities that interest them.

SE-305 Children will comply more often to their parents' requests when parents reduce the number of requests they ask of their children.

- There is a limit to how much children can respond to their parents' requests.
- If parents simply reduce the number of times they ask their children to do something, children will appear more cooperative even if they do not increase their number of responses.

SE-306 Children are more likely to comply with parents' requests when parents engage in frequent, reciprocal interactions with them.

- Cooperation requires that parents and children respond to the requests or desires of each other.
- Interacting reciprocally with their parents helps children learn the habit of cooperation.

SE-307 Parents can gain children's cooperation by giving them frequent opportunities to make choices.

- Children are more likely to cooperate when they have choices about what to do or how to cooperate with their parents.
- Being able to make their own choice is one of the most basic motivators of children's early learning and development.
- When parents are flexible in requesting children to do things, children are more apt to form the habit of cooperation.

SE-308 Transitions are often difficult for children to cooperate with.

- The children who have the greatest difficulty with transitions are children with a "difficult" temperament who react intensely to almost any novel situation or change of routine.
- Children experience transitions as a process of being pulled away from their current activities without understanding what will happen in the future.
- Children are fundamentally egocentric: they have difficulty leaving activities that interest them.

SE-309 Parents can reduce the stress of children's transitions.

- They need to anticipate how their child is likely to react during a transition.
- They should learn to divert their child's interests.
- They should comfort their child through transitions.

RT Strategies That Promote Cooperation

112 ***Play frequently together.*** Play is an ideal way to interact with your child. Engage in several brief episodes of play with your child throughout the day. Play as often as possible, particularly when your child is alert and ready to engage in playful interaction.

Practical Suggestions

- Consider how often you play with your child and what kinds of things you do together.
- Find out what kinds of toys your child is most likely to play with at his or her current developmental age level (libraries and Web sites are great resources for this).
- Professionals can model various types of play with the child.
- Professionals can invite parents to join them as they play with the child and gradually encourage the parent to take over playing with the child.
- Professionals can share with parents the kinds of games they like to play with children.

235 ***Interpret noncompliance as a choice or lack of ability.*** Children communicate their intentions by "not complying" with what you ask them to do. Often children do not comply with their parents' request because they (a) feel that what their parents are asking them to do is too difficult, or (b) their parents are trying to coax them to do something that does not interest them. When what you are asking your child to do is not critically important, a very effective way of keeping your child interacting with you is letting your child not comply.

Practical Suggestions

- Consider that accepting your child's choice not to comply does not teach your child to be disobedient. When you do this you are actually responding to your child's interests and limitations. The more you recognize and respond to your child's limitations and desires, the more successful you will be at gaining your child's voluntary cooperation.

313 ***Give my child frequent opportunities to make choices.*** While interacting with your child, wait for your child to choose what he or she wants to do and how he or she wants to do it. Follow your child's choice of toys and activities, particularly if they are appropriate to the situation and not harmful to the child or to others.

Practical Suggestions

- Your child may have difficulty choosing what to do when one or a combination of three things occurs. First, the toys or activities are too difficult for your child to use alone. Second, the toys are out of your child's reach. Third, your child is not able to manipulate or control these toys alone. If your child is having difficulty making choices, give your child several toys and activities that are within his or her range of ability that he or she can get to, handle, and operate alone.

423 ***Turn routines into games.*** Transform routine childcare activities—such as dressing, feeding, bathing, putting your child to bed, driving from one place to another, or transitioning your child from one routine or situation to another—into games. Even if you are tired and not feeling up to playing with your child, a dose of playfulness will encourage your child to be more cooperative and enjoyable.

Practical Suggestions

- Make ordinary routines playful by accompanying your child with songs, nursery rhymes, or games like "I'm going to get you."
- Consider what you typically do to get your child to smile or laugh. Try to infuse these into the routine activities with your child that you find tedious and trying.

443 ***Accept whatever my child does.*** Respond supportively to any behaviors your child does, except for behaviors that are harmful, disrespectful, or incompatible with your family's values and priorities.

Practical Suggestions

- There are long-term implications to your responding to whatever your child does. Although your responsiveness will encourage your child to repeat behaviors he or she is currently doing, it *will not* prevent your child from learning new developmental behaviors. Rather than reinforcing undesirable behavior, your responding communicates that you value and accept what your child is doing. Over time, your repetitive, positive feedback will help your child form self-perceptions of being competent and capable.
- Consider how your parents influenced your development. Did your parents play a strong role in helping you learn specific behaviors, or in help-

ing you form your own self-concept and personality? If you become too focused on the behaviors your child is not able to do, you may be overlooking the potentially negative impact that you might be having on how your child feels about him- or herself.

- Consider that if we help a child learn a behavior, but at the same time give negative messages by not accepting the behaviors he or she is able to do, will the new behavior that we have helped the child learn compensate for the negative feedback he or she received?

513 ***Request actions that match my child's developmental level.*** Limit your requests for your child to do or say things to behaviors that are within your child's range of accommodation. Your child will have difficulty responding to behaviors and communications that exceed his or her range of accommodation.

Practical Suggestions

- Review a videotape of you and your child playing together. Write down the behaviors that you have asked your child to do. Look up these behaviors on the *Developmental Rainbow* or other developmental profile. Notice how your child was more reactive and engaged when you asked him or her to do things that were within his or her range of accommodation. Notice how he became passive or ignored you when you asked him to do things that are difficult (e.g., beyond his range of accommodation).
- Consider how you respond when you are asked to do something that you do not know how to do.
- Increase your child's opportunities to be successful with you by asking him or her to do things that he or she has the developmental capabilities to do.

516 ***Have developmentally appropriate rules and expectations.*** You are more likely to gain your child's cooperation, and your child will be less likely to act out or misbehave, if your rules and expectations are compatible with what most children are able to do at your child's current level of social–emotional functioning.

Practical Suggestions

- Use a developmental observation guide such as the *Developmental Rainbow* to determine your child's current level of social–emotional functioning. Many children have levels of social–emotional functioning that are different from their current age level and from their level of communication and cognitive development.
- Identify common situations where your child typically acts out or does not conform to your expectations. Review the *Developmental Rainbow* or other social–emotional profile to determine whether your rules or expectations are compatible with your child's current level of social–emotional functioning. If your rules and expectations are too high, try to modify them so they are more consistent with your child's social–emotional capabilities.

Developmental Domain: Social–Emotional Functioning

Pivotal Behavior: Self-Regulation

SE-4 Self-Regulation refers to the degree to which children are able to soothe themselves when they are upset or frustrated. Periods of tantruming and crying are infrequent and brief in duration. Children are able to comfort themselves by holding a favorite toy or becoming engaged in a different play activity. They make transitions easily, adapting quickly to changes in the environment or routine.

Facts To Consider About Self-Regulation

SE-401 Self-regulation—learning to cope with emotions.

Young children react instinctively to the way that they feel. When babies feel distressed, uncomfortable, hungry, or need physical contact, they react by crying. Likewise, when babies are happy, excited, or pleased to see someone, they react by smiling. Most infants are incapable of holding back their emotions. They do not think about how to react to their feelings—they simply react.

One of the major differences between the emotional reactions of young children and those of adults are related to self-regulation. Adults are capable of self-regulating or controlling their emotions. When they are in pain, sad or uncomfortable, they may feel like crying, yet they refrain from crying, particularly if they are in a situation in which crying would be socially inappropriate. Similarly, when adults are angry, they can refrain from acting aggressively toward others by using alternative coping strategies. When they have strong emotional feelings, they generally try to control their reactions, at least until they are in a more appropriate setting to act out their feelings.

Young children do not have the internal capabilities necessary to regulate their emotions. They cry primarily because they have no capacity to regulate their reactions to the negative emotions they are experiencing. They bite, hit, or destroy things because they do not have internal strategies for controlling their anger. Young children do not necessarily have more negative feelings than adults, but they cry and act out more than adults do because they have no alternative way to deal with their emotions.

During early childhood, children gradually develop strategies for coping with, or regulating, their own emotional responses. Children become less emotionally volatile as they develop a better understanding of the nature of their feelings and of the routines their caregivers typically implement to help them deal with their emotions. In addition, as children develop language, they acquire more effective ways of communicating their needs than by crying or acting aggressively. But perhaps equally important, children develop internal strategies or mechanisms that help them to cope with their feelings and regulate their reactions to their feelings.

SE-402 Children develop their coping skills with time.

Most children cry, tantrum, and even act aggressively on a regular basis throughout the early childhood years. For many children, these behaviors seem to increase up to 2 years of age and do not subside until much later in childhood. One reason for this is that children begin to develop their abilities to cope with their emotions at about 2 years of age.

Self-regulation is a competency that children develop throughout the early childhood years. For most children this process is not fully developed until about 10 to 12 years of age. It is a slow process, but if parents keep a record of how often their children act out, they will find that their children become increasingly capable of managing and coping with their emotions with each successive year.

Some parents try to deal with their children's negative reactions by coercing them to suppress their crying and aggressive behavior through threats or punishment. In some cases this works. Children's fear of their parents motivates them to suppress their crying and acting out. However, the fact that children suppress their reactions to these negative emotions does not mean that they have learned to cope with the emotions that fueled them. Children may still feel pain, anger, or anxiety, even though they have learned not to express them. By coercing their children not to cry or act out, parents are dealing with the symptoms of their children's emotions without necessarily helping them deal with their feelings. For some children, this can result in their having persistent feelings of anxiety, fearfulness, and anger, none of which are of the kinds of feelings that lead to long-term emotional well-being.

Helping children learn to cope with their emotions is very different than coercing them to suppress their negative behaviors. Parents can help children cope by treating their negative emotions as legitimate feelings. Parents do this by comforting, soothing, and empathizing with their children during their times of distress. Parents can try to respond to what may be causing their children to react negatively by alleviating their discomfort, feeding them if they are hungry, or soothing them when they are tired and irritable. When children are emotionally distraught, parents provide them the comfort, support, and reassurance that will help them de-escalate their negative feelings and regain their composure. Although it is difficult not to be irritated by children's negative reactions, *parents must exercise patience and understand that their children do not have the same capabilities to manage their emotions as adults do.* When parents persist at helping their children buffer their emotional reactions, in time their children will develop the skills they need to cope with their emotions.

SE-403 Children's behavioral style or temperament plays a major role in the ease with which they learn to self-regulate.

There are considerable differences in the amount of time it takes children to learn to regulate their emotions. For some, emotional regulation is never a concern. These children seldom cry, they are slow to become angry, they readily adapt to new situations, and if they do become emotionally distraught, they are easy to calm. But these children are the exception, not the rule. More typical are children who have frequent and regular episodes of crying and acting out but who are able to calm down with a moderate amount of support. Seldom do these children carry out these episodes for excessive periods of times. In other words, although they are emotionally reactive, it is relatively easy to help them regain their composure. Yet, there is another group of children who seem not to miss an opportunity to overreact, who get angry quickly, who almost always have strong reactions to change and novelty, and who are difficult, if not impossible, to calm down.

By the time the first group of children (e.g., easy temperament) is 2 years old, their parents may find that they seldom cry, are not hostile and aggressive towards others, and generally tend to be happy or content. At 2 years, the second group may still be a handful, but they have more episodes of being happy and content than of acting out. Although at times they push their parents to their limits, they are generally manageable and show encouraging signs of becoming more so. The third group of children may continue to show little mercy to their parents when they are 2, 3, or even 4 years of age. They tend to be more aggressive and have considerably more episodes of reacting negatively than the other two groups. Their parents will likely struggle to find ways to please and soothe them. Many of these children will not begin to settle down and become manageable until they are between 7 and 9 years of age, and even at this age their parents may continue to feel uncertain as to how to deal with them.

What causes this variability? Why are children so different from each other? *One of the factors that contribute to children's ability to regulate their emotions is their developing cognitive and communication skills.* As children reach higher levels of developmental maturity, they have both a better understanding of the nature of their feelings and more effective ways of communicating to get their needs met.

Yet, the children who have difficulty regulating their emotions are not necessarily limited in their ability to think or communicate. What distinguishes these children from the other two groups, and what is one of the major contributors to children's ability to self-regulate, is temperament. These *children are born with a biological predisposition to overreact to almost any form of stress.* They seem to have a neurological system that is on high alert 24 hours a day, 7 days a week. As a result, they react intensely to almost any negative feeling or any person or event they perceive as obstructing them from doing what they want. They do not have different ways of understanding or greater sensitivity to discomfort and negative feelings than do other children, but they react completely differently to situations that the other two groups of children seem to handle in stride.

Because these children are so temperamentally reactive, they need to develop stronger self-regulation or coping mechanisms to attain emotional stability than do other children. It takes longer for them to do this because the process of self-regulation is so much more difficult than it is for children who have easy or moderately reactive behavioral styles or temperaments.

SE-404 Tantruming—children's reaction to stress or frustration.

It is difficult to understand how young children—who have few cares in the world—can nonetheless have a considerable amount of stress to deal with. But the fact is, they do. Their stress is caused by their lack of ability to cope with their negative feelings, as well as by their frustration of not being able to do what they want. As children attain higher levels of developmental functioning, they develop greater awareness of their world. This enables them to recognize the vast range of possibilities that they could be doing. It also makes them more aware of their vulnerability, which leads to fears, which are often fueled by their incomplete understanding. Children become stressed when they are frustrated and when they are unable to do things that are compatible with their increasing understanding of the world.

Children become aggressive and tantrum when the stress or frustration they are experiencing exceeds their capabilities to cope or regulate their emotions. When children have no effective strategies for coping or regulating their stress, they react with emotional outbursts. A tantrum for a child is the equivalent of a nervous breakdown for an adult; in both cases, their reactions are fueled by strong feelings that they are unable to control.

Almost every child has episodes of tantruming and aggression, but there are tremendous differences in the frequency, duration, and intensity of these reactions. This is highly related to children's biologically determined temperament. If children have an easy temperament, they do not to react strongly to stress. They tend not to cry and scream excessively, or lash out by hitting or biting, and they are often able to regain their composure within relatively short periods of time. However, if children have a difficult temperament, they react strongly to even minor stressors, because they are in such a high state of emotional arousal and they have not yet developed their abilities to regulate their feelings. Children with difficult temperaments tantrum frequently, with great intensity, and for long durations of time.

For all children, *tantruming and aggressive behavior decrease as they develop strategies for regulating their emotions.* The rate at which these behaviors decrease depends both on the speed with which children develop these coping strategies and on the nature of the stressors with which children need to cope. Generally, *children with a difficult temperament must develop greater self-control to mange their behavior effectively.* They may develop their coping skills at the same rate as children with an easy temperament, but it takes longer for them to reduce their frequency of tantruming and acting out simply because they experience stress so much more intensely than do other children.

SE-405 Children do not tantrum just to get their way.

There is a common notion that *children use tantrums as a means of getting their own way.* In other words, many parents view tantruming as a conscious strategy children use to impose their will over their parents. It is understandable why parents might interpret children's tantrums this way, because tantrums commonly occur when parents or others prevent children from doing what they want. However, this is not the only situation that precipitates tantrums—children may also tantrum when they are fearful or when they discover they are unable to do something they would like to do.

Responsive parenting views tantrums as resulting from children's inability to cope with stress. That is, tantrums are thought to be reactions to stress that children are not capable of managing. In contrast to the interpretation that children use tantrums as a means of getting their own way, this view implies that children do not use tantrums to purposely manipulate or defy their parents. Rather, it emphasizes that tantrums result from children's limited ability to control their emotions.

These two views of tantrums have very different implications for how parents treat children. Parents who interpret children's tantrums as willful acts intended to manipulate them feel justified in trying to extinguish children's tantrums by ignoring or punishing them. On the other hand, parents who view tantrums as involuntary reactions to stress resulting from children's inability to cope are more likely to empathize with their children and provide support and nurturance to help them cope more effectively with their feelings.

Most children first begin to tantrum at about 18 months of age. At this age, children are unaware that tantruming can be used to attempt to persuade their parents to give them what they want. *If parents give in to children when they tantrum, children may learn to use tantrums as a strategy for getting their way.* However, if parents maintain their focus on their children's emotional state and address their children's tantrums by providing comfort and support, this pattern of responding will reduce the likelihood that children would ever consider that tantrums can be used to get what they want.

SE-406 Comfort and acceptance help children learn to soothe themselves.

As adults, *many of us have learned strategies to help ourselves deal with stress, anger, or frustration.* For example, when we become angry we may (a) change the topic, (b) insert humor to de-escalate growing tensions, (c) leave the situation, or (d) engage in a physical activity that will enable us to release our anger. When we are stressed, we often engage in activities that calm us: watch TV, go for a walk, eat, or take a nap. In other words, many of us have learned to deal with anger and stress by engaging in some type of activity that de-escalates the tension and gives us time to regain control of our emotions.

Young children do not have strategies for dealing with anger, stress, or anxiety. They are limited not only by their physical capabilities but also by their lack of awareness of alternatives for calming themselves. As a result, children frequently react to stress and frustration by crying or acting aggressively. Early in life they may discover a few strategies that are somewhat effective at helping them calm themselves. These include strategies like sucking their fingers or hand; cuddling up to soft, warm materials such as a blanket; or falling asleep. But these are strategies children discover by chance and are not strategies they can control. The less these strategies are available to children, the more likely they will respond to stress or anger with outbursts and aggressive behavior.

When parents try to soothe children by holding, touching, talking, and singing, or gently rocking or bouncing them, they are providing their children supports that will help to calm them. These supports are especially helpful for babies because they have such limited resources for self-soothing or controlling their emotions. Parents act as emotional blankets to their children. In doing this, they both teach children ways that they can calm themselves and serve as a means to reduce children's emotional reactions until children are able to calm themselves. *The more parents provide children comfort and nurturance during their times of distress, the quicker children acquire their own strategies for learning to cope with their emotions.*

If parents leave their children alone during their times of distress, children are more apt to become emotionally spent, and they will miss important opportunities to learn how to calm themselves. Parents' responding to children when they are distressed does not reinforce crying or encourage more frequent episodes of crying. To the contrary, when parents comfort their children, they both de-escalate the intensity of children's emotional reactions and teach their children to comfort themselves. Responding to children's distress and anger helps children develop their ability to cope or self-regulate. This makes them less apt to become emotionally distraught during subsequent episodes of stress and frustration.

SE-407 Parental anger aggravates children's frustration.

Children's outbursts of crying, tantruming, or aggressive behavior frequently unnerve parents, especially if they feel stressed or worn out. *Most parents have had the experience of becoming angry at their children's emotional outbursts* and of responding by yelling or treating their children harshly. This is a natural reaction to the stress that parents experience. Nonetheless, it does little to help children resolve their own distress.

When parents react with anger at their children's distress, their reaction heightens their children's feelings of distress and exacerbates their outbursts. When parents are stressed out, they can easily forget that their children are crying and acting out because of their limited capacity to control their own reactions to stress. But parents cannot afford to forget this. Expecting young children to have the same kinds of emotional controls as adults does not make these children more capable of controlling their emotions. Rather, it creates expectations for children to behave in ways they are incapable of doing. By reacting with anger and hostility, parents may sometimes be successful at getting their children to stifle their emotional outbursts. Yet, the frustration, anger, or fears that precipitated children's reactions will likely go unresolved.

It is important that children become sensitive to and respectful of their parents' emotional state. Most children develop these sensitivities in the first year of life, particularly when their parents are sensitive and responsive to their own emotional states. However, it is also important that parents understand and respect children's emotional state.

Parents need to control their own emotions to deal effectively with their children's emotional distress. To do this, parents must become aware of how they tend to react to their children in various situations. If they tend to become angry at their children's outbursts, they need to develop plans to avoid such outbursts. If they become so stressed when their children act out that it is difficult for them to control their own emotions, they need to consider what they can do to manage themselves more effectively. This might mean that they plan a time-out from their children, perhaps by taking a nap or engaging in some kind of physical exercise, or by asking other people to provide them respite from their children. If a spouse is available to help with childcare responsibilities, parents need to plan ways they can support each other. If parents wait until they are so stressed that they are no longer able to manage their feelings, it will be difficult to avoid negative interactions with their children.

SE-408 Parents are most successful at managing their children's behavior when they expect them to react according to their temperament or behavioral style.

As child psychologists have begun to take a closer look at the effects of temperament on children's behavior, it has become increasingly apparent that much of children's misbehavior early in their lives is less a function of their intentions to misbehave and more a result of biological tendencies that children cannot control. Parents are unlikely to be successful at managing their children's behavior if they demand their children to control behaviors over which they have little voluntary control. A more effective strategy for managing children's behavior would be to *have rules and expectations that match the manner in which children are most likely to respond.* For example, if children are physically active, parents will be more successful at gaining children's cooperation if they expect them to be active, as opposed to quiet and sedate, and if they provide children opportunities for physical activity throughout their daily routine.

This approach to managing children's behavior is based upon the assumption that children will become more cooperative when adults' expectations are compatible with or supportive of children's natural predispositions. *By accommodating to children's natural predispositions, parents can make it easier for their children to behave or cooperate.* As children develop their capacity to control their behavior, parents can gradually "up the ante," or increase their expectations, for their children.

Conversely, children will become more difficult to manage if parents' expectations and behavior requests are incompatible or mismatched with children's natural predispositions. *Expecting children to behave in ways that are contrary to their natural tendencies only heightens parents' conflict and tension with their children.* This makes it more difficult for children to develop the strategies and coping mechanisms they need to regulate their own behavior.

SE-409 Give children room to react.

Most children who are highly emotionally reactive have biological predispositions that they cannot control. If parents demand that these children to control themselves when they become emotionally distraught, they are demanding their children to do something that they are unable to do.

One way *parents can reduce the conflict they have with children who have difficult temperament is to give these children room to react in a typical way.* For example, if children become upset when they are required to sit at the dinner table for 20 minutes while the family eats, allow children to leave the table after 5 minutes or to not sit at the table at all. If children are fearful when they are left in the presence of strangers, stay close to children or hold and comfort them until they are ready to act more independently with the stranger. If children have difficulty falling asleep at their regular bedtime (e.g., 8:00), let children stay up later (e.g., 9:00) before trying to put them to sleep. If children have difficulty sharing their toys with their brothers or sisters, provide duplicates of toys so that more than one child can play with the same toy at a time. If children become upset when they are required to transition from one activity to another, give children an opportunity to express their feelings and regain their composure before insisting that they become involved in the other activity.

Adults are unlikely to win battles that require children to suppress behaviors that are dictated by their temperament or biological predispositions. In time, *children will learn to comply with most of the behavioral expectations parents have for them, so long as parents maintain these expectations as long-term goals.* By being flexible and accommodating to children's behavioral style or temperament early in their lives, parents avoid fueling episodes of emotional upheaval with their children. Parents should never give up their desire for the children to engage in appropriate, civil behavior. However, they need to realize that it is more important to give their children the time and support they need to learn to manage the situations and activities that they find stressful than it is for their children to behave according to what parents consider to be appropriate or necessary.

Parents who insist that their children do *what* they want them to do, *when* they want them to do it, and in *the way* they think it should be done, may win the battle of getting their children to comply with their expectations, but they risk losing the war of helping their children learn how to regulate their emotional reactions.

Discussion Points

SE-401 Self-regulation—learning to cope with emotions.

- Young children react instinctively to the way they feel.
- Young children do not have the internal capabilities necessary to regulate their emotions.
- During early childhood, children gradually develop strategies for coping with, or regulating, their own emotional responses.

SE-402 Children develop their coping skills with time.

- Self-regulation is a competency that children develop throughout the early childhood years.
- Helping children learn to cope with their emotions is very different than coercing them to suppress their negative behavior.
- Parents must exercise patience and understand that their children do not have the same capabilities to manage their emotions as adults do.

SE-403 Children's behavioral style or temperament plays a major role in the ease with which they learn to self-regulate.

- There are considerable differences in the amount of time it takes children to learn to regulate their emotions.
- One of the factors that contributes to children's ability to regulate their emotions is their developing cognitive and communication skills.
- Some children are born with a biological predisposition to overreact to almost any form of stress.

SE-404 Tantruming—children's reaction to stress or frustration.

- Children become aggressive and tantrum when the stress or frustration they are experiencing exceeds their capabilities to cope or regulate their emotions.

- Tantruming and aggressive behavior decrease as children develop strategies for regulating their emotions.
- Children with a difficult temperament must develop greater self-control to manage their behavior effectively.

SE-405 Children do not tantrum just to get their way.

- Tantrums commonly occur when parents or others prevent children from doing what they want.
- Tantrums are reactions to stress that children are not capable of managing.
- Only if parents give in to children when they tantrum will children learn to use tantrums as a strategy for getting their way.

SE-406 Comfort and acceptance help children learn to soothe themselves.

- Many of us have learned strategies to help ourselves deal with stress, anger, or frustration.
- Young children do not have strategies for dealing with anger, stress, or anxiety.
- The more parents provide children comfort and nurturance during their times of distress, the quicker children acquire their own strategies for learning to cope with their emotions.

SE-407 Parental anger aggravates children's frustration.

- Most parents have had the experience of becoming angry at their children's emotional outbursts.
- When parents react with anger at their children's distress, their reaction heightens children's feelings of distress and exacerbates their children's outbursts.
- Parents need to control their own emotions to deal effectively with their children's emotional distress.

SE-408 Parents are most successful at managing their children's behavior when they expect them to react according to their temperament or behavioral style.

- Parents need to have rules and expectations that match the manner in which children are most likely to respond.
- By accommodating to children's natural predispositions, parents can make it easier for their children to behave or cooperate.
- Expecting children to behave in ways that are contrary to their natural tendencies only heightens parents' conflict and tension with their children.

SE-409 Give children room to react.

- Children are reactive because of biological predispositions that they cannot control.

- Parents can reduce the conflict they have with children who have difficult temperament by giving these children room to react in a typical way.
- Children will learn to comply with most of the behavioral expectations parents have for them, so long as parents maintain these expectations as long-term goals.

RT Strategies That Promote Self-Regulation

133 ***Join perseverative play (make it interactive).*** When your child is perseverating or playing in self-stimulatory ways, enter into your child's world and make the play interactive. After you have successfully entered your child's world, gradually show your child other ways to play.

Practical Suggestions

- If your child does the same thing with every toy (e.g., pretend that all objects are "trains"), join your child's play rather than try to force your child to use objects in a different way. It is more important to use anything that interests your child as an opportunity for interaction than it is for your child to break his or her compulsive behaviors. Compulsive behaviors almost always decrease over time.
- Often, children use stereotypic, repetitive behaviors (e.g., rocking, flapping their hands) to avoid interacting with others. Make your child's stereotypic behavior an opportunity to interact with you. Place yourself next to your child, imitate your child's stereotypic behavior, and notice how your child starts to pay attention to you.
- If your child engages in stereotypic behavior such as "hand flapping" while interacting with you, ignore the behavior and focus on the activity you are doing with your child.
- Never imitate or encourage self-destructive or harmful behavior. For self-destructive behaviors (e.g., head banging, biting self) make sure your child has protective clothing (e.g., gloves, long sleeve shirts) or equipment (e.g., helmet). A developmental pediatrician or neurologist may be able to prescribe medication that might reduce some of these behaviors.

223 ***Discipline promptly and comfort.*** When your child misbehaves, discipline him or her immediately to stop these behaviors. The discipline you use should be stern enough to get your child's attention, yet appropriate to your child's physical and developmental level (e.g., a stern "No!" to restrain your child from doing something). Timing is important for effective discipline. Discipline your child while he or she is misbehaving or immediately afterward. Comfort your child no more than a few minutes after you discipline him or her. The positive affection children receive from you will help them understand that you disciplined them because of what they did, and that you still love them as you always have.

Practical Suggestions

- Discipline is one way that parents respond to children's behavior. Think of discipline as a natural and immediate consequence to your child's undesirable or harmful behavior.
- Regardless what strategy you use to discipline your child (e.g., sharp rebuke, restraining), discipline should be sufficiently forceful to get your child's attention and to let your child know that he or she has done something wrong. Discipline should never physically harm or injure your child.
- If you are disciplining your child more than you think you should, explore the possibility that you may not be interacting enough with your child when he or she is behaving. You will become more effective at disciplining your child, the more time you spend engaging with your child in highly responsive interactions.
- Consider that when you comfort your child after disciplining him or her, you are helping your child learn to cope with emotions and you are also reassuring your child of your love.

516 ***Have developmentally appropriate rules and expectations.*** You are more likely to gain your child's cooperation, and your child will be less likely to act out or misbehave if your rules and expectations are compatible with what most children are able to do at your child's current level of social–emotional functioning.

Practical Suggestions

- Use a developmental observation guide such as the *Developmental Rainbow* to determine your child's current level of social–emotional functioning. Many children have levels of social–emotional functioning that are different from their current age level and from their level of communication and cognitive development.
- Identify common situations in which your child typically acts out or does not conform to your expectations. Review the *Developmental Rainbow* or other social–emotional profile to determine whether your rules or expectations are compatible with your child's current level of social–emotional functioning. If your rules and expectations are too high, try to modify them so they are more consistent with your child's social–emotional capabilities.

521 ***Read my child's behavior as an indicator of interest.*** To read your child's behavior, engage in two activities while interacting with your child. First, observe carefully the subtle as well as obvious behaviors your child is doing. Second, use context cues to interpret your child's interests.

Practical Suggestions

- Your child's interests are likely to be very different than yours. Objects or activities to which your child attends, which seem unexciting to you, can be interesting to your child—particularly because many of these are novel experiences for your child.

- Consider that your child's interests can change from moment to moment. What interests your child on one day may not interest him or her on the next.
- Not all of your child's interests may be strong. If your child is attending or doing something but is not actively engaged, what your child is doing is still an indicator of his or her interest.
- Use the following questions to interpret your child's behavior: "What does that behavior reflects about my child's interests?" "What is my child trying to communicate by doing that?"
- While interacting with a child, professionals can describe the cues that they see as indicators of the child's interests.
- Professionals should ask parents to describe what their children are interested in doing and help parents think of their children's behaviors as indicators of interest.

523 ***Follow my child's lead.*** Respond to your child in a manner that is compatible with or complements your child's activity and intentions. Play with toys or engage in activities in the same manner as your child. Do not make your child play with toys in the manner for which the manufacturer designed them unless that is the way your child chooses to play with them.

Practical Suggestions

- Whatever your child is playing with is what interests your child at the moment. Consider how you are much more motivated to engage in activities that interest you and to learn and remember information that you find interesting. Your child is no different than you are when it comes to the motivating power of interest.
- When you follow your child's lead, you are actually responding to your child's interests. The more you respond to your child's interests, the greater the number of interests your child will have and the stronger these interests will be.

532 ***Observe how my child ordinarily engages in interaction.*** Soon after they are born, children develop a fairly consistent style of reacting to people and to changes in their environment. Because this style of interaction is strongly influenced by children's genetic makeup, it is not something children can easily control in the early childhood years. The more you are aware of your child's behavioral style, the easier it is to anticipate and adjust to how your child will typically react.

Practical Suggestions

Determine what your child's behavioral style is by considering the following questions:

- Is my child active or passive?
- Is my child generally happy or more inconsistent in his or her moods?
- How does my child react to me and to other familiar people? How does he or she react to strangers?

- How does my child react to touch and physical stimulation?
- Does my child have regular routines with regard to sleeping, hunger, and bowel movements, or does he or she have inconsistent routines?
- What does my child do when routines change, such as when he or she goes to new places?
- Is my child easy to console, or does it take him or her a long time to calm down?
- In general, is my child an easy child, a slow to warm-up child, or a difficult child?

533 ***Respond to my child's behavioral state.*** Identify and respond to the cues your child uses to indicate whether he or she is ready to engage in interaction with you.

Practical Suggestions

- Your child likely has periods of time when he or she is receptive to interacting with you and periods of time when he or she prefers to be left alone. Identify the cues that your child uses to indicate his or her disposition for interacting. Use his or her cues to regulate your interactive episodes with your child.
- Children typically engage and then disengage for periods of time. Your child can be next to you and yet want to interact by himself and not with you. Identify the behaviors your child uses to disengage from you.
- Let your child go when he or she attempts to disengage from you. If you continue to attend to your child when he or she is disengaged, your child will soon return to interact with you.
- If your child prefers to be alone and actively avoids interacting with you, interject yourself into the child's activity. A good way to do this is often to join in your child's activity by doing what your child is doing.

534 ***Have expectations that conform to my child's behavioral style.*** If your child is slow to warm up to new situations, expect your child to behave this way in future situations. If your child can only interact with you or others for a few minutes at a time, do not expect your child to react positively to situations that require sustained periods of interaction.

Practical Suggestions

- Consider that your child cannot change his or her behavioral style just because the situation demands it. For example, 2-year-olds who are naturally active and impulsive will still be active and impulsive in public places, where such behavior is not appropriate (e.g., church, restaurants, stores, friends' homes).
- Make accommodations for how your child typically reacts. Do not expect your child to behave more appropriately in public places than he or she typically behaves. Understand that your child's reactions are not ones that

he or she is able to control. To avoid conflict that arises when your child is unable to conform to the behavioral norms that are required for different situations, either avoid these situations, or get a babysitter so that you can go without your child.

- Plan activities that will help your child adjust to difficult or stressful situations (e.g., use a favorite toy to coax your child to leave a place or activity that he or she is enjoying; talk to your child about what will happen; go to a restaurant or sit in a section of the restaurant where your child can leave the table and wander without harming him- or herself).

535 ***Match my child's interactive pace.*** When you interact with your child, use an interactive pace that is similar to your child's.

Practical Suggestions

- Consider that your child's pace of interaction may be faster in movement and slower in thinking and interpretive processing than is yours. You and your child can miss connecting with each other when your child is on an action fast-track and you are on a thinking fast-track.
- Give your child silent time to initiate contact with you. Silent time can be a signal for your child to interact.

Developmental Domain: Social–Emotional Functioning

Pivotal Behavior: Feelings of Confidence

SE-5 Feelings of Confidence refers to the degree to which children have positive feelings about their ability to carry out both social and nonsocial tasks. Children have a positive view of themselves and are motivated to interact with people and try new things. They take pride in themselves and are willing to try new behaviors and activities.

Facts To Consider About Feelings of Confidence

SE-501 Children's ability alone does not determine how they feel about themselves.

There is a popular children's story called "The Little Engine Who Could," about a small and outdated railroad engine and how this engine accomplished a task normally done by much larger and more powerful engines, primarily because he refused to believe that he was not capable of performing it. The moral of this story is that success is not only dependent upon how strong or capable an individual is, but is equally, if not more, dependent upon a person's ability to believe in and to see him- or herself as competent and capable, regardless of how much ability the person actually has.

This is an important message for all children who often compare themselves to other children and who frequently see themselves as not quite measuring up to others. It is an even more important message for children with developmental problems who, in fact, may not be as capable as other children, and who often need to rely on their own will and determination to get things done. Children who have limited abilities can, like the Little Engine Who Could, still accomplish many things. If they view themselves as capable they can accomplish feats that many would think to be out of their reach. *Whether children succeed at a task is less dependent upon how much ability they possess than it is upon their believing in themselves* and feeling that they have the ability to do what needs to be done. The heroes in this world are the legions of overachievers who refuse to see themselves as incapable.

An important goal of early intervention is not only to maximize children's developmental potential but, what is perhaps more important, to help children develop their sense of competency and their belief that they possess the capabilities to do what they want. *Children will learn to feel confident in themselves when we make sure they have frequent opportunities to be successful.* One way we can do this is by asking them to do things that they *can* do rather than things that are beyond their current capabilities.

What have we accomplished if we help children gain more knowledge, communicate, and function better if they do not also believe in themselves and feel that they are capable of rising to the challenges they must inevitably face. *Helping children develop their self-confidence should be the highest goal of early intervention* and must never be subjugated to efforts to encourage children to learn and develop skills they do not yet know.

SE-502 Even at early ages, children form internal models of who they are.

Long before children communicate and express their feelings, they have many of the emotions and feelings that older and more expressive children have. In the first year of life, children have the emotions of happiness, excitement, anticipation, surprise, fear, sadness, anger, and even depression. They are also beginning to develop internal feelings about themselves. They may feel loved, wanted, and even begin to feel that they are capable or incapable.

Children's feelings of confidence are strongly affected by the kinds of interactions they have with their parents. Young children whose parents make a big deal about each of their new accomplishments, who take delight in whatever they do, who constantly tell them that they are "so big," "so cute," and "so clever," and "light up" when they are with them are continually giving their children messages that they are competent, unique, and worthwhile. Given a daily diet of these messages, children gradually internalize them and think of themselves as competent, regardless of how competent they actually are.

But not all children regularly have these kinds of experiences with their parents. Parents may communicate negative messages to their children when they are tired and depressed or spend little time playing with and enjoying their child. If parents see much of what their children do as an annoyance, or if they worry about their children's development and express little joy in what they are doing because they are so focused on what they are not doing, parents may negatively affect how their children feel about themselves.

Regardless how much love and affection parents have for their children, their actions can unintentionally communicate that their children are less than perfect, less than desirable, and less than competent. Just as children form positive images when their parents give positive messages, so too *daily exposure to negative messages will eventually result in children forming negative perceptions about how capable or worthwhile they are.*

Children's routine, daily experiences shape the feelings they have about themselves, even from the earliest ages. *From the earliest days of their lives, experiences of success during routine activities with their parents can have major influences on children's self-confidence.* Over time, these experiences gradually shape children's perceptions of who they are, what they can do, and what their worth is. The feelings of confidence children develop in early childhood will continue to shape their self-perceptions for the remainder of their lives.

SE-503 Children feel good about themselves when adults express pleasure or take delight in what the children do.

Praise is words and expressions of affection that adults use to let children know that they have accomplished what they were expected to do. One of the major ways *adults use praise is to encourage children to increase the frequency that they attempt to produce a behavior they want them to do. Acceptance means valuing children, regardless of what they do*. Acceptance involves words and expressions of affection that adults use to tell children how terrific they are. The main difference between praise and acceptance involves the contingencies for these behaviors. Praise is contingent on the child's meeting the expectation of the adult. The only contingency for acceptance is that the child be him- or herself.

If parents frequently praise children but seldom give them unconditional acceptance, they inform children that they are valued primarily for doing what others expect of them. *Too much praise could result in children defining their self-worth solely on the basis of being able to meet the expectations of others.* However, if parents use praise to reinforce their children occasionally for accomplishing tasks they want them to do, but balance praise with frequent expressions of acceptance, parents are both rewarding children for their accomplishments while giving them frequent feedback that they are valued for who they are, regardless of what they do.

In the early childhood years, it is critical to let children know that they are valued and accepted for who they are and not only for what they accomplish. Too often when children have developmental problems, parents and adults focus on what their children are not doing and what they need to learn, and they fail to take pleasure in the things that their children do on a regular basis—to let their children know that they are accepted for who they are. Expressing delight and taking pleasure in what children do will not prevent children from striving to do or learn what they need. On the contrary, *acceptance will help children develop the feelings of confidence or self-esteem that are so crucial to their realizing their full developmental potential.*

SE-504 Success breeds self-confidence; failure breeds lack of confidence.

Feelings of confidence do not simply result from how bright or capable people are but rather from how they feel about themselves and their ability to do things. Why do some people feel confident in themselves while others do not?

For a number of years, psychological research has been interested in these questions. Several studies have been reported in which psychologists have artificially rigged the outcomes of tasks they have asked people to do. For some, tasks have been arranged so that, regardless of what the participants do, they cannot succeed. For others, tasks have been arranged so that people succeed, or at least feel they are successful, regardless of what they do. What psychologists have discovered is that after a number of trials, participants who experience the failure condition begin to see themselves as not being able to do the task, they begin to lose interest in the task, and they quickly give up. Participants who succeed react in the opposite way. Over time, their confidence that they know how to do the task increases, they maintain their interest in the task, and they persist longer at the task.

Children's routine experiences of success and failure in their interactions with parents and other adults affect their feelings of confidence. *The more children's interactions are successful (i.e., they are able to do what their parents ask them), the more likely they are to form positive concepts of themselves.* Conversely, the more their interactions with their parents are failures (i.e., they are unable to do what their parents ask), the more likely they will form negative concepts of themselves.

In the first 3 to 5 years of life, children form their self-perceptions primarily from the way they relate to their parents. How they relate to their parents is far more critical to their self-perceptions (feelings of confidence) than are their relationships with their siblings, friends, or any other adults. No matter how limited children's ability might be, parents can help their children perceive themselves as competent by asking them to perform activities they are able to do. Conversely, *no matter how bright and capable children are, parents can cause their children to form negative feelings about themselves by asking or expecting their children to do things they are not able to do.*

SE-505 Children fail when they are unable to do what they are asked to do.

Like success, failure is a relative phenomenon. Whether a person fails is based upon his or her inability to do what others expect him or her to do. When expectations are greater than a person is able to achieve, the probability of failure is high regardless of how bright or capable a child is. *Whether people fail has more to do with whether they can meet expectations that have been set out for them than with how capable they are.*

If parents ask or expect children with developmental problems to perform at age-appropriate levels, they will increase their children's experience of failure. By definition, children with developmental problems are less capable in at least one developmental area than are typically developing children who are the same age. To expect children with developmental problems to do things that, although age appropriate, exceed their current capabilities is to increase the likelihood they will fail.

The probability that children with developmental problems will fail decreases as their parents' expectations or requests become more aligned with their capabilities. Yet, the line between the point at which children succeed or fail is very narrow. Even when parents' expectations only slightly exceed their capabilities, the possibility that children will fail is almost as great as when their expectations greatly exceed their capabilities. Children who have most, but not all, of the skills needed to ride a bike are as likely to fall off the bike as children who have none at all.

Children first experience failure in the context of their interactions with their parents. Any time parents ask or suggest that children do something that they cannot do on their own, children experience failure. *If parents constantly focus on encouraging their children to do things they cannot do, inadvertently they are teaching their children to expect to fail* at whatever they are asked to do. Over time, these expectations result in children forming negative perceptions of themselves.

SE-506 Long-term learning is more dependent on how children feel about themselves than on the specific skills and behaviors that are taught them.

The children who tend to achieve best in elementary school are the children who are successful in first grade. However, there is nothing magical about the content that children learn in first grade that can account for why the first grade is so important. In fact, children who do not master the first-grade subjects in first grade usually learn them rapidly when they get to second grade. Probably the most important thing children learn in the first grade is about their own ability to learn. If they are successful in first grade, they likely interpret their experience as an indication that they have the potential to succeed at school. If they are not successful they may come to view themselves as not able to do schoolwork. The specific skills and behaviors children learn in their early school years are less important to their lifelong learning than the attitudes they form about themselves.

The same principle applies to children's early interactions with their parents. Children are not born understanding what success is. They learn about success from their parents. When parents expect their children to do the things they are able to do, their children will have repeated opportunities to be successful. Because they experience success in this early period of their lives, they begin to perceive themselves as "able to learn." *Even if they have limited capacity to learn, children will learn to believe in their capabilities when they experience high levels of success* during their routine activities.

Thus, children's personal experiences of success are closely linked to what their parents ask them to do. Children experience success when parents are proud of them and expect them to be who they are, enjoy themselves, and be happy. *When children are able to do what their parents expect them to do, children experience higher levels of success and they begin to believe in their capacity to learn, which has major benefits for their lifelong learning.*

Parents of children with developmental problems have a right to be concerned and should hope for and expect their children to do better. But parents must be careful not to translate these hopes and expectations into requests and demands that are impossible for their children to do. They must recognize that one of the major ways to help their children develop feelings of confidence is to make sure they experience success. To do this, parents must expect children to do the things they are able to do during each of the routine interactions parents have with them.

SE-507 Children who feel confident confront challenges and assert themselves in cognitive and social tasks.

Intervention cannot teach children everything they need to know or be able to do. The majority of what children learn is dependent upon their own ability to be learners and to deal with the challenges and demands in their world. *It is far more important that intervention help children acquire the competencies and skills they need to become effective learners than it is to teach them everything they need to know.* Feelings of confidence, or how children feel about their ability to learn, are one of these key competencies.

Children who feel they are competent are much more likely to persist in activities, especially activities that are difficult or challenging, than those who do not feel competent. Development is a process of children discovering the challenges in their world and determining through a process of trial and error what they need to do to deal with these challenges. This requires that children have the feelings of competence that are necessary to remain actively involved in interactions, to be interested in their world, and to not give up when they encounter challenges or obstacles.

Discussion Points

SE-501 Children's ability alone does not determine how they feel about themselves.

- Whether children succeed at a task is less dependent upon how much ability they possess than it is upon their believing in themselves.

- Children will learn to feel confident in themselves when we make sure they have frequent opportunities to be successful.
- Helping children develop their self-confidence should be the highest goal of early intervention.

SE-502 Even at early ages, children form internal models of who they are.

- Children's feelings about themselves are strongly affected by the kinds of interactions they have with their parents.
- Daily exposure to negative messages will eventually result in children forming negative perceptions about how capable or worthwhile they are.
- From the earliest days of their lives, success experiences during routine activities with their parents can have major influences on children's self-confidence.

SE-503 Children feel good about themselves when adults express pleasure or take delight in what the children do.

- Adults use praise to encourage children to increase the frequency with which they attempt to produce a behavior the adults want them to do.
- Acceptance means valuing children, regardless of what they do.
- Too much praise could result in children defining their self-worth solely on the basis of being able to meet the expectations of others.
- Acceptance will help children develop the feelings of confidence or self-esteem that are so crucial to their realizing their full developmental potential.

SE-504 Success breeds self-confidence; failure breeds lack of confidence.

- The more children's interactions are successful (i.e., they are able to do what their parents ask them), the more likely they are to form positive concepts of themselves.
- No matter how bright and capable children are, parents can cause them to form negative feelings about themselves by asking or expecting them to do things they are not able to do.

SE-505 Children fail when they are unable to do what they are asked to do.

- Whether people fail has more to do with whether they can meet expectations that have been set out for them than how capable they are.
- If parents ask or expect children with developmental problems to perform at age-appropriate levels, they will increase children's experience of failure.
- If parents constantly focus on encouraging their children to do things they cannot do, inadvertently they are teaching their children to expect to fail.

SE-506 Long-term learning is more dependent on how children feel about themselves than on the specific skills and behaviors that are taught them.

- Even if they have limited capacity to learn, children will learn to believe in their capabilities when they experience high levels of success.
- When children are able to do what their parents expect them to do, children experience higher levels of success and they begin to believe in their capacity to learn, which has major benefits for their lifelong learning.

SE-507 Children who feel confident confront challenges and assert themselves in cognitive and social tasks.

- It is far more important that intervention help children acquire the competencies and skills they need to become effective learners than it is to teach them everything they need to know.
- Children who feel they are competent are much more likely to persist in activities, especially activities that are difficult or challenging.

RT Strategies That Promote Feelings of Confidence

134 ***Play with my child with toys.*** When you play with your child with toys, begin by playing with the toys as your child does, then gradually show him or her new ways to use them.

Practical Suggestions

- Play with the toys your child is playing with. Your child will attend and interact more with you when you play with the things that your child has chosen.
- Consider that it is important for your child to be able to interact with you without needing to do anything "right" or to engage in any particular activity with toys.
- After you have established routine patterns of back-and-forth play with toys, gradually introduce new or more appropriate ways of play with your child.

231 ***Respond to unintentional vocalizations, facial displays, and gestures as if they were meaningful conversation.*** Often children make sounds for sensory play but not for communicating intentionally. Every action your child makes can become a communication. The more you respond to your child's actions, the quicker your child will learn to use these actions to exchange meanings with you and others.

Practical Suggestions

- Get into the habit of responding to your child's sounds even when they may be just for self-play and do not have any obvious meaning or communicative intent.
- If your child makes sounds while playing, but does not use sounds to communicate his or her intentions, he or she has not yet learned that

sounds can get people's attention. To help your child learn to use his or her sounds as communication, respond more to your child's sounds than to his or her facial displays or touches.

441 ***Value what my child is doing.*** View what your child is doing as important, interesting, and meaningful. Do not dismiss what your child does simply because it is not what other children do at your child's age level.

Practical Suggestions

- Make a list of the things your child has done since the last intervention session. Focus on the positive aspects of your child's behavior.
- Videotape your child in several situations: playing alone, playing with you, and playing with other children. Review the video to identify what your child is doing. Keep this video as a record of your child's accomplishments.
- Professionals should consistently comment on what children are doing during intervention sessions. Celebrate what children are doing. Discuss with parents the importance, or developmental significance, of their children's behavior.

442 ***Treat my child's fears as meaningful and legitimate.*** Early in their lives, children develop fears of people, places, lights, sounds, and so forth, which may not seem fearful to adults. Understand that your child's fears stem from the limited understanding he or she has of different people and events. Comfort and support your child to help him or her cope with fears.

Practical Suggestions

- As your child develops, his or her understanding of people, places, and sensations constantly changes. For example, fear of strangers typically begins at about 8 to 12 months of developmental age when children begin to perceive their parents as unique sources of support and protection. At this time, children become fearful of strangers they previously did not fear because they lack confidence that these strangers will protect them from harm.

443 ***Accept whatever my child does.*** Respond supportively to any behaviors your child does, except for behaviors that are harmful, disrespectful, or incompatible with your families' values and priorities.

Practical Suggestions

- There are long-term implications to your responding to whatever your child does. While your responsiveness will encourage your child to repeat behaviors he or she is currently doing, it *will not* prevent your child from learning new developmental behaviors. Rather than reinforcing undesirable behavior, your responding communicates that you value and accept what your child is doing. Over time, your repetitive, positive feedback will help your child form self-perceptions of being competent and capable.

- Consider how your parents influenced your development. Did your parents play a strong role in helping you learn specific behaviors or in helping you form your own self-concept and personality? If you become too focused on the behaviors your child is not able to do, you may be overlooking the potentially negative impact that you might be having on how your child feels about him- or herself.
- Consider the following: If we help children learn a behavior but at the same time give them negative messages about themselves by not accepting the behaviors they are able to do, will the new behavior that we have helped them learn compensate for the negative feedback they received?

444 ***Talk about the novel, funny, and good things my child is doing.*** Talk about the positive and amusing things that your child does. Engage in these conversations not only during intervention sessions but also in routine interactions with spouses, friends, and relatives.

Practical Suggestions

- Talk about positive experiences and stories about your child to friends and relatives. The more you get into the habit of focusing on the positive and amusing things your child does, the easier it becomes to value and accept what your child is doing.
- The more you focus on your child's developmental problems or disabilities, the more difficult it becomes to truly accept your child for who he or she is. It is difficult to ignore your child's developmental problems, because these are issues that have lifelong implications. However, when you talk about the things that make your child "a child" as opposed to a "person with a problem," you are more apt to accept and nurture your child than to fight the developmental problems over which your child has little control.
- Professionals should ask parents at the beginning of each intervention session to describe a funny experience or anecdote that happened with their child since the last session.

513 ***Request actions that match my child's developmental level.*** Limit your requests for your child to do or say things to behaviors that are within your child's range of accommodation. Your child will have difficulty responding to behaviors and communications that exceed his or her range of accommodation.

Practical Suggestions

- Review a videotape of you and your child playing together. Write down the behaviors that you have asked your child to do. Look up these behaviors on the *Developmental Rainbow* or other developmental profile. Notice how your child was more reactive and engaged when you asked him or her to do things that were within his or her range of accommodation. Notice how your child became passive or ignored you when you asked him or her to do things that are difficult (e.g., beyond his or her range of accommodation).

- Consider how you respond when you are asked to do something that you do not know how to do.
- Increase your child's opportunities to be successful with you by asking him or her to do things he or she has the developmental capabilities to do.

514 Act in ways that my child can act. When you interact with your child, modify what you do and the way you do it so that your behaviors mirror the kinds of activities that your child typically does.

Practical Suggestions

- Imitate some of your child's actions. Notice how your child stays with you and attends more to you when you do this.
- Play with the toys and objects that your child is playing with and in the same way as your child. Your child will attend and interact more actively when you interact with the toys and objects your child prefers.
- Review a videotape of you playing with your child. How well are you matching your actions to your child's spontaneous behavior?
- When you match your child's actions, talk with your child, using words that fit your child's actions such as *come, go, eat, mom, dog,* or *truck.* These words are more meaningful to your child and thus easier to learn than words like *two, three, red, yellow, horse,* and *barn.*

Developmental Domain: Social–Emotional Functioning

Pivotal Behavior: Feelings of Control

SE-6 Feelings of Control refers to the degree to which children demonstrate mastery of activities and an awareness that they can control the outcome of activities. Children are self-reliant as opposed to dependent upon others. They frequently make choices about what to do. They purposefully do things to influence what others do and prefer to control rather than be controlled.

Facts To Consider About Feelings of Control

SE-601 Children have a basic need to control their environment.

In a classic child development study (Watson & Ramey, 1972), infants were observed while lying in their cribs with their heads resting on a pillow that contained a switch that activated a mobile mounted above them. When children turned their heads in one direction, they activated the switch and the mobile would move; when they turned their heads in the other direction, the switch was not activated and the mobile did not move.

Researchers discovered that by as early as 3 months of age children quickly discovered how to operate the switch. Although they initially activated the mobile by accident, after a few chance encounters, they discovered that they could control the mobile by turning their head in a certain direction. As children learned this contingency, they increased the frequency they activated the mobile. Furthermore, each time they activated the mobile, children reacted with pleasure by smiling or laughing.

This study is an important illustration of how *being able to control is a basic developmental drive.* From very early ages, children are delighted by their ability to control their environment. In addition, *when they identify situations in which they are capable of exerting control, children are more active and engaged.*

One of the basic factors that motivate children in any situation is the opportunity to exert control. This is one of the main motivators for children trying to learn new information or skills. Children are more apt to become actively engaged in learning experiences in which they can determine (i.e., control) what takes place. Children's desire to control or influence what happens to them is a strong motivator for them to learn advanced developmental skills.

SE-602 Children learn to control by controlling others.

Children's earliest experiences in learning to control occur in interactions where they have opportunities to control what parents and others do with them. When children get their parents' attention by crying, they learn how to use crying to influence (i.e., control) what their parents do with them. Similarly, when children elicit a response from their parents using signals such as smiling, eye gaze, or general body activity, they learn to use these social signals to influence the behavior of others.

Children learn to control by having repeated experiences of controlling people in their interactions with them. *How well children develop their ability to control is dependent upon the willingness of parents and others to respond to their early social signals.* If parents respond only infrequently to children's social signals, children will not have enough opportunities to develop their ability to control. However, if parents are highly responsive to children's social signals, children have numerous opportunities to develop and refine their ability to control others.

As children grow older they will have increasing opportunities to exert control over toys and other objects they play with. Yet, the children who have learned to control in their interactions with their parents are the ones who are most likely to exert control during their solitary play. *The more proficient children become at controlling the behavior of parents and other familiar people, the more likely they will exert control as the opportunity arises in new situations.*

SE-603 Children have no choice if parents always tell them what to do.

Children learn to control when they have opportunities to choose or decide what they want to do. The opportunity to learn to control can occur at any time throughout the daily routine, such as when children choose what toys to play with, how they play with them, whom to interact with, and when and what to eat or drink.

Parents need to make numerous choices for their children throughout the day. These include choices about what to wear, when to bathe, what and when to eat, where to be, how to get to places, and when to go to sleep. Parents would not be acting responsibly if they did not make these choices.

But within most of these situations there is considerable leeway about what is done and how it is done. For example, when parents and children play together, there are choices about what toys to play with and what to do with them. When parents and children communicate with each other, there are choices about what to communicate and who should initiate the communication. Similarly, while parents should make nutritional choices for their children and establish a regular routine for meals, there is still a wide range of choices about how much children eat and how they should eat. These are only a few examples of the opportunities children and parents have to share choice making.

Sometimes parents dominate opportunities for making choices with their children. This might happen if parents are focused on completing a task, if they view a situation as having only one solution, or if they feel the need to help their children learn and do things in a particular way. However, *if parents dominate interactions with their children, they limit their children's opportunities to make choices and thereby impede them from learning to control.*

Parents need to give their children as many opportunities to make choices as possible. They can do this by allowing their children to initiate actions or conversations, following their lead, and supporting the choices they make. Parents must never give up their responsibility to make the choices that are essential for their children's survival and well-being. Yet, the more they refrain from telling their children what to do, the more they encourage their children to make their own choices, and thus help them develop their ability to control.

SE-604 How young children make choices.

A popular preschool curriculum, the *High/Scope Preschool Curriculum* (Hohmann & Weikert, 1995), uses an instructional format referred to as "Plan–Do–Review" to maximize children's opportunities to choose what they do in their classrooms. In the "Planning" phase, children discuss with their teachers what they would like to do, and in the "Do" phase, children carry out the activity they have chosen to do.

This curriculum is effective because many preschool children, particularly 4- and 5-year-olds, are capable of making choices about what they want to do at least a few minutes before they actually follow through with their choice. In other words, the *High/Scope Curriculum* provides preschool aged children a procedure for choice-making that is compatible with their ability to make choices.

But children who are developmentally younger than 3 years commonly have difficulty engaging in Plan–Do–Review. Part of the reason for this is that they make choices very differently than 4- and 5-year-olds. Most children below the 3-year stage of development do not have the capacity to choose from a range of alternatives, stick with their choice, or even understand the consequences of their choice for more than a few minutes at a time.

Young children have limited ability to weigh the merits of various alternatives. *Young children's choices are the objects or activities that are most appealing to them at the moment.* Consequently, they stay with these activities so long as they are interested in them. Choosing one thing rather than another reflects the degree to which they were attracted to the activity they chose. Their choices are better described as a preference to do something rather than a conscious choice not to do the alternative activity. Because of this, *young children frequently change their minds about what they want.* Often they decide (choose) to become involved in the same activity that they rejected only a few moments ago.

Children's choices are reflected in what they do. If they pick up a toy and play with it, they have in fact chosen the toy with which they are playing. If they put the toy down and move on to another toy, then they have chosen to discontinue playing with one toy and to play with another. *Children's choices are often short lived and are seldom a commitment to stay a long time with the activity they have chosen.*

SE-605 Activities that children choose are just as important as those that parents choose.

Parents dominate interactions with their children when they decide what to do and how to do it more than 50% of the time. One reason parents dominate interactions is that they often feel that it is necessary for their children to do certain things or to learn the activities that they have selected. Thus, when children are playing by putting figures in and out of a toy bus, parents may divert their children to playing with stacking rings because they feel that the information that stacking rings afford (e.g., colors, size, sequence) is more important than the toy bus. Yet, when parents dominate interaction with their children in this way, they deprive their children of opportunities to make their own choices and learn to exert control.

To help children develop their ability to control, parents must give their children frequent opportunities to make their own choices and refrain from dominating the interaction. At the same time, they must also make sure that their children engage in meaningful activity. In most cases, these two goals can be achieved at the same time.

For example, if we consider the situation of the child playing with the toy bus in which the parent diverted the child to the stacking rings, there are two issues to consider. First, *children can learn new information from any activity they choose.* Although the stacking rings provide an opportunity for children to learn different information than the toy bus, valuable information can be learned from either activity. The stacking rings are not a better learning opportunity; they are merely a different opportunity. In fact, the toy bus can afford children opportunities to learn some of the same concepts as the stacking rings, including colors, sizes, and shapes.

Second, by supporting what children choose to do, parents are more likely to provide guidance and information that is directly related to what interests them. *Children are more likely to learn from activities that they have chosen and are interested in than from activities that parents choose that may not interest them.* At the same time children have the opportunity to learn from activities they have chosen, they are also learning to make choices and to develop their feelings of control.

SE-606 Learned helplessness—not feeling able to control.

Many children with developmental problems become "helpless" later in their lives. They tend to be passive and nonassertive. They often wait to be told what to do rather than take the initiative to do things on their own. This phenomenon has been described as "learned helplessness." It is not caused by the learning problems that children have. Rather, *helplessness is a motivational trait children learn from their early life experiences.* Often, these children know what to do and how to do it. Their lack of initiative is more a reflection of their inability to take charge, to make their own decisions, and to assert themselves.

Not every child with learning problems becomes helpless. There are many people who have very significant learning problems who are quite confident and capable of asserting themselves and initiating appropriate actions to address a situation. The question is, what is it that distinguishes children with learning problems who are capable of taking control from children with learning problems who are helpless and unable to assert themselves?

Many parents of children with learning problems become highly directive and controlling with their children. This results from their efforts to teach their children the skills and behaviors that are central to their developmental problem. However, by encouraging their children to learn these behaviors, these parents often deprive them of opportunities to learn to make choices and pursue their own interests.

This pattern of interaction is not limited to children's experiences with their parents. Special education can also be a highly directive and controlling experience. Commonly, special education focuses on directly teaching children the skills and competencies that are focal to their learning problems. Like parents, special education teachers often teach children by using highly structured procedures in which children's role is to respond to their direction and requests. Although these instructional methods may be effective at encouraging children to comply, they fail to enhance children's ability to assert themselves and make decisions.

It is not surprising that *when children's life experiences are dominated by others making decisions and controlling their lives, they learn to be helpless* and dependent upon the guidance and help of others, rather than taking the initiative and asserting themselves.

SE-607 Children with high feelings of control confront challenges.

One of the most important competencies children must develop during the early childhood period is learning to assert themselves in the face of challenge. Child development research has reported that *the children who are most likely to address challenges are children who have strong personal feelings of control* and are not necessarily the brightest or most capable children. Children who have learning problems tend to give up more quickly than children without learning problems when they are faced with a challenging situation. This tendency is partly related to children's accurately appraising that they are not capable of dealing with a challenging situation, no matter how hard they try. Yet, there are some children with learning problems who give up in challenging situations even though they have many, if not all, of the skills or competencies needed to deal with the situation.

Children will have difficulty moving forward in life if they are unwilling to attempt situations they find challenging. This is even truer if children have learning problems. Parents and adults can help their children become more assertive in challenging situations. They can do this by making sure that their children have frequent opportunities to develop their feelings of control. *Children can develop strong feelings of control even though they have significant learning problems if their parents make special efforts to allow them to initiate and exert control during joint activities with them.* Parents must constantly remind themselves that to help their children develop a strong sense of control, they need to routinely allow their children to express their interests, make choices, and initiate and sustain the activities that interest them.

Discussion Points

SE-601 Children have a basic need to control their environment.

- Being able to control is a basic developmental drive.
- When they are capable of exerting control, children are more active and engaged.

SE-602 Children learn to control by controlling others.

- Children's earliest experiences in learning to control occur in interactions where they have opportunities to control what parents and others do with them.
- How well children develop their ability to control is dependent upon the willingness of parents and others to respond to their early social signals.
- The more proficient children become at controlling the behavior of parents and others, the more likely they will exert control as the opportunity arises in new situations.

SE-603 Children have no choice if parents always tell them what to do.

- Children learn to control when they have opportunities to choose or decide what they want to do.
- If parents dominate interactions with their children, they limit their children's opportunities to make choices and impede them from learning to control.
- Parents need to give their children as many opportunities to make choices as possible.

SE-604 How young children make choices.

- Young children's choices are the objects or activities that are most appealing to them at the moment.
- Young children frequently change their minds about what they want.
- Children's choices are often short lived and are seldom a commitment to stay a long time with the activity they have chosen.

SE-605 Activities that children choose are just as important as those that parents choose.

- Children can learn new information from any activity they choose.
- Children are more likely to learn from activities that they have chosen and are interested in than from activities that parents choose that do not interest them.

SE-606 Learned helplessness—not feeling able to control.

- Many children with learning problems appear "helpless" later in their lives.
- Helplessness is a motivational trait children learn from their early life experiences.
- When children's life experiences are dominated by others making decisions and controlling their lives, they learn to be helpless.

SE-607 Children with high feelings of control confront challenges.

- The children who are most likely to address challenges are children who have strong personal feelings of control.
- Children can develop strong feelings of control if their parents make special efforts to allow them to initiate and exert control during joint activities with them.

RT Strategies That Promote Feelings of Control

221 ***Respond quickly to my child's signals, cries, or nonverbal requests.*** Before children talk, they cry or use nonverbal cues to make their needs known. Respond promptly to your child's nonverbal signals or cries to help your child learn how to use these behaviors and to increase the rate that he or she begins to use more sophisticated behaviors to communicate.

Practical Suggestions

- Review the child development research findings by Bell and Ainsworth (1992), which indicated that parents who responded quickly to their children's cries during the first year of life had children who were better communicators in their second year of life.
- Consider that prompt responding to your child's cries and other nonverbal signals will not reinforce lower forms of behavior. Rather, it will teach your child how to use these behaviors more effectively in social interactions.
- Respond promptly to your child's nonverbal signals and cries. Observe how your child becomes more attentive and responsive to you when you do this.

222 ***Respond immediately to little behaviors.*** Little behaviors are behaviors such as burps, change of visual regard, kicking legs, waving hands, facial displays, and others.

Practical Suggestions

- Even if your child is not directing his or her "little behaviors" to you, and even though these behaviors have no apparent purpose or meaning, by responding immediately you can transform these behaviors into meaningful social interaction.
- Immediate responding to your child's solitary play and self-speech will help your child become more aware of you and more apt to engage in social exchanges.
- Review videotaped observations to see how quickly you respond to your child's behavior.

235 ***Interpret noncompliance as a choice or lack of ability.*** One way your child communicates his or her intention is by "not complying" with what you ask him or her to do. Often children do not comply with their parents' requests because they (a) feel that what their parents are asking them to do is too difficult or (b) their parents are trying to coax them to do something that does not interest them. When what you are asking your child to do is not critically important, a very effective way of keeping your child interacting with you is by letting your child not comply.

Practical Suggestions

- Consider that accepting your child's choice not to comply does not teach your child to be disobedient. When you do this you are actually responding to your child's interests and limitations. The more you recognize and respond to your child's limitations and desires, the more successful you will be at gaining your child's voluntary cooperation.

313 ***Give my child frequent opportunities to make choices.*** While interacting with your child, wait for your child to choose what he or she wants to do and how he or

she wants to do it. Follow your child's choice of toys and activities, particularly if it is appropriate to the situation and not harmful to your child or to others.

Practical Suggestions

- Your child may have difficulty choosing what to do when one or a combination of three things occur. First, the toys or activities are too difficult for your child to use by him- or herself. Second, the toys are out of your child's reach. Third, your child is not able to manipulate or control these toys on his or her own. If your child is having difficulty making choices, give your child several toys and activities that are within his or her range of ability that he or she can get to, handle, and operate alone.

424 ***Repeat activities my child enjoys.*** Keep doing activities that your child finds fun and amusing. The more you emphasize these activities, the more you and your child will enjoy being with each other.

Practical Suggestions

- Unlike adults, children may do things many times before they get tired of the activity. When you repeat activities your child enjoys, you may tire of the activity long before your child does. However, if you continue this activity to promote your child's enjoyment, your child will learn that interacting with you is an enjoyable activity.
- Children develop a sense of humor when parents join in their amusement. The more you support activities your child enjoys, the more your child will learn to share amusing and enjoyable things with you. Your child will make the effort to bring joy to you the more you make your child's enjoyment a focus of your interactions with him or her.

523 ***Follow my child's lead.*** Respond to your child in a manner that is compatible with, or complements, your child's activity and intentions. Play with toys or engage in activities in the same manner as your child. Do not make your child play with toys in the manner for which the manufacturer designed them unless that is the way your child chooses to play with them.

Practical Suggestions

- Whatever your child is playing with is what interests your child at the moment. Consider how you are much more motivated to engage in activities that interest you and to learn and remember information that you find interesting. Your child is no different than you are when it comes to the motivating power of interest.
- When you follow your child's lead you are actually responding to your child's interests. The more you respond to your child's interests, the greater the number of interests your child will have and the stronger these interests will be.

References

Ainsworth, M. D., & Bell, S. M. (1974). Mother–infant interaction and the development of competence. In K. Connolly & J. Bruner (Eds.), *The growth of competence* (pp. 97–118). New York: Academic Press.

Applebaum, M., Batten, D. A., Belsky, J., Boller, K., Friedman, S., Phillips, D., et al. (2000). The relation of child care to cognitive and language development. *Child Development, 71*(4), 960–980.

Atkinson, J. W. (1964). *An introduction to motivation.* Princeton, NJ: Von Nostrand.

Bagnato, S., Neisworth, J., Salvia, J. J., & Hunt, F. M. (1999). *Temperament and Atypical Behavior Scale.* Baltimore: Brookes.

Baird, S., & Peterson, J. E. (1997). Seeking a comfortable fit between family-centered philosophy and infant–parent interaction in early intervention: Time for a paradigm shift? *Topics in Early Childhood Special Education, 17*(2), 139–164.

Basani, C. (2003). A look at changing parental ideologies and behaviors in Japan. *Sociological Research Online, 8*(1).

Bates, E., Benigni, L., Bretherton, I., Camaioni, L., & Volterra, V. (1979). *The emergence of symbols: Cognition and communication in infancy.* New York: Academic Press.

Beckwith, L., & Cohen, S. E. (1989). Maternal responsiveness with preterm infants and later competency. In M. H. Bornstein (Ed.), Maternal responsiveness: Characteristics and consequences. *New Directions for Child Development, 43,* 75–87.

Biringen, Z., & Robinson, J. (1991). Emotional availability in mother–child interactions: A reconceptualization for research. *American Journal of Orthopsychiatry, 61*(2), 258–271.

Bornstein, M. H. (1989). Between caretakers and their young: Two modes of interaction and their consequences for cognitive growth. In M. H. Bornstein & J. S. Bruner (Eds.), *Interaction in human development* (pp. 32–47). Hillsdale, NJ: Erlbaum.

Bornstein, M. H., Tamis-LeMonda, C. S., & Haynes, O. M. (1999). First words in the second year: Continuity, stability, and models of concurrent and predictive correspondence in vocabulary and verbal responsiveness across age and context. *Infant Behavior and Development, 22*(1), 65–85.

Bowlby, J. (1969). *Attachment and loss.* New York: Basic Books.

Boyce, G. C., Marfo, K., Mahoney, G., Spiker, D., Price, C., & Taylor, M. J. (1996, March). *Parent–child interaction in dyads with children at risk for developmental delays: A factor analytic study.* Poster presented at Gatlinburg Conference on Research and Theory in Mental Retardation and Developmental Disabilities, Gatlinburg, TN.

Bradley, R. (1989). HOME measurement of maternal responsiveness. In M. H. Bornstein (Ed.), Maternal responsiveness: Characteristics and consequences. *New Directions for Child Development, 43,* 63–74.

Bronfenbrenner, U. (1974). *Is early intervention effective? A report on longitudinal evaluations of preschool programs* (Vol. 2). Washington, DC: Department of Health, Education and Welfare.

Bronfenbrenner, U. (1979). Contexts of child rearing: Problems and prospects. *American Psychologist, 34*(10), 844–850.

Brooks-Gunn, J., & Lewis, M. (1984). Maternal responsivity in interactions with handicapped infants. *Child Development, 55,* 782–793.

Brooks-Gunn, J., McCarton, C. M., Casey, P. H., McCormick, M. C., Bauer, C. R., Bernbaum, J. C., et al. (1994). Early intervention in low birthweight, premature infants. *Journal of the American Medical Association, 272,* 1257–1262.

Brown, R., & Hanlon, C. (1970). Derivational complexity and order of acquisition in child speech. In J. R. Hayes (Ed.), *Cognition and the development of language* (pp. 122–139). New York: Wiley.

Bruner, J. (1974). From communication to language: A psychological perspective. *Cognition, 3,* 255–277.

Bruner, J. (1983). *Child talk.* New York: Norton.

Camarata, S. M., Nelson, K. E., & Camarata, M. N. (1994). Comparison of conversational-recasting and imitative procedures for training grammatical structures in children with specific language impairment. *Journal of Speech and Hearing Research, 37*(6), 1414–1423.

Carpenter, M., Nagell, K., & Tomasello, M. (1998). Social cognition, joint attention, and communicative competence from 9 to 15 months of age. *Monographs of the Society for Research in Child Development, 63*(4, V-143).

Crockenberg, S., & Litman, C. (1990). Autonomy as competence in two-year-olds: Maternal correlates of child compliance, defiance and self-assertion. *Developmental Psychology, 26,* 961–971.

Dale, P. (1976). Language *development: Structure and function.* New York: Holt, Rinehart & Winston.

De Wolff, M. S., & van Ijzendoorn, M. H. (1997). Sensitivity and attachment: A meta-analysis of parental antecedents of infant attachment. *Child Development, 68*(4), 571–591.

Dunst, C., Mahoney, G., & Buchan, K. (1996). Promoting the cognitive competence of young children with or at-risk for developmental disabilities. In S. Odom & M. McLean (Eds.), *Early intervention for infants and young children and their families* (pp. 159–195). Austin, TX: PRO-ED.

Eccles, J. S., Wigfield, A., & Schiefele, U. (1998). Motivation. In W. Damon (Series Ed.) & N. Eisenberg (Vol. Ed.), *Handbook of child psychology: Vol. 4. Social and personality development.* New York: Wiley.

Feldman, R., & Greenbaum, C. W. (1997). Affect regulation and synchrony in mother–infant play as precursors to the development of symbolic competence. *Infant Mental Health Journal, 18*(1), 4–23.

Fewell, R. R., Casal, S. G., Glick, M. P., Wheeden, C. A., & Spiker, D. (1996). Maternal education and maternal responsiveness as predictors of play competence in low birth weight, premature infants: A preliminary report. *Developmental and Behavioral Pediatrics, 17*(2), 100–104.

Fewell, R. R., & Deutscher, B. (2004). Contributions of early language and maternal facilitation variables to later language and reading abilities. *Journal of Early Intervention 26*(2), 132–145.

Field, T. M., Hossain, Z., & Malphurs, J. (1999). Depressed fathers' interactions with their infants. *Infant Mental Health Journal, 20*(3), 322–332.

Findley, M. J., & Cooper, H. M. (1983). Locus of control and academic achievement: A literature review. *Journal of Personality and Social Psychology, 44*(4), 419–427.

Girolametto, L., Pearce, P. S., & Weitzman, E. (1996). Interactive focused stimulation for toddlers with expressive vocabulary delays. *Journal of Speech and Hearing Research, 39*(6), 1274–1283.

Goleman, D. (1995). *Emotional intelligence.* New York: Bantam.

Greenspan, S., & Wieder, S. (1998). *The child with special needs.* Reading, MA: Addison-Wesley.

Hart, B., & Risley, T. (1995). *Meaningful differences in the everyday experience of young American children.* Baltimore: Brookes.

Hart, S., Field, T., del Valle, C., & Pelaez-Nogueras, M. (1998). Depressed mothers' interactions with their one year old infants. *Infant Behavior and Development, 21*(3), 519–525.

Hoff-Ginsberg, E., & Shatz, M. (1982). Linguistic input and the child's acquisition of language. *Psychological Bulletin, 92,* 3–26.

Hohmann, M., & Weikert, D. P. (1995). *Educating young childen: Active learning practices for preschool and child care programs.* Ypsilanti, MI: High/Scope Press.

Isabella, R. A. (1993). Origins of attachment: Maternal interactive behavior across the first year. *Child Development, 64,* 605–621.

Kaiser, A. P., Hemmeter, M. L., Ostrosky, M. M., Fischer, R., Yoder, P., & Keefer, M. (1996). The effects of teaching parents to use responsive interaction strategies. *Topics in Early Childhood Special Education, 16*(3), 375–406.

Kaiser, A., & Hester, P. (1994). Generalized effects of enhanced milieu training. *Journal of Speech and Hearing Research, 37*(6), 1320–1340.

Kochanska, G. (1997). Mutually responsive orientation between mothers and their young children: Implications for early socialization. *Child Development, 68,* 94–112.

Kochanska, G. (1998). Mother–child relationship, child fearfulness, and emerging attachment: A short-term longitudinal study. *Developmental Psychology, 34,* 480–490.

Kochanska, G., Forman, D. R., & Coy, K. C. (1999). Implications of the mother–child relationship in infancy for socialization in the second year of life. *Infant Behavior and Development, 22*(2), 249–265.

Koegel, R. L., Koegel, L. K., & Carter, C. M. (1999). Pivotal teaching interactions for children with autism. *School Psychology Review, 28*(4), 576–594. Baltimore: Brookes.

Koegel, R. L., Koegel, L. K., & McNerny, E. K. (2001). Pivotal areas in intervention for autism. *Journal of Clinical Child Psychology, 30*(1), 19–32.

Koegel, R., Koegel, L., Shoshan, Y., & McNerney, E. (1999). Pivotal response intervention II. Preliminary long-term outcome data. *Journal of the Association for the Severely Handicapped, 24*(3), 186–198.

Landry, S. H., & Chapieski, M. L. (1989). Joint attention and infant toy exploration: Effects of Down syndrome and prematurity. *Child Development, 60*(1), 103–118.

Lay, K. L., Waters, E., & Park, K. A. (1989). Maternal responsiveness and child compliance: The role of mood as a mediator. *Child Development, 60,* 1405–1411.

Leadbeater, B. J., Bishop, S. J., & Raver, C. C. (1996). Quality of mother–toddler interactions, maternal depressive symptoms, and behavior problems in preschoolers of adolescent mothers. *Developmental Psychology, 32,* 280–288.

Linder, T. W. (1993). *Transdisciplinary play-based assessment: A functional approach to working with young children* (Rev. ed.). Baltimore: Brookes.

MacDonald, J. (1985). Language through conversation: A model for language delayed persons. In A. Rogers-Warren & S. Warren, *Teaching functional language.* Austin, TX: PRO-ED.

MacDonald, J. D. (1989). *Becoming partners with children: From play to conversation.* San Antonio, TX: Special Press.

MacDonald, J. (2004). *Communicating Partners: 30 years of building relationships with late-talking children: Including Autism, Asperger's syndrome, Down syndrome and typical development.* London: Jessica Kingsley Press.

MacDonald, J., & Blott, J. (1974). An experimental parent assisted treatment program for preschool language delayed children. *Journal of Speech and Language Disorders, 39,* 244–266.

MacDonald, J., & Gillette, Y. (1984). Conversational engineering. *Educational Seminars in Speech and Language, 5*(3), 171–183.

MacDonald, J., & Gillette, Y. (1986). Communicating with persons with severe handicaps: Roles of parents and professionals. *Journal of the Association of Severe Handicaps, 11*(4), 255–265.

MacDonald, J., & Gillette, Y. (1992). Turntaking: The key to communication for language delayed children. *Exceptional Parent, 15,* 49–54.

Mahoney, G. J. (1988a). Communication patterns between mothers and developmentally delayed infants. *First Language, 8,* 157–172.

Mahoney, G. J. (1988b). Maternal communication style with mentally retarded children. *American Journal of Mental Retardation, 93,* 352–359.

Mahoney, G. (1999). *The Maternal Behavior Rating Scale–Revised.* Available from the author, Mandel School of Applied Social Sciences, 11235 Bellflower Rd., Cleveland, OH 44106-7164.

Mahoney, G., Boyce, G., Fewell, R., Spiker, D., & Wheeden, C. A. (1998). The relationship of parent–child interaction to the effectiveness of early intervention services for at-risk children and children with disabilities. *Topics in Early Childhood Special Education 18*(1), 5–17.

Mahoney, G. J., Finger, I., & Powell, A. (1985). The relationship between maternal behavioral style to the developmental status of mentally retarded infants. *American Journal of Mental Deficiency, 90,* 296–302.

Mahoney, G. J., Fors, S., & Wood, S. (1990). Maternal directive behavior revisited. *American Journal of Mental Retardation, 94,* 398–406.

Mahoney, G. J., Kim, J. M., & Lin, C. S. (in press). Parental responsiveness and children's pivotal behavior: The keys to intervention effectiveness. *Infants and Young Children.*

Mahoney, G., & Neville-Smith, A. (1996). The effects of directive communications on children's interactive engagement: Implications for language intervention. *Topics in Early Childhood Special Education, 16*(2), 236–250.

Mahoney, G. J., & Perales, F. P. (1996). *Developmental Rainbow: Early Childhood Developmental Profile.* Tallmadge, OH: Family Child Learning Center.

Mahoney, G., & Perales, F. (2003). Using relationship-focused intervention to enhance the social–emotional functioning of young children with autism spectrum disorders. *Topics in Early Childhood Special Education, 23*(2), 77–89.

Mahoney, G., & Perales, F. (2005). A comparison of the impact of relationship-focused intervention on young children with Pervasive Developmental Disorders and other disabilities. *Journal of Developmental and Behavioral Pediatrics, 26*(2), 77–85.

Mahoney, G., & Powell, A. (1986). *The transactional intervention program: Teacher's guide.* Farmington, CT: Pediatric Research and Training Center.

Mahoney, G., & Powell, A. (1988). Modifying parent–child interaction: Enhancing the development of handicapped children. *Journal of Special Education, 22*, 82–96.

Mahoney, G., Robinson, C., & Powell, A. (1992). Focusing on parent–child interaction: The bridge to developmentally appropriate practices. *Topics in Early Childhood Special Education, 12*(1), 105–120.

Mahoney, G., & Wheeden, C. A. (1997). Parent–child interaction: The foundation for family-centered early intervention practice: A response to Baird and Peterson. *Topics in Early Childhood Special Education, 17*(2), 165–184.

Mahoney, G., & Wheeden, C. (1998). Effects of teacher style on the engagement of preschool aged children with special learning needs. *Journal of Developmental and Learning Disorders, 2*(2), 293–315.

Mahoney, G. J., & Wheeden, C. A. (2000). *Family ties: A preschool parent education program.* Washington, DC: Model Demonstration Project, Office of Special Education Programs, U.S. Department of Education.

Mahoney, G., Wheeden, C. A., & Perales, F. (2004). Relationship of preschool special education outcomes to instructional practices and parent–child interaction. *Research in Developmental Disabilities, 25*(6), 493–595.

Mangelsdorf, S. C., McHale, J. L., Diener, M., Heim Goldstein, L., & Lehn, L. (2000). Infant attachment: Contributions of infant temperament and maternal characteristics. *Infant Behavior and Development, 23*, 175–196.

Manolson, A., Ward, B., & Dodington, N. (1995). *You make the difference: In helping your children learn.* Available from The Hanen Centre, 1075 Bay St., Suite 403, Toronto, ON M5A 4K2.

McCollum, J. A., & Hemmeter, M. L. (1997). Parent–child interaction intervention when children have disabilities. In M. J. Guralnick (Ed.), *The effectiveness of early intervention* (pp. 549–576). Baltimore: Brookes.

Miserandino, M. (1996). Children who do well in school: Individual differences in perceived competence and autonomy in above-average children. *Journal of Educational Psychology, 88*, 203–214.

Morales, M., Mundy, P., Delgado, C. E. F., Yale, M., Messinger, D., Neal, R., & Schwartz, H. (2000). Responding to joint attention across the 6- through 24-month age period and early language acquisition. *Journal of Applied Developmental Psychology, 21*(3), 283–298.

Mundy, P., Sigman, M., & Kasari, C. (1990). A longitudinal-study of joint attention and language-development in autistic children. *Journal of Autism and Developmental Disorders, 20*(1), 115–128.

Nelson, K. (1973). Structure and strategy in learning to talk. *Monographs of the Society for Research in Child Development, 38.*

Pepper, J., & Weitzman, E. (2004). *It takes two to talk: A practical guide for parents of children with language delays.* Toronto: The Hanen Center.

Phillips, D. A. (1984). The illusion of incompetence among academically competent children. *Child Development, 55*, 2000–2016.

Phillips, D. A. (1987). Socialization of perceived academic competence among highly competent children. *Child Development, 58*, 1308–1320.

Phillips, D. A., & Zimmerman, M. (1990). The development course of perceived competence and incompetence among competent children. In R. J. Sternberg & J. Kolligian (Eds.), *Competence considered.* New Haven, CT: Yale University Press.

Piaget, J. (1963). The *psychology of intelligence.* Totowa, NJ: Littlefield, Adams.

Rotter, J. B. (1990). Internal versus external control of reinforcement: A case history of a variable. *American Psychologist, 45*(4), 489–493.

Seligman, M. E. P. (1975). *Helplessness: On depression, development, and death.* San Francisco: Freeman.

Siller, M., & Sigman, M. (2002). The behaviors of parents of children with autism predict the subsequent development of their children's communication. *Journal of Autism and Developmental Disorders, 32*(2), 77–89.

Skinner, E. A., Zimmer-Gembeck, M. J., & Connell, J. P. (1998). Individual differences in the development of perceived control. *Monographs of the Society for Research in Child Development, 63.*

Spiker, D., Ferguson, J., & Brooks-Gunn, J. (1993). Enhancing maternal interactive behavior and child social competence in low birth weight, premature infants. *Child Development, 64*, 754–768.

Stipek, D. J. (1980). A causal analysis of the relationship between locus of control and academic achievement in first grade. *Contemporary Educational Psychology, 5*, 90–99.

Stipek, D. J., & Weisz, J. R. (1981). Perceived personal control and academic achievement. *Review of Educational Research, 51*, 101–137.

Tamis-LeMonda, C. S., Bornstein, M. H., & Baumwell, L. (2001). Maternal responsiveness and children's achievement of language milestones. *Child Development, 72*(3), 748–767.

Thomas, A., Chess, S., & Birch, H. G. (1968). *Temperament and behavior disorders in children.* New York: New York University Press.

van den Boom, D. C. (1994). The influence of temperament and mothering on attachment and exploration: An experimental manipulation of sensitive responsiveness among lower-class mothers with irritable infants. *Child Development, 65,* 1457–1477.

van den Boom, D. (1995). Do first-year intervention effects endure? Follow-up during toddlerhood of a sample of Dutch irritable infants. *Child Development, 66,* 1798–1816.

Vereijken, C. M. J. L., Ricksen-Walraven, M., & Kondo-Ikemura, K. (1997). Maternal sensitivity and infant attachment security in Japan: A longitudinal study. *The International Society for the Study of Behavioural Development, 21*(1), 35–49.

Vygotsky, L. (1978). *Mind in society.* Cambridge, MA: Harvard University Press.

Watson, J. S., & Ramey, C. T. (1972). Reactions to response contingent stimulation in early infancy. *Merrill-Palmer Quarterly, 18,* 219–227.

Weiner, B. (1980). *Human motivation.* New York: Holt, Rinehart & Winston.

Zeanah, C. H. (Ed.). (2000). *Handbook of infant mental health* (2nd ed., pp. 129–144). New York: Guilford Press.

Recommended Materials to Supplement Responsive Teaching

Recommended Readings

Bowman, B. T., Donovan, M. S., & Burns, M. S. (Eds.). (2001). *Eager to learn: Educating our preschoolers.* Washington, DC: National Research Council.

Brazelton, T. B. (1992). *Touchpoints: Your child's emotional and behavioral development.* Cambridge, MA: Perseus.

Brazelton, T. B., & Greenspan, S. I. (2000). The *irreducible needs of children: What every child must have to grow, learn, and flourish.* Cambridge, MA: Perseus.

Bruner, J. S. (1983). *Child's talk: Learning to use language.* New York: Norton.

Eliot, L. (2000). *What's going on in there? How the brain and mind develop in the first five years of life.* New York: Bantam Dell.

Elkind, D. (1987). *Miseducation: Preschoolers at risk.* New York: Knopf.

Elkind, D. (2001). *The hurried child: Growing up too fast too soon.* Reading, MA: Addison-Wesley.

Golinkoff, R. M., & Hirsh-Pasek, K. (Eds.). (1999). *How babies talk: The magic and mystery of language in the first three years.* New York: Dutton/Penguin Press.

Gopnik, A., Meltzoff, A. N., & Kuhl, P. K. (1999). *The scientist in the crib: Minds, brains, and how children learn.* New York: HarperCollins.

Gottman, J. M., & DeClaire, J. (1997). *Raising an emotionally intelligent child.* New York: Fireside.

Greenspan, S. I., & Weider, S. (1998). *The child with special needs: Encouraging intellectual and emotional growth.* Cambridge, MA: Perseus.

Heller, S. (2002). *Too loud, too bright, too fast, too tight: What to do if you are sensory defensive in an overstimulating world.* New York: HarperCollins.

Hirsh-Pasek, K., & Golinkoff, R. M. (Eds.). (2003). *Einstein never used flash cards: How our children really learn and why they should play more and memorize less.* Emmaus, PA: Rodale Press.

MacDonald, J. (2004). *Communicating partners: 30 years of building responsive relationships with late-talking children.* London: Jessica Kingsley.

Segal, M. (1998). *Your child at play: Birth to one year.* New York: Newmarket Press.

Segal, M. (1998). *Your child at play: One to two years.* New York: Newmarket Press.

Segal, M. (1998). *Your child at play: Two to three years.* New York: Newmarket Press.

Segal, M. (1998). *Your child at play: Three to five years.* New York: Newmarket Press.

Shelov, S. P., & Hannemann, R. E. (Eds.). (1998). *FAAP: The complete and authoritative guide: Caring for your baby and young child birth to age 5.* Elk Grove, IL: American Academy of Pediatrics.

Stern D. (2001). *First relationship: Infant and mother.* Cambridge, MA: Harvard University Press.

Recommended Videos

Videos by James MacDonald available through Child Development Media, Inc., 5632 Van Nuys Blvd., Suite 286, Van Nuys, CA 91401 (info@childdevelopmentmedia.com)

ECO Video II: Balance

ECO Video II: Match

ECO Video II: Responsiveness

ECO Video II: Nondirectiveness

ECO Video II: Emotional Attachment

ECO Video II: Adult Communication Styles w/Preconversational Infants–Toddlers–Preschoolers (set)

Videos and materials from the Hanen Center available through Child Development Media, Inc., 5632 Van Nuys Blvd., Suite 286, Van Nuys, CA 91401 (info@childdevelopmentmedia.com)

It Takes Two to Talk

Hanen Resources for Parents of Children with Language Delays

Together We Can Know the World

Together We Can Know the World: Moving Forward with Music

Together We Can Know the World: Sharing Books

Together We Can Know the World: Creating Together

Together We Can Know the World: Playing Games

Together We Can Know the World: It Takes Two to Sing

About the Authors

Gerald Mahoney, PhD, is the Verna Houck Motto Professor of Families and Community at the Mandel School of Applied Social Sciences at Case Western Reserve University. He has been involved in research and higher education for more than 25 years. He received his doctoral degree in mental retardation and special education from Peabody College of Vanderbilt University. Since that time, he has held faculty positions at UCLA, University of Michigan, University of Connecticut, Winthrop University, and Kent State University. From 1991 through 2001, Dr. Mahoney was the director of the Family Child Learning Center, an early intervention research and training center that is sponsored by Children's Hospital of Akron and Kent State University. Dr. Mahoney's research has focused primarily on parent and family influences on children's development and social–emotional functioning. He has conducted numerous studies on parent influences on the development of children at risk or with disabilities as well as on the application of research findings from the parent–child literature to early intervention practice.

Currently, Dr. Mahoney is the Director of the Center on Interventions for Children and Families. This center is involved in providing training and technical assistance for parents and professionals on the Responsive Teaching curriculum. Information on research and training opportunities can be accessed online (www.ResponsiveTeaching.org).

James D. MacDonald, PhD, has spent more than 30 years investigating how persons with disabilities socialize and communicate. He earned his doctoral degree at the University of Minnesota studying communicative disorders and behavioral psychology.

For 24 years, Dr. MacDonald was a member of the faculty in Speech and Hearing Science at Ohio State University, where he was involved in clinical, research, and teaching efforts at the Nisonger Center for Developmental Disabilities. At the Nisonger Center he directed the Parent–Child Communication Clinic and implemented several research and training projects related to intervention for social and communicative development.

Early on, Dr. MacDonald's research focused on the natural roles of parents in children's language development. Several studies resulted in identifying five global responsive strategies that predicted increases in children's communication. These research findings were the basis for a parent-based intervention model called The ECO (Ecological) Language Program. Dr. MacDonald's extensive clinical experiences using the ECO program with more than 1,000 families of children with autism, Down syndrome, speech disorders, and other late-talking conditions provided the experiential foundation for many of the clinical strategies and concepts in the Responsive Teaching curriculum.

Currently, Dr. MacDonald directs the Communicating Partners Center in Columbus, Ohio. The center is a clinical and teaching network of many parents and professionals who have completed training in the model.

He personally provides clinical service to many families and communicates to over 1,000 people on an Internet discussion group. His primary concern is to work to ensure that children with autism and other late-talking concerns develop stable social relationships.

Information on his work can be accessed online (www.jamesdmacdonald.org).